EXPERIMENTS IN BIOCHEMISTRY

Experiments in Biochemistry

MAX S. DUNN, Ph.D.

*Professor of Chemistry, University
of California, Los Angeles*

WILLIAM DRELL, Ph.D.

*Research Fellow, California Institute of Technology,
Pasadena; formerly Teaching Assistant and Research
Fellow, University of California, Los Angeles*

First Edition

1951

New York   Toronto   London

McGRAW-HILL BOOK COMPANY, INC.

EXPERIMENTS IN BIOCHEMISTRY

PREFACE

Experiments in Biochemistry is designed as a laboratory guide and reference book for students in beginning biochemistry. Experiments of wide scope and uniform quality have been provided. Opportunities are presented to become skilled in the use of common and special biochemical apparatus, to become proficient in the quantitative determination of biological substances in a variety of naturally occurring materials, and to gain experience in the synthesis, isolation, purification, and analysis of typical biological compounds. The student's understanding of, and appreciation for, the development, use, and application of biochemical procedures is furthered by detailed explanations and discussions of the principles underlying chemical reactions and techniques and of background and related current investigations. The more than 900 references to the original and the review literature should aid in increasing the student's comprehension of biochemical subject matter.

Among the new experiments which have been found to interest students are the synthesis of an aromatic amino acid, synthesis of a peptide, asymmetric-enzymatic synthesis of an optically amino acid derivative, isolation and analysis of an amino acid amide, isolation of a sterol, polarimetric analyses of amino acids and carbohydrates, separation and identification of purines and pyrimidines by paper chromatography, identification of amino acids in a mixture of amino acids, identification of carbohydrates in a mixture of carbohydrates, determination of nicotinic acid by microbiological assay with a lactobacillus, determination of choline by microbiological assay with a mutant strain of *Neurospora crassa*, and determination of vitamin D by the chick bone-ash method.

If it is to be expected that the student will put forth his best efforts, the results of his work should be evaluated by objective standards. For this reason the authors have employed analytically pure unknowns in the quantitative experiments, have applied the recovery principle in experiments on the determination of biological substances in naturally-occurring materials, and have estimated the precision of analyses and the purity of preparations on the basis of the student's analytical data.

Precise directions for the preparation of special reagents, complete lists of apparatus and reagents, precautions in the conduct of experiments, discussions of biochemical principles and techniques, and a summary of the results obtained by students in the authors' classes over a period of more than fifteen years are given in the Appendix.

The authors have the hope and belief that *Experiments in Biochemistry* will be stimulating to students and useful to instructors.

MAX S. DUNN
WILLIAM DRELL

LOS ANGELES, CALIF.
July, 1951

CONTENTS

EXPERIMENT 1

DETERMINATION OF THE EQUIVALENT WEIGHT OF AN UNKNOWN ORGANIC ACID

This experiment is to test the ability of the student in performing simple quantitative manipulations and calculations.

EXPERIMENTAL

Obtain approximately 1.0 g. of an unknown solid organic acid. Transfer the sample to a dry weighing bottle. Transfer about 1.0 g. (weighed to ±1 mg.) of the solid acid to a 100-ml. volumetric flask. Add about 50 ml. of distilled water, rotate the flask until the solid dissolves, and add distilled water to the mark. Stopper the flask and thoroughly mix the liquids.

Pipette a 25.0-ml. aliquot of this solution into each of three 125-ml. conical flasks. Add 2 drops of phenolphthalein indicator solution to each flask and titrate each solution with standard, approximately 0.1 N, sodium hydroxide delivered from a burette.

EXPERIMENT 2

SYNTHESIS OF GLYCINE

Glycine (sugar of gelatin), the simplest amino acid, was first isolated from an acid hydrolysate of gelatin by Braconnot (1820, 1827). It tastes more sweet than other amino acids but less so than sucrose, some other sugars, and compounds such as dulcin ($C_2H_5OC_6H_4NHCONH_2$) and saccharin ($C_6H_4SO_2NHCO$) (Cameron, 1947).

Glycine was first synthesized in about 20 per cent yield from bromoacetic acid and ammonia (Perkin and Duppa, 1858; Cahours, 1858, 1859). It was crystallized as the copper salt because separation (in the free form) was difficult from the ammonium salts of iminodiacetic acid (called diacid) and trimethyleneaminetricarboxylic acid (called triacid) (see equations below).

$$BrCH_2COOH + NH_2CH_2COOH + 3NH_3 \rightarrow NH(CH_2COONH_4)_2 + NH_4Br$$

$$BrCH_2COOH + NH(CH_2COONH_4)_2 + 2NH_3 \rightarrow N(CH_2COONH_4)_3 + NH_4Br$$

Kraut (1890, 1891) increased the yield of glycine to about 50 per cent by increasing the molar ratio of ammonia to halogen acid to 20:1. At a molar ratio of 220:1 Robertson (1927) obtained nearly the theoretical yield of glycine. Excess ammonia and chloride ions were removed by treating the crude product with silver oxide. Orten and Hill (1931) found that glycine could be purified more conveniently by crystallizing it from 85 per cent (by volume) aqueous methanol.

Purified glycine has been prepared in 55 to 60 per cent yield by the reaction at 60 to 65° of a mixture containing ammonia, carbonate, and chloroacetic acid in an equivalent ratio of 5:4:1 (Chadwick and Pacsu, 1941; Cheronis and Spitzmueler, 1941; Dunn, Butler, and Frieden, 1941). Robertson obtained the same yield at room temperature with a 60:1 molar ratio of ammonia to chloroacetic acid. The effectiveness of small amounts of carbonate in depressing the production of the di- and triacids and in increasing the yield of glycine has been explained by the conversion of glycinate ions to alkali-stable carbaminoglycinate ions.

$$CO_2 + 2NH_3 \rightarrow NH_2COO^- + NH_4^+$$

$$NH_2COO^- + NH_3 + ClCH_2COO^- \rightarrow {}^-OOCNHCH_2COO^- + NH_4Cl$$

Various methods for the synthesis of glycine have been discussed by Clark (1943), Carter and Hooper (1944), Dunn (1943), Dunn and Rockland (1947), and Block (1946). The synthesis of glycine labeled with radioactive (C^{14}) carbon has been described by Sakami, Evans, and Gurin (1947), Loftfield (1947), and Ostwald (1948).

Animals convert glycine to creatine (Bloch and Schoenheimer, 1941), uric acid (Shemin and Rittenberg, 1947), serine (Sakami, 1949), and the protoporphyrin ($C_{34}H_{34}O_4N_4$) moiety of hemoglobin (Wittenberg and Shemin, 1949). According to Shemin (1945) the nitrogen, as well as the carboxyl and adjacent carbons, of serine are utilized in the in vivo synthesis of glycine. In animals glycine is incorporated into the proteins of intestinal tissue, liver, and spleen (Friedberg, Winnick, and Greenberg, 1947; Winnick, Friedberg, and Greenberg, 1947). The yeast *Torulopsis utilis* transforms glycine into serine (Ehrensvärd, Sperber, Saluste, Reio, and Stjernhelm, 1947), proline (Ehrensvärd *et al.*, 1947), and purines (Abrams, Hammarsten, and Shemin, 1948). The conjugation of glycine with benzoic acid and other aromatic acids to form hippuric acid (benzoylglycine) and analogous derivatives has been reviewed by Young (1939), Stekol (1941), Lewis (1941), Quick (1944), and Handler and Perlzweig (1945). Glycine is indispensable for growth of the chick, but not of the rat and other animals. It has been employed clinically for the alleviation of muscular disfunctions although its curative powers have been questioned (Burman, 1943).

Glycine is to be synthesized by the reaction of chloroacetic acid and ammonia ($ClCH_2COOH + 2NH_3 \rightarrow NH_2CH_2COOH + NH_4Cl$). It is readily crystallized from 80 per cent aqueous methanol, since it is only slightly soluble while NH_4Cl is almost entirely soluble in this solvent.

EXPERIMENTAL

Mark a 500-ml. round-bottomed pyrex flask at the 100-ml. level with a wax pencil. Place 162 g. (1.3 moles) of technical ammonium carbonate,[1] (see end of experiment for footnotes) 190 ml. of distilled water, and 75 ml. (1.1 moles) of 15 N ammonium hydroxide in the flask. Stir the mixture thoroughly and heat it on a water bath at 60° until the solid dissolves. Prepare a solution containing 35 g. (0.37 mole) of chloroacetic acid (m.p. 62 to 64°) in 60 ml. of distilled water, and add this solution slowly, with stirring, to the ammoniacal solution in the flask. Label the flask, cover the neck of the flask with an inverted beaker, and place the covered flask in an oven at 60 to 65° for 24 hr. or longer. The yield and quality of the glycine are not altered by heating the mixture longer than 24 hr.

Set up the reduced-pressure distillation apparatus shown in Fig. 7 (see Distillation in the Appendix).

Close the screw clamp on the tubing leading to the safety flask. Turn on the valve controlling the flow of water from the water pump. Open the screw clamp sufficiently to permit rapid evolution of gas from the liquid in the distilling flask, and as the gas evolution diminishes, heat the water bath sufficiently to maintain rapid distillation. Continue the heating and distillation under reduced pressure until the volume of the solution has been reduced to about 100 ml. Add 100 ml. of distilled water to the flask and repeat the distillation process until the volume of the solution has been reduced to about 100 ml.

Transfer the residual solution to a 1-liter beaker and add 500 ml. of methanol. Stir the mixture thoroughly, cover the beaker with a watch glass, label the beaker, and place the covered beaker in a refrigerator overnight or for longer time. Transfer the supernatant liquid to a Buchner funnel and filter it with suction. Add 100 ml. of methanol to the beaker, stir the mixture for about 3 min., and transfer the alcoholic suspension of crystals to a Buchner funnel. Apply suction until the crystalline precipitate is nearly dry. Resuspend the glycine in 75 ml. of methanol, stir the mixture for about 3 min., transfer the suspension to a Buchner funnel and apply suction until the crystals are nearly dry. Transfer the alcoholic filtrates to the container provided for that purpose to permit recovery of the alcohol. Transfer the crystals to an evaporating dish, label and cover the dish, and place the covered dish overnight in an oven at 50°. Transfer the dry product to a labeled, tared (weighed) sample bottle, and submit the (stoppered) bottle to the instructor. Calculate the percentage yield of glycine and submit the calculations to the instructor.

NOTE

1. Technical ammonium carbonate is a mixture of anhydrous and monohydrated ammonium carbonate, ammonium bicarbonate, and ammonium carbamate (NH_4OOCNH_2). It has an apparent equivalent weight of 60 to 65, and it is assumed to be principally ammonium carbonate monohydrate.

EXPERIMENT 3

PREPARATION OF GLYCINE METHYL ESTER HYDROCHLORIDE

Glycine ester is utilized for the preparation of ethyl hydantoate (Harries and Weiss, 1903), glycine anhydride (Fischer, 1906; Dickinson and Marshall, 1929), polyglycine esters (Frankel and Katchalski, 1942; Fraenkel-Conrat, Cooper, and Olcott, 1945) and optically active peptides (Bergmann and Fruton, 1941; Sheehan and Frank, 1949).

Glycine methyl ester hydrochloride is to be prepared by passing dry hydrogen chloride into a suspension of glycine in anhydrous methanol. This procedure, first described by Curtius and Goebel (1888), is commonly employed for the preparation of the ester hydrochlorides of amino acids and peptides. The free esters are readily liberated with base and separated by ether extraction.

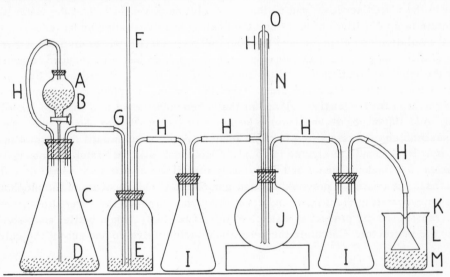

Fig. 1. APPARATUS FOR GENERATION OF HYDROGEN CHLORIDE AND PREPARATION
OF GLYCINE METHYL ESTER HYDROCHLORIDE.

A — 125-ml. separatory funnel
B — 85-ml. concentrated commercial sulfuric acid
C — 500-ml. conical flask
D — Solution containing 18 g. NaCl and 42 ml.
     concentrated hydrochloric acid
E — 25-ml. concentrated commercial sulfuric acid
F — Glass tube, 3 mm. diameter
G — Glass tube, 8 mm. diameter

H — Rubber tubing
I — 125-ml. flask (trap)
J — 200-ml. round-bottomed flask
K — 600-ml. beaker
L — Glass funnel
M — 100-ml. 6 N sodium hydroxide solution
N — T-tube, large bore
O — Glass rod

EXPERIMENTAL

Set up the apparatus shown in Fig. 1.

Place 15 g. of purified glycine and 75 ml. of anhydrous methanol in the 200-ml. round-bottomed flask. Admit a small stream of concentrated sulfuric acid from the dropping funnel on to the mixture of sodium chloride and concentrated hydrochloric acid in the 500-ml. conical flask. The sulfuric acid should be added at such a rate that the liberated hydrogen chloride bubbles in a steady stream through the sulfuric acid in the widemouthed bottle into the reaction mixture in the 200-ml. flask. If any hydrogen chloride escapes into the room, reconstruct the apparatus. Manipulate the stirring rod in the tube to prevent clogging of the delivery tube with solid glycine methyl ester hydrochloride. Immerse the reaction flask at intervals in an ice-water bath to prevent the temperature from rising above the boiling point of the alcoholic suspension. The temperature of the suspension should be maintained high enough to prevent crystallization of the product. A clear solution should form in about 30 min.

Transfer this solution to a beaker and rinse the flask with two 10-ml. portions of hot methanol. Immerse the beaker for 30 min. in an ice-water bath. Filter the suspension on a Buchner funnel. Redissolve the precipitate in the minimum volume (about 6 ml. per g.) of hot methanol; if undissolved material is present, filter the suspension. Transfer the solution (or filtrate) to a beaker, cover and label the beaker, and allow the covered beaker to stand 30 min. in an ice-water bath or overnight in the refrigerator.

Filter the suspension on a Buchner funnel, cover the funnel with a watch glass, and apply suction (for 10 min.) until nearly all the methanol is removed. Transfer the crystals to an evaporating dish, cover and label the dish, and allow the covered dish to stand overnight in an oven at 50°. Submit the product to the instructor in a tared, labeled sample bottle. Calculate the percentage yield and submit the calculations to the instructor.

EXPERIMENT 4

PREPARATION OF GLYCINE ANHYDRIDE (DIKETOPIPERAZINE)

Glycine anhydride is formed by the spontaneous decomposition of glycine ester in water (Fischer, 1906), although it is prepared more conveniently in about the same yield (45 per cent) by dehydrating and condensing glycine in hot glycerol (Blanchetière, 1927; Maillard, 1914a, 1914b; Morrow and Sandstrom, 1935) or ethylene glycol (Sannié, 1942). A modification of Sannié's method is to be employed in this experiment.

EXPERIMENTAL

Place 80 ml. of technical ethylene glycol in a 125-ml. conical flask, suspend a 360° thermometer in the flask, and heat the flask in a hydrogenated-cottonseed-oil bath until the temperature of the ethylene glycol reaches 185°. Add 15 g. (0.20 mole) of technical glycine, initially in 1-g. portions to avoid frothing and loss of the ethylene glycol mixture by sudden liberation of water vapor. Maintain the mixture at about 180° and stir it until the glycine dissolves. Maintain a temperature of about 175° for 45 min. while stirring the solution at intervals. Remove the flask from the bath and cool it in air or under running water. Stopper and label the flask and allow it to stand 30 min. in an ice-water bath or overnight in the refrigerator.

Decant (and discard) as much of the supernatant liquid as possible. Add 5 ml. of methanol to the suspension and filter the mixture on a Buchner funnel. Disconnect the pressure tubing leading to the filter flask, add 10 ml. of methanol to the dark-brown precipitate in the funnel, and stir the suspension thoroughly without disturbing the filter paper. Attach the pressure tubing and apply suction until the precipitate is nearly dry. Press the precipitate with an inverted glass stopper until as much solvent as possible is removed. Repeat this process, using a second 10-ml. portion of methanol.

Dissolve the precipitate in the minimum volume (10 ml. per g.) of boiling distilled water, and if undissolved solid is present, filter the mixture. Transfer the filtrate to a flask and cool the flask for 30 min. in an ice-water bath or overnight in the refrigerator.

Filter the suspension on a Buchner funnel and wash the precipitate on the funnel with distilled water. Transfer the precipitate to a 125-ml. flask and dissolve it in the minimum volume of boiling distilled water. Add 1 g. of decolorizing carbon, heat the mixture to boiling, and continue heating for 5 min. Filter the hot suspension on a Buchner funnel which has been thoroughly heated by immersing it in hot water. Triturate the carbon residue with 10 ml. of hot distilled water. If the filtrate is colored, repeat the decolorizing procedure using 0.5 g. of carbon. Transfer the filtrates and any crystalline material in the filter flask to a 125-ml. conical flask. Use distilled water to wash traces of crystals from the flask. Stopper and label the flask and allow it to stand for 30 min. in an ice-water bath or overnight in the refrigerator. Filter the suspension of crystals and wash the crystals as previously described, first with 10 ml. of 50 per cent methanol and then with 10 ml. of methanol.[1] Transfer the precipitate to an evaporating dish, cover and label the dish, and allow the covered dish to stand overnight in an oven at 50°. Submit the product to the instructor in a tared, labeled sample bottle. This product is sufficiently pure for the preparation of glycylglycine hydrochloride, but recrystallization from water would be required to yield an analytically pure product. Calculate the percentage yield and submit the calculations to the instructor.

NOTE

1. An additional crop (0.5 g.) may be obtained by evaporating the combined filtrate and washings *in vacuo* to about 25 ml. and allowing the residual liquid to stand overnight in the refrigerator.

EXPERIMENT 5

PREPARATION OF GLYCYLGLYCINE HYDROCHLORIDE MONOHYDRATE

Glycylglycine hydrochloride monohydrate is readily prepared by acid hydrolysis of glycine anhydride under the conditions described by Fischer and Fourneau (1901) and Schott, Larkin, Rockland, and Dunn (1947). The prescribed time of heating should be observed closely, since both peptide bonds would be split and glycine, rather than glycylglycine, formed by prolonged heating.

EXPERIMENTAL

Heat concentrated hydrochloric acid (12 ml. per g. of glycine anhydride) to boiling, add the purified glycine anhydride prepared in Exp. 4, and maintain the solution at the boiling point for 1 min. Immediately immerse the flask in an ice-water bath. After 15 min. transfer the flask to the refrigerator and allow it to stand overnight. Filter the suspension on a Buchner funnel. Recrystallize the product from the minimum volume (about 35 ml. per g.) of hot 80 per cent ethanol. Dry the product in air[1] and submit it to the instructor in a tared, labeled sample bottle. The product should be nearly analytically pure. Calculate the percentage yield and submit the calculations to the instructor.

NOTE

1. Glycylglycine hydrochloride monohydrate is stable at $70°$, but it loses part, although not all, of its water of hydration when heated for 5 hr. at $110°$.

EXPERIMENT 6

PREPARATION OF GLYCYLGLYCINE

Glycylglycine may be prepared from glycylglycine hydrochloride monohydrate by neutralizing the hydrochloride with base (Fischer, 1906). Silver oxide is a satisfactory base for laboratory preparations, but it is too expensive for large-scale work. Sodium hydroxide is unsatisfactory, because glycylglycine and sodium chloride are difficult to separate by fractional crystallization from water or other solvents. Ammonium hydroxide is satisfactory because ammonium chloride is more soluble in methanol than glycylglycine.

EXPERIMENTAL

Dissolve the glycylglycine hydrochloride monohydrate prepared in Exp. 5 in the minimum volume (4.5 ml. per g.) of distilled water in a small beaker. Add sufficient concentrated ammonium hydroxide (1 ml. per g. of glycylglycine hydrochloride monohydrate) to bring the solution to pH 7.0. Test the pH of the solution with nitrazine paper, which changes from yellow-green to blue color over the pH range 6.0 to 7.5. Determine the shade of color to be expected by testing a buffer solution at pH 7.0 or by reference to a color chart.

Add methanol (1.3 ml. per ml. of solution) and immerse the beaker in an ice-water bath for 25 min. Filter the suspension of crystals on a Buchner funnel and wash the precipitate with two 10-ml. portions of methanol. Transfer the crystals to an evaporating dish and allow the product to dry in air for 30 min. Cover and label the dish and allow it to stand overnight in an oven at 50°. Submit the product to the instructor in a tared, labeled sample bottle. Calculate the percentage yield and submit the calculations to the instructor.

EXPERIMENT 7

SYNTHESIS OF HIPPURIC ACID

N-Benzoylglycine was named hippuric acid from the Greek words "hippos" (horse) and "ouron" (urine) because of its abundance in horse urine. It is present in relatively high concentration in the urine of herbivorous animals, and 0.6 g. is excreted daily in the urine of an adult person. Hippuric acid is synthesized in the liver and the kidney at the rate of about 1.5 g. per hr. on a constant input of sodium benzoate. Hippuric acid formation is considered to be a process for the detoxification of benzoic acid. Benzoic acid in the body is derived primarily from foods (such as cranberries) in which it occurs naturally or to which its sodium salt has been added as preservative. Most of the glycine utilized for conjugation with benzoic acid is derived from body protein or is synthesized in vivo, since only a small part of the isotopic (N^{15}) nitrogen present in ingested "tagged" glycine was found in the urinary hippuric acid (Rittenberg and Schoenheimer, 1939).

Hippuric acid is to be synthesized by the reaction of benzoyl chloride and glycine (Schotten, 1888; Baumann, 1886). The reaction mixture is kept cold, and it is maintained at pH 9 to 11. Under these conditions hydrolysis of benzoyl chloride is minimized, sodium chloride rather than hydrochloric acid is formed, and benzoylation of the glycine is nearly complete.

EXPERIMENTAL

Add 15 g. (0.2 mole) of purified glycine and 100 ml. of distilled water to a 1-liter three-necked flask. Rotate the flask until the glycine dissolves. Add 6 N sodium hydroxide (about 35 ml.) to pH 9 to 11 as shown by test (blue color) with thymolphthalein indicator. Add ice to the solution until the temperature is reduced to about 2° and immerse the flask in an ice-water bath. Stir the mixture vigorously (motor stirrer) while adding 24.5 ml. (0.21 mole) of benzoyl chloride from a dropping funnel at the rate of about 1 ml. (20 drops) per min. At 3-min. intervals check the pH of the solution and add 6 N sodium hydroxide as required to maintain the solution at pH 9 to 11. Add ice to the solution if necessary to keep the temperature below 5°. When all the benzoyl chloride has been added, continue stirring for an additional 20 min.

Filter the solution to remove any suspended particles and add concentrated hydrochloric acid from a dropping funnel to the filtrate with stirring until the solution is at about pH 3, as shown by test (blue color) with congo red paper. Filter the suspension of hippuric acid and wash the precipitate four times with 15-ml. portions of ice-cold distilled water to remove sodium chloride. Wash the precipitate three times with 15-ml. portions of isopropyl ether to remove benzoic acid. Dry the product in air in a tared, covered evaporating dish and show it to the instructor before starting the next experiment. Calculate the percentage yield and submit the calculations to the instructor.

EXPERIMENT 8

SYNTHESIS OF PHENYLALANINE

The Perkin reaction (condensation of an aldehyde with an active methylene group) was first adapted to the synthesis of phenylalanine by Plöchl (1884), but the most extensive early investigations were made by Erlenmeyer (1886–1904b). Sodium amalgam was first employed to reduce the azlactone, but hydriodic acid and red phosphorus were utilized by later workers (Harington and McCartney, 1927; Lamb and Robson, 1931) to effect the reduction and hydrolysis of the azlactone simultaneously. Gillespie and Snyder (1943) have described the laboratory preparation of phenylalanine. According to Breslow and Hauser (1939) acetic anhydride acts as a dehydrating agent and sodium acetate as a base causing enolization of the hippuric acid. The synthesis of phenylalanine by other methods has been discussed by Block (1946), Carter and Hooper (1944), Dunn (1943), and Dunn and Rockland (1947).

Phenylalanine is an essential dietary nutrient (Rose, 1938), and normally it is oxidized in the body. Some individuals whose metabolic processes are deranged excrete relatively large amounts of abnormal products such as *p*-hydroxyphenylpyruvic acid ("tyrosinuria"), 2,5-dihydroxyphenylacetic acid or homogentisic acid ("alkaptonuria"), and phenylpyruvic acid ("phenylpyruvic oligophrenia"). Garrod (1923) has discussed these inborn errors of metabolism. The biochemical error in phenylpyruvic oligophrenia is believed to result from a block in the hydroxylation of phenylalanine to tyrosine. Hall, Sydenstricker, and Rawls (1948) and Lanyar (1942) have investigated the formation by alkaptonurics of homogentisic acid from the optical isomers of phenylalanine and tyrosine. Cataracts and granulocytes are produced in animals on phenylalanine-deficient diets (Hall, Bowles, Sydenstricker, and Schmidt, 1948). Analogues of phenylalanine inhibit the growth of vaccinia virus (Thompson and Wilkins, 1948), *Neurospora crassa* mutants (Mitchell and Niemann, 1947), lactic acid bacteria (Beerstecher and Shive, 1947), other organisms (Dittmer, 1949), and the rat (Ferger and du Vigneaud, 1949).

Phenylalanine is to be synthesized by (a) condensing benzaldehyde with hippuric acid in the presence of acetic anhydride and sodium acetate and (b) reducing and hydrolyzing the resulting azlactone (lactimide) by heating it with concentrated hydriodic acid and red phosphorus (equations below).

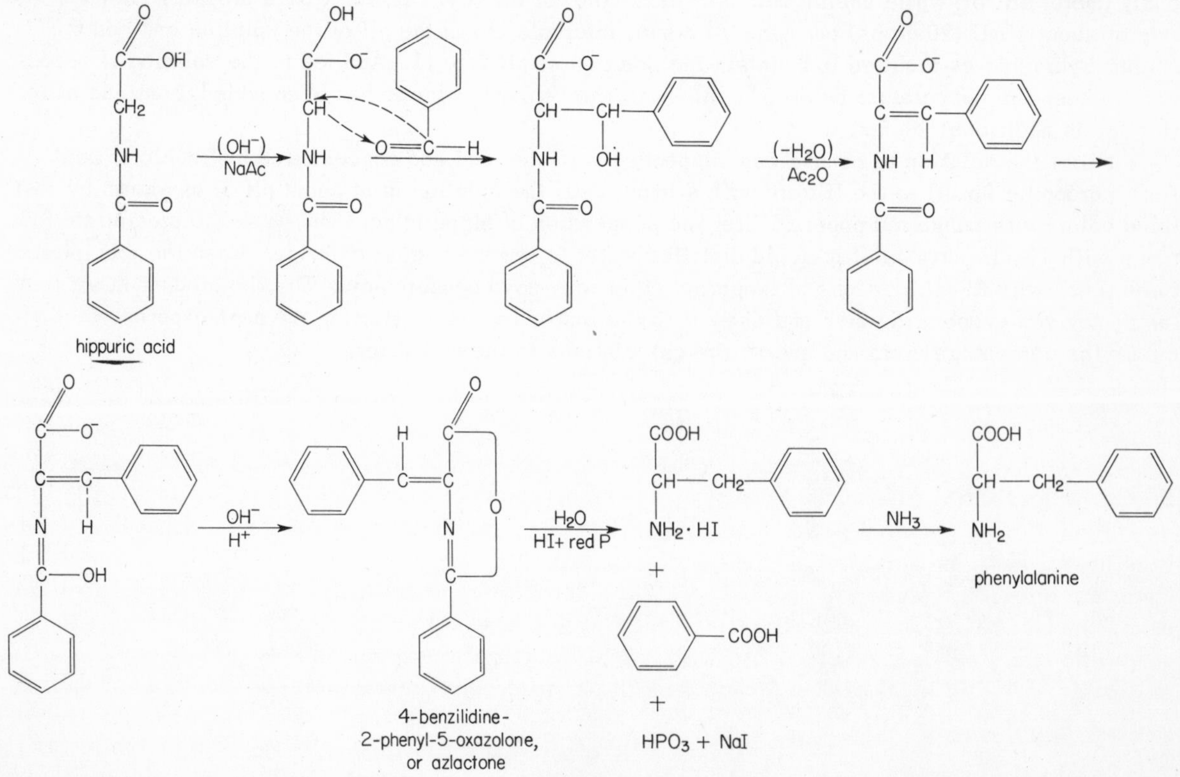

4-benzilidine-
2-phenyl-5-oxazolone,
or azlactone

— 10 —

EXPERIMENTAL

4-Benzylidine-2-phenyl-5-oxazolone. Place 16.4 g. (0.2 mole of anhydrous sodium acetate, 35.8 g. (0.2 mole) of hippuric acid, 20 ml. (0.2 mole) of benzaldehyde, and 72 ml. (0.77 mole) of acetic anhydride in a 1-liter three-necked flask. Fit the flask with a 110° thermometer, a 3-ft. reflux condenser with an attached calcium chloride drying tube, and a Hershberg (1936) stirrer, as shown in Fig. 2.

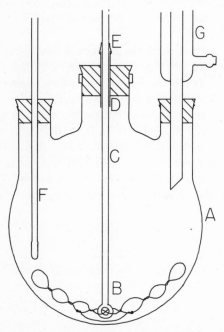

A—1-liter 3-necked round-bottomed flask

B—Hershberg stirrer, sttached to a hollow 8-mm. glass shaft (C)

C—Hollow, 8-mm. glass shaft

D—Glass bearing, 8-mm. fire-polished glass tubing

E—Rubber tubing which fits C snugly over 2-mm. length and is attached securely to D. In attaching E to D moisten the latter with glycerol. During stirring E should be lubricated at the point of attachment to D

F—110° thermometer

G—3-ft. condenser to which a calcium chloride drying tube is attached

Fig. 2. HERSHBERG STIRRER ASSEMBLY.

Heat the mixture on the water bath with vigorous stirring until the temperature rises rapidly to 75° owing to the heat of the reaction. Keep the temperature below 90° by cooling (ice water, if necessary) the flask. Note the formation of an orange solution and the deposition of solid material on the walls of the flask. Break up this cake with a stirring rod so that it will not insulate the solution and delay cooling. After precipitation appears to be complete, replace the ice bath with a hot-water bath, heat the bath to boiling, and continue heating at this temperature for 1 hr. Allow the mixture to cool to room temperature. Add distilled water slowly with stirring to decompose the excess acetic anhydride. A violent reaction may ensue if the water is added too rapidly or in too large portions. Allow the mixture to cool to room temperature while stirring it at intervals, filter the suspension of yellow needle-like crystals, and wash the precipitate on the Buchner funnel with three 50-ml. portions of boiling distilled water. Allow the solid to dry overnight at 50° in a tared, covered evaporating dish. Show the product to the instructor. Calculate the percentage yield.

Phenylalanine. Place 35 g. (0.14 mole) of 4-benzilidine-2-phenyl-5-oxazolone, 20 g. (0.64 mole) of red phosphorus, and 180 ml. (1.37 moles) of constant-boiling (57 per cent) hydriodic acid in a 1-liter round-bottomed flask. Fit the flask with a 3-ft. reflux condenser to which is attached a rubber tube leading to the sink. The purpose of this tube is to carry away any phosphine (PH_3) which may be formed. Phosphine is poisonous; it is readily ignited; and when mixed with air, it is explosive.

Heat the mixture slowly and carefully to the boiling point with a gas flame, and allow the mixture to reflux for about an hour until all the solid oxazolone dissolves to form a green solution. Remove the flame and allow the solution to cool to room temperature. Add an additional 17.5 g. (0.70 mole) of the oxazolone slowly, to avoid excess heating which would cause the solution to boil over. Allow the mixture to reflux continuously for 6 hr. Discontinue heating and add immediately, but slowly and cautiously, 0.5 g. of solid carbon dioxide through the condenser. Add a total of about 10 g. of the

— 11 —

carbon dioxide while observing these precautions. Sufficient gaseous carbon dioxide is liberated to flush all the phosphine from the flask. Add 300 ml. of distilled water, filter the suspension, and wash the precipitate of benzoic acid and (excess) phosphorus on the Buchner funnel with a total of 150 ml. of distilled water.

Distill the combined filtrate and washings to dryness, using the reduced-pressure distillation apparatus shown in Fig. 7 (see Distillation in the Appendix). Add 50 ml. of distilled water to the flask, stir or heat the suspension until the solid dissolves, add 5 g. of decolorizing carbon, stir the mixture for 5 min., and filter the suspension. Add 15 N ammonium hydroxide slowly with stirring to the filtrate until the pH is about 6, as tested (yellow color) with methyl red indicator. Allow the mixture to stand overnight.

Filter the suspension on a Buchner funnel and apply suction until the product is nearly dry. Dissolve the solid in boiling distilled water (20 ml. per g.), and add 5 g. of decolorizing carbon to the solution (or suspension, if suspended material is present). Stir the mixture at the boiling temperature for 5 min. and filter the suspension on a Buchner funnel which has been preheated by immersion in hot water. Add slowly an equal volume of 95 per cent ethanol to the filtrate and allow the solution to cool spontaneously to room temperature with frequent shaking. Place the solution in the refrigerator and allow it to stand overnight or longer. Filter the suspension and wash the crystals twice on the Buchner funnel with 15-ml. portions of 95 per cent ethanol. Allow the product to dry overnight in a covered evaporating dish at 50°. Submit the product to the instructor in a tared, labeled sample bottle. Calculate the percentage yield based on (a) hippuric acid and (b) the azlactone. Submit the calculations to the instructor.

EXPERIMENT 9

KJELDAHL ANALYSIS OF AN AMINO ACID OR AMINO ACID DERIVATIVE

The historical development of the Kjeldahl method, first described by Johan Kjeldahl (1883), has been reviewed by Bradstreet (1940) and Vickery (1946). It is employed to determine the purity of nitrogen-containing organic compounds and to characterize plant and animal materials in terms of total nitrogen.

Nitrogen in organic compounds is converted to ammonium ion by the action of boiling concentrated sulfuric acid and catalysts, the ammonium ion is transformed to ammonia with strong base, the liberated ammonia is distilled into acid, and the excess acid is titrated with base.

Copper sulfate is an effective catalyst for most amino acids containing only alpha-amino nitrogen, but more active catalysts are required for histidine, lysine, and some other amino acids. According to Chibnall, Rees, and Williams (1943), 12 to 16 hr. digestion time is required to liberate completely the nitrogen of lysine and most proteins when a digestion mixture composed of K_2SO_4, $CuSO_4$, H_2SO_4, and Na_2SeO_4 is employed. Jonnard (1945) has reported that digestion first with a mixture of H_2SO_4, K_2SO_4, and HI and then with SeO_2 in H_2SO_4 is usually complete in 2 to 5 hr. but is complete for lysine, histidine, and casein only after 12 to 16 hr. Excellent results were obtained by Miller and Houghton (1945) with 12 amino acids when digestion with a mixture of K_2SO_4, HgO, and H_2SO_4 was continued for 6 hr. after the solution became clear. Other catalysts which have been recommended include $HgCl_2$, V_2O_3, Se, $K_2S_2O_8$, and $HClO_4$.

The ammonia liberated by the Kjeldahl digestion process may also be determined by titrating the ammonium ion with standard base, by photometric determination of the product formed with Nessler's reagent (see Exp. 46), and on the basis of the pH of its boric acid solution (see Exp. 20).

The effectiveness of the Kjeldahl method has been investigated by Meredith (1946) and by Miller and Miller (1948). If nitrates, nitrites, or nitro derivatives of organic compounds are present, they must be reduced to the corresponding amines (prior to Kjeldahl digestion) by treatment with a mixture of salicylic acid and sodium thiosulfate or other reducing agent.

The purity of an amino acid or amino acid derivative is to be determined in this experiment by Kjeldahl analysis of its total nitrogen.

EXPERIMENTAL

Obtain three approximately 1-g. samples of an unknown amino acid or amino acid derivative. Obtain assignment to a Kjeldahl digestion apparatus and a Kjeldahl distillation apparatus. Proceed simultaneously with the analysis of the three samples.

Digestion of Sample. Transfer 1 g. (weighed to ±1 mg.) of the amino acid sample quantitatively to a 100-ml. volumetric flask, add about 25 ml. of 0.5 N sulfuric acid, and rotate the flask until the sample dissolves. Add 0.5 N sulfuric acid to the mark and mix the liquids thoroughly. Pipette a 25.0-ml. aliquot of the amino acid solution into each of three 800-ml. Kjeldahl flasks. Pipette a 25-ml. aliquot of the 0.5 N sulfuric acid into each of two 800-ml. Kjeldahl flasks.[1] Add (from a graduate) to each Kjeldahl flask 20 ml. of the digestion reagent (cupric sulfate and sodium sulfate in 18 N sulfuric acid). Place the flasks on a Kjeldahl digestion rack and heat the mixture in each flask to boiling. (Care should be taken that the fume hood connected with the digestion apparatus is operating efficiently, since sulfur dioxide, irritating to the eyes and throat, is evolved during the digestion process.) Maintain gentle, but constant, boiling until the water is driven off, the brown color first formed disappears, and dense white fumes of sulfur trioxide appear in the flask. Continue gentle boiling for at least 1 hr., at which time the solution should be colorless or colored pale blue-green.[2]

Cool each flask in air and then to about 40° under running water. Add 350 ml. of distilled water to the warm solution in each flask to prevent caking of the white sodium sulfate which precipitates, and rotate each flask until the liquids are thoroughly mixed. Allow each solution to cool to room temperature.

Distillation of the Ammonia. Clean the distillation apparatus by distilling water from a Kjeldahl flask until about 250 ml. of distillate have collected in the receiver. (This precaution may be omitted if it is certain that the apparatus has been thoroughly steamed previously.)

Pipette 50.0 ml. of 0.1 N sulfuric acid[3] into each of the required number of 500-ml. filter flasks, each of which is fitted with a short piece of rubber tubing on the side arm. Insert the side arm of each filter flask into the neck of a rubber balloon and tie the neck of the balloon to the side arm with stout thread.[4] Add 4 to 6 drops of methyl red and p-nitrophenol mixed indicator[5] solution to each filter flask. Connect each flask to a delivery tube of the distillation apparatus by means of a tightly fitting rubber stopper. Dry each flask on the outside and dry 1 in. on the inside in order that the rubber stopper may fit tightly. Open the faucet which controls the flow of water to the condenser to permit a small, but steady, stream of water to flow from the condenser. Turn on the switch which controls the electricity to the heating coils (or light the gas burners).

Add about 0.5 g. of granular zinc so that hydrogen liberated by reaction with the alkali will promote quiet boiling. Incline each flask in turn at an angle of about 30° from the horizontal position. Add 30 ml. of 18 N (saturated), carbonate-free sodium hydroxide from a graduate in such a manner that the alkali does not come in contact with the inch of dry surface inside the flask. Hold the flask in this position until the alkali runs down the inner wall of the flask and collects as a layer beneath the liquid. Connect each flask in turn to the distillation apparatus and make certain that the flask fits tightly on the rubber stopper. Rotate the flask gently until the acidic and basic layers mix smoothly and form a homogeneous solution. Lower each flask until it rests on its heating unit.

When about half of the liquid has distilled, turn off the electricity (or gas) and allow the flask to cool (5 to 10 min.). Remove the flask and discard the solution. Remove the receivers from the distillation apparatus and titrate each solution in turn with standard 0.1 N sodium hydroxide measured from a 50-ml. burette.

NOTES

1. Omit this step if the blank value is furnished by the instructor. Only one blank determination is required for a particular set of reagents.

2. Unknowns will be limited to amino acids which digest within 2 hr. If digestion is continued for a longer time, additional (5 to 10 ml.) of digestion reagent may be required to replace the sulfuric acid (as sulfur dioxide) and water lost by vaporization.

3. The same 0.1 N sulfuric acid should be employed throughout the experiment. It is unnecessary that the exact normality of this acid be known, since the ammonia in the sample is calculated from the difference in volumes of standard base used to titrate the excess acid in the blank and unknown solutions.

4. In conventional Kjeldahl distillation apparatus the delivery tube extends into the acid in the receiver. At the start of distillation small quantities of ammonia are trapped in bubbles of air which pass through the solution. For this reason ammonia is lost, and the analysis is inaccurate. Bradley (1942) has eliminated this error by attaching a rubber balloon to the side arm of the receiver. It was observed that the pressure developed by distilling into a closed system was insufficient to burst the balloon and that there was no water condensate on the walls of the balloon which would absorb ammonia. Under these conditions 99.9 per cent of the ammonia was recovered. Analytical results of comparable accuracy are attainable by distilling the ammonia from an all-glass apparatus by a micro or semimicro procedure.

5. Solutions of mixed indicators are advantageous in titrating ammonia with a strong acid, since the color change at the end point is sharper and more distinct than that obtained with a single indicator. Mixed indicators consisting of methyl red and methylene blue, methyl red and guinea red, and other combinations have been described by Johnson and Green (1930).

EXPERIMENT 10

ANALYSIS OF AN AMINO ACID BY THE VAN SLYKE VOLUMETRIC NITROUS ACID METHOD

Nitrous acid procedures for the determination of amino nitrogen by volumetric macro- and micro- and manometric methods have been described by Van Slyke (1911, 1912, 1913–1914, 1915b, 1929b).

The simple aliphatic alpha-amino acids react quantitatively with nitrous acid in about 4 min. at room temperature. The time for complete reaction of beta-, gamma-, delta-, and epsilon-amino acids increases directly with the distance of the amino from the carboxyl group (Dunn and Schmidt, 1922). About 30 min. is required for the complete reaction with lysine. Arginine, cystine, glycine, histidine, tryptophan, and serine yield higher than the theoretical amount of nitrogen, particularly at elevated temperatures (Schmidt, 1929). These amino acids give extra nitrogen because nitrous acid is reduced by intermediate products as well as by the original amino acid.

Kendrick and Hanke (1937, 1940) reported that these abnormalities were prevented by introducing potassium iodide into the deaminizing mixture (manometric apparatus). Preferential oxidation by iodine rather than by nitrous acid was assumed to explain the iodide effect, but Dunn and Porush (1939) proposed that an unreactive mercuric iodide complex was formed. Compounds such as ammonia, urea, asparagine, creatinine, and purines react slowly with nitrous acid.

An unknown amino acid is to be analyzed by the Van Slyke volumetric macro nitrous acid procedure. Nitrous acid, formed by mixing sodium nitrite solution and 3 N hydrochloric acid, reacts with the amine solution in the deaminizing chamber to form a hydroxy compound, nitric oxide, water, and nitrogen.

$$NaNO_2 + HCl \rightarrow NaCl + HNO_2$$

$$3HNO_2 \rightarrow HNO_3 + 2NO + H_2O$$

$$RNH_2 + HNO_2 \rightarrow ROH + N_2 + H_2O$$

The gaseous products are shaken with alkaline permanganate solution, which oxidizes the nitric oxide to potassium nitrate.

$$NO + KMnO_4 \rightarrow KNO_3 + MnO_2$$

The volume of residual nitrogen is measured in a gas burette at atmospheric pressure and room temperature. The weight of nitrogen in the sample is calculated from these data by applying gas-law principles or, more conveniently, by employing the conversion factor in the table of factors prepared by Van Slyke.

EXPERIMENTAL

Obtain approximately 0.5 g. of an unknown amino acid and assignment to a volumetric macro Van Slyke apparatus (shown in Fig. 3). Transfer 0.5 g. (weighed to ± 1 mg.) of the sample quantitatively to a 25-ml. volumetric flask, add 10 ml. of 0.5 N sulfuric acid, and rotate the flask until the sample dissolves. Add distilled water to the mark and mix the liquids thoroughly.

Adjustment of the Apparatus. The glass parts should be clean and connected tightly with heavy-walled soft-rubber tubing. The stopcocks should be well lubricated, turn easily, and be attached to the apparatus with rubber or wire. The lower bulb and the tube leading to the upper bulb of the Hempel pipette should be filled with alkaline potassium permanganate solution saturated with nitrogen (shaken with air for about a minute). The upper bulb should contain only a few milliliters of the permanganate reagent. The gas burette should be filled and the level bulb about one-third filled with 0.5 N sulfuric acid.

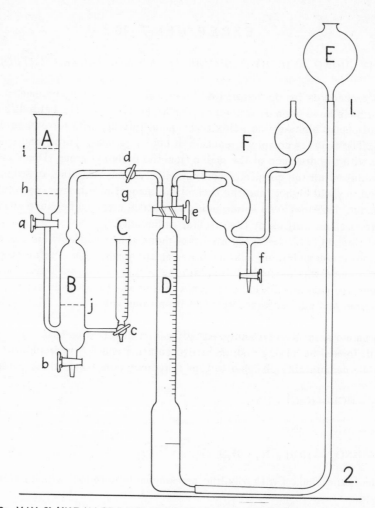

Fig. 3. VAN SLYKE MACRO VOLUMETRIC AMINO NITROGEN APPARATUS.

Place bulb E in position 2, open stopcock e to the Hempel pipette H, and allow the permanganate solution to fill the bore of stopcock e.[1] Close stopcock e, raise bulb E to position 1, turn stopcock d so that it connects with exit tube g, open stopcock e to connect with stopcock d, and allow the sulfuric acid to flow until it fills the bore of stopcock d. Close stopcock e. Make certain that no air bubbles are present in the capillary tubes.

Removal of Air from Reagents and Deaminizing Chamber. Turn stopcock d to connect the deaminizing chamber B with exit tube g. Close stopcocks a, b, and c. Add sufficient (about 8 ml.) 3 N hydrochloric acid to fill funnel A to mark h. Open stopcock a and admit the acid solution into the deaminizing chamber B. Close stopcock a and add 30 per cent sodium nitrite solution sufficient (about 33 ml.) to fill funnel A to mark i. Open stopcock a, allow all but 1 or 2 ml. of the sodium nitrite solution to run from funnel A into deaminizing chamber B, and close stopcock d.

Agitate the deaminizing chamber with the motor at a uniform rate such that nitric oxide is generated rapidly with no strain on the apparatus. Although the rate of shaking is unimportant, the same rate should be employed for all determinations. Continue the shaking until the liquid is forced down to mark j, stop the motor, and open stopcock d to permit the gas (nitric oxide and residual air) to escape through g. When nearly all the solution has run from A into B, close stopcock d. Turn on the motor and allow the deaminizing chamber to shake until the liquid has been forced down to j. Close stopcock a. Turn stopcocks d and e so that the deaminizing chamber B is connected to gas burette D.

Reaction of Amino Acid with Nitrous Acid. Transfer quantitatively 5.00 ml. of the unknown amino acid solution from the 25-ml. volumetric flask to burette C by means of a 5-ml. pipette. Place bulb E in position 2. Turn stopcock c so that burette C is open into B. Admit all but about 0.2 ml. of the amino acid solution into B. Close stopcock c and rinse burette C with approximately 4 ml. of distilled water delivered from a wash bottle. Turn stopcock c so that all but about 0.2 ml. of the liquid is admitted to B. Close stopcock c and add 1 ml. of distilled water to C. Turn stopcock c so that all but about 0.2 ml. of the liquid is admitted to B. Turn on the motor and allow the deaminizing chamber to shake for 5 min. at the rate employed previously. Open stopcock a and allow the liquid in A to run into B until all the gas above the liquid in B has been forced into burette D. Close stopcock e.[2]

Removal of Nitric Oxide and Measurement of Nitrogen. Place bulb E in position 1. Open stopcock e so that burette D is connected with the Hempel pipette H. When all the gas has been forced into the lower bulb of H, close stopcock e. Agitate the Hempel pipette H slowly for 5 min. (with the motor or by hand). Lower bulb E to position 2, turn stopcock c to connect H and D, and when the unabsorbed gas in H has been forced past the bore of stopcock e into D, close stopcock e. Allow the burette to drain for 1 min. Lower bulb E to a position close to burette D such that the meniscus of the liquid in the burette and the surface of the liquid in bulb E are at the same height. Read the volume of the gas in burette D to 0.01 ml. Return the gas in D to H by the technique previously described, agitate the Hempel pipette for 1 min., return the gas to D, and read the volume of the gas in D. If the observed volumes do not differ by more than 0.02 ml., it can be assumed that the nitric oxide has been completely absorbed. If the volumes differ by more than this amount, repeat the absorption procedure.

Read the thermometer and the barometer. Record the temperature and the corrected pressure (see Pressure in the Appendix).

When the analysis has been completed, open stopcock b and allow the liquid to drain from B. Rinse A, B, and C with distilled water. Analyze a second 5-ml. aliquot of the unknown amino acid solution. The volumes of nitrogen gas should agree within 0.05 ml. If necessary, perform additional analyses until the volumes of nitrogen in two consecutive analyses agree within 0.05 ml.

Determination of Nitrogen from Reagents. Repeat the described procedures with 5.0-ml. volumes of the 0.5 N sulfuric acid until the volumes of nitrogen gas agree within 0.05 ml. Reagents suitable for the analysis of amino acids should give not more than 0.4 ml. of residual gas.

Conversion Factor. See the accompanying table for factor with which to convert the corrected volume of nitrogen to weight of nitrogen.

MILLIGRAMS OF AMINO NITROGEN CORRESPONDING TO ONE MILLILITER OF NITROGEN GAS[a]

Temperature, °C	Corrected pressure, mm. Hg							
	730	732	734	736	738	740	742	744
16	0.5570	0.5585	0.5600	0.5615	0.5630	0.5645	0.5660	0.5675
17	0.5540	0.5555	0.5575	0.5590	0.5605	0.5620	0.5635	0.5650
18	0.5515	0.5530	0.5545	0.5560	0.5580	0.5595	0.5610	0.5625
19	0.5490	0.5505	0.5520	0.5535	0.5550	0.5565	0.5580	0.5595
20	0.5460	0.5475	0.5495	0.5510	0.5525	0.5540	0.5555	0.5570
21	0.5435	0.5450	0.5465	0.5480	0.5495	0.5510	0.5525	0.5540
22	0.5410	0.5425	0.5440	0.5455	0.5470	0.5485	0.5500	0.5515
23	0.5380	0.5395	0.5410	0.5425	0.5440	0.5455	0.5470	0.5485
24	0.5350	0.5365	0.5380	0.5400	0.5415	0.5430	0.5445	0.5460
25	0.5325	0.5340	0.5355	0.5370	0.5385	0.5400	0.5415	0.5430
26	0.5295	0.5310	0.5325	0.5340	0.5355	0.5370	0.5365	0.5400
27	0.5265	0.5280	0.5295	0.5310	0.5325	0.5340	0.5355	0.5370
28	0.5235	0.5250	0.5265	0.5280	0.5295	0.5310	0.5325	0.5340
29	0.5210	0.5220	0.5235	0.5250	0.5265	0.5280	0.5295	0.5310
30	0.5175	0.5190	0.5205	0.5220	0.5235	0.5250	0.5265	0.5280

MILLIGRAMS OF AMINO NITROGEN CORRESPONDING TO ONE MILLILITER OF NITROGEN GAS[a]
(Cont'd)

Temperature, °C.	Corrected pressure, mm. Hg							
	746	748	750	752	754	756	758	760
16	0.5690	0.5710	0.5725	0.5740	0.5755	0.5770	0.5785	0.5800
17	0.5665	0.5680	0.5695	0.5710	0.5730	0.5745	0.5760	0.5775
18	0.5640	0.5655	0.5670	0.5685	0.5700	0.5715	0.5730	0.5745
19	0.5610	0.5630	0.5645	0.5660	0.5675	0.5690	0.5705	0.5720
20	0.5585	0.5600	0.5615	0.5630	0.5645	0.5660	0.5675	0.5690
21	0.5555	0.5575	0.5590	0.5605	0.5620	0.5635	0.5650	0.5665
22	0.5530	0.5545	0.5560	0.5575	0.5590	0.5605	0.5620	0.5635
23	0.5500	0.5515	0.5530	0.5545	0.5560	0.5575	0.5595	0.5610
24	0.5475	0.5490	0.5505	0.5520	0.5535	0.5550	0.5565	0.5580
25	0.5445	0.5460	0.5475	0.5490	0.5505	0.5520	0.5535	0.5550
26	0.5415	0.5430	0.5445	0.5460	0.5475	0.5490	0.5505	0.5520
27	0.5385	0.5400	0.5415	0.5430	0.5445	0.5460	0.5475	0.5490
28	0.5355	0.5370	0.5385	0.5400	0.5415	0.5430	0.5445	0.5460
29	0.5325	0.5340	0.5355	0.5370	0.5385	0.5400	0.5415	0.5430
30	0.5295	0.5310	0.5325	0.5340	0.5355	0.5370	0.5385	0.5400

[a]The figures in the table are the milligrams of nitrogen per milliliter of nitrogen gas liberated from the amino acid. The weight of nitrogen actually liberated is twice that indicated, since half the gas is derived from the amino acid and half from the nitrous acid.

NOTES

1. The alkaline permanganate solution should be in contact with stopcock *e* as short a time as possible, since it is attacked by the alkali and discolored by the manganese dioxide. When the apparatus is not in use, force the permanganate solution into the Hempel bulbs. As a further safeguard, run the 0.5 *N* sulfuric acid solution throu the bore of stopcock *e*. The efficiency of the permanganate solution as an oxidant for nitric oxide diminishes with use, as may be noted by the accumulation of manganese dioxide in the Hempel pipette. For this reason, record the number of determinations and, after 10 runs, drain the permanganate solution from the Hempel pipette, rinse the pipette and connecting tubes with 0.5 *N* sulfuric acid, and rinse them finally with distilled water. Refill the Hempel pipette with the permanganate solution.

2. If more than 100 ml. of gas collects in the gas burette *D*, place bulb *E* in position 1 to prevent displacement of all the liquid in *D*, turn stopcock *e* to connect *D* with the Hempel pipette, and permit about 20 ml. of the gas to enter the Hempel pipette. Turn stopcock *e* to connect *D* with the deaminizing chamber *B*, and lower bulb *E* to position 2. These manipulations should be performed as quickly as possible to minimize the danger and loss of gas caused by the pressure developed in *B* while the latter is a closed system.

EXPERIMENT 11

VOLHARD ANALYSIS OF AMINO ACID OR PEPTIDE HYDROCHLORIDE

Chloride ion may be determined accurately by precipitating and weighing silver chloride, but this procedure is less rapid and convenient than volumetric methods. The oldest and simplest volumetric procedure is that described by Mohr (1856). An aqueous solution of the hydrochloride is titrated with standard silver nitrate in the presence of sodium chromate. Silver chloride is precipitated, and, at the end point, red-colored silver chromate is formed. Disadvantages of this method are that silver chromate is not formed in solutions more acid than pH 5 and that chloride in blood and urine cannot be determined since silver salts of purines and other substances may be precipitated.

Volhard's (1874, 1878) method, or a modification, is used commonly for the determination of chloride. An excess of standard silver nitrate solution is added to the solution of the unknown hydrochloride, the suspension of silver chloride is filtered, a soluble ferric salt is added to the filtrate, and the excess silver ions are titrated with standard thiocyanate solution. White silver thiocyanate is precipitated, and, at the end point, intensely red-colored ferric thiocyanate is formed. It was first pointed out by Drechsel (1877) that, unless the silver chloride is removed, the end-point color fades, owing to the reaction of the more soluble silver chloride with ferric thiocyanate to give ferric chloride and the less soluble silver thiocyanate.

Alternative procedures have been proposed in which the excess silver ions are titrated in the presence of silver chloride, which is coagulated, and hence rendered insoluble, by the addition of ether (Rothmund and Burgstaller, 1909), caprylic alcohol (McLean and Van Slyke, 1915a, 1915b), acetone (Patterson, 1928; Smirk, 1927), glacial acetic acid and chloroform (McKittrick and Schmidt, 1945), or nitrobenzene (Caldwell and Moyer, 1935). Chloride may be determined also by titration with standard silver nitrate in the presence of fluorescein or a related dye (Kolthoff, 1935). The dye is adsorbed on the silver chloride coagulum, and, at the end point, red-colored silver fluoresceinate is formed. Sendroy (1937) has described a gasometric method for the determination of chloride.

The purity of an unknown amino acid hydrochloride or peptide hydrochloride is to be determined by Caldwell and Moyer's modification of the Volhard method. Nitric acid, nitrobenzene, and an excess of standard silver nitrate are added to a solution of the hydrochloride, the precipitated silver chloride is coagulated, ferric alum indicator is added, and the excess silver ions are titrated with standard thiocyanate. The end point is sharp, and satisfactory analyses are readily made.

EXPERIMENTAL

Obtain an approximately 1-g. sample of each of three unknown amino acid or peptide hydrochlorides. Transfer 1 g. (weighed to ± 1 mg.) of one of the samples quantitatively to a 100-ml. volumetric flask. Add 50 ml. of distilled water, rotate the flask until the sample dissolves, add 2 ml. of concentrated nitric acid, add distilled water to the mark, mix the liquids thoroughly, and stopper the flask. Prepare solutions of the other samples similarly.

Pipette three 25.0-ml. aliquots of one of the unknown solutions into separate 100-ml. glass-stoppered bottles (or flasks). Add 5 ml. of reagent-grade nitrobenzene to each bottle. Add standard, approximately 0.1 N, silver nitrate solution from a 50-ml. burette until no further precipitation of silver chloride is observed. Stopper and rotate the bottle to coagulate the silver chloride suspension, allow the suspension to settle, and add 1 drop of the standard silver nitrate solution. If no additional precipitation occurs, add 2.00 ml. of the standard nitrate solution. Stopper the bottle and shake it vigorously for 30 sec. Rinse the stopper and inside neck of the bottle with distilled water. Add 1 ml. of ferric alum indicator solution. Titrate the excess silver ions with standard, approximately 0.05 N, potassium thiocyanate solution to a faint-pink color which is permanent for at least 30 sec. Repeat this procedure using the other unknown solutions.

EXPERIMENT 12

ISOLATION OF L-TYROSINE FROM SILK OR CASEIN HYDROLYSATE

Tyrosine was first isolated from casein by Liebig (1846, 1847). Since the alkali-fusion procedure employed for the liberation of tyrosine was not satisfactory, proteins were hydrolyzed with hydrochloric acid by Bopp (1849) and with sulfuric acid by Hinterberger (1849). Later investigators have liberated tyrosine from proteins by the action of microorganisms (Emmerling, 1897) and by enzymatic digestion with pepsin (Borkel, 1903), trypsin (Cohn, 1895), and papain (Emmerling, 1902; Bergmann and Niemann, 1938).

Crude tyrosine can be readily isolated from protein hydrolysates because of its low solubility at the isoelectric point, pH 5.7. It may be purified by crystallization from water, although large volumes of water and large containers are required. Dilute ethanol was employed by Bopp, but this solvent is unsatisfactory. Extraction of the leucine from the crude tyrosine was proposed by Habermann and Ehrenfeld (1902), and the purification of tyrosine by precipitating it as its phosphotungstate (Sjollema and Rinkes, 1911), ethyl ester hydrochloride (Plimmer, 1913), or mercuric chloride complex (Hanke, 1925) has been suggested.

The best source of tyrosine is silk, which contains from 15 to 30 per cent of a gummy protein, sericin, and from 70 to 85 per cent of a fibrous protein, silk fibroin. The tyrosine content of silk fibroin from Chinese, Indian, Italian, Japanese, and Russian sources varies from 3.5 to 13 per cent. Casein contains about 6 per cent tyrosine.

L-Tyrosine is to be isolated by precipitating it at the isoelectric point from the hydrochloric acid hydrolysate of casein or silk.

EXPERIMENTAL

Add 100 g. of silk waste or commercial casein and 300 ml. of 8 *N* hydrochloric acid to a 2-liter round-bottomed flask. Place the flask in a sand bath and attach a reflux condenser. Heat the bath sufficiently to dissolve the protein and cause the acid solution to boil gently. Continue gentle boiling for 12 hr.

Filter the hot, dark-colored hydrolysate on a Buchner funnel with the aid of celite. Wash the precipitate on the funnel with three 20-ml. portions of boiling distilled water. Transfer the filtrate and washings to a 1-liter round-bottomed flask and set up the reduced-pressure distillation apparatus shown in Fig. 7 (see Distillation in the Appendix). Distill the solution under reduced pressure on a water bath to a sirup. Add 100 ml. of hot distilled water and distill the solution under reduced pressure on a water bath to a sirup. Immediately, add 250 ml. of hot distilled water and stir the mixture until it is homogeneous. Heat the solution to boiling, remove the flame, add 10 g. of decolorizing carbon in small portions with occasional stirring. Add 5 g. of celite and filter the suspension on a Buchner funnel. Wash the precipitate on the funnel with two 25-ml. portions of boiling distilled water.

Place the combined filtrate and washings in a 1.5-liter beaker and add sufficient (about 375 ml.) 3 *N* sodium hydroxide to bring the pH to 5.7. Determine the pH of the solution by test with methyl red indicator, which changes color from red to yellow over the pH range 4.4 to 6.0. Determine the shade of color to be expected by testing a buffer solution at pH 5.7. Allow the beaker (covered and labeled) to stand overnight in the refrigerator. Filter the suspension on a Buchner funnel and wash the precipitate on the funnel with two 25-ml. portions of distilled water.

Transfer the precipitate to a 600-ml. beaker and add 300 ml. of distilled water. Add 3 *N* sodium hydroxide slowly from a dropping funnel with stirring until the solid dissolves. Filter the solution on a

Buchner funnel to remove any suspended material. Transfer the filtrate to a 600-ml. beaker and add sufficient (volume same as that of the 3 N sodium hydroxide added previously) 3 N hydrochloric acid to bring the solution to pH 5.7. Immerse the beaker for 30 min. in an ice-water bath or allow it to stand overnight in the refrigerator. Filter the suspension on a Buchner funnel and wash the precipitate on the funnel with 25 ml. of distilled water.

Dissolve the wet product in the minimum volume (200 ml. per g.) of boiling distilled water in a large beaker. The rate of solution may be slow. If suspended material is present, filter the solution and allow the filtrate to stand overnight in a beaker (covered and labeled) in the refrigerator. Filter the suspension and wash the crystals on the funnel with 25 ml. of distilled water and two 25-ml. portions of methanol. Dry the product in an evaporating dish (covered and labeled) at 50°. Submit the product[1] to the instructor in a tared, labeled sample bottle.

NOTE

1. An additional crop (0.5 g.) may be obtained by evaporating the combined filtrate and washings to a small volume and recrystallizing the resulting crude tyrosine from the minimum volume of distilled water.

EXPERIMENT 13

PHOTOMETRIC ANALYSIS OF TYROSINE BASED ON THE MILLON REACTION

The Millon procedure, first described by Weiss (1919), has been employed by Folin and Marenzi (1929a) and other investigators. Tyrosine has also been determined by an iodometric bromination method (Plimmer and Phillips, 1924) and by the photometric analysis of the blue-colored complex formed with a phosphotungstic acid—phosphomolybdic acid reagent (Looney, 1926) and of the red- to yellow-colored complex with diazotized sulfanilic acid (Fürth and Fleishmann, 1922; Hanke, 1928).

The purity of the tyrosine prepared in Exp. 12 is to be determined by a modification of Arnow's (1937) photometric Millon method. The construction and operation of a visual colorimeter are described in the Appendix (see Photometry) and will be demonstrated by the instructor.

EXPERIMENTAL

Obtain three L-tyrosine unknowns and assignment to a visual colorimeter. Transfer approximately 0.25 g. (weighed to ± 1 mg.) of each sample quantitatively to a 500-ml. volumetric flask. Add 100 ml. of 0.5 N sulfuric acid to each flask and rotate each flask until the sample dissolves. Add 0.5 N sulfuric acid to the mark and mix the liquids in each flask thoroughly.

Pipette 1-ml. aliquots of the three unknown solutions and the standard solution, containing approximately 0.5 mg. per ml. of purified L-tyrosine, to four separate 6-in. test tubes. Add 5 ml. of 15 per cent mercuric sulfate in 6 N sulfuric acid to each tube with the aid of a 10-ml. graduate. Mix the solutions in each tube and immerse the tubes for 10 min. in a boiling water bath. Remove the tubes and allow them to cool to room temperature. Place a small funnel in a 25-ml. volumetric flask and transfer one of the solutions quantitatively to the flask. Rinse the funnel with distilled water, add 5 ml. of 0.2 per cent sodium nitrite solution, add distilled water to the mark, and mix the liquids thoroughly (flask should be stoppered the minimum time, since nitric oxide is evolved). Transfer each of the other solutions in turn to a 25-ml. volumetric flask as described and treat each solution similarly. After the solutions have stood for 5 min., compare their color intensities in turn in a visual colorimeter with that of the standard, which has been developed simultaneously.

EXPERIMENT 14

PHOTOMETRIC DETERMINATION OF TYROSINE IN CASEIN

The reaction of phenols with a mixture of mercurous and mercuric nitrites to give red-colored products was discovered by Millon (1849) and was first applied to tyrosine by Hoffman (1853). Gibbs (1926, 1927) and Lugg (1938) have discussed this test.

Values ranging from 4.5 to 6.5 per cent tyrosine in casein have been reported. Fischer (1901) found 4.5 per cent by isolation, and Osborne and Guest (1911) considered this percentage to be the most reliable. Folin and coworkers obtained values from 5.3 to 6.4 per cent by photometric determination with their phenol (phosphotungstic acid—phosphomolybdic acid) reagent (Folin and Denis, 1912) and with their Millon's reagent (Folin and Ciocalteu, 1927; Folin and Looney, 1922). Values ranging from 5.5 to 6.0 per cent have been found more recently by photometric (Beach *et al.*, 1941; Williamson, 1944) and microbiological (Gunness, Dwyer, and Stokes, 1946) assays. Tyrosine has also been determined by spectrophotometric (Goodwin and Morton, 1946), chromatographic (Moore and Stein, 1949; Stein and Moore, 1949; Tristram, 1946), and L-amino acid decarboxylase (Hanke, 1948) methods.

Tyrosine in casein is to be determined by Block and Bolling's (1945) modification of the Millon-Folin method. The protein is hydrolyzed with sodium hydroxide rather than acid, which partially destroys tyrosine. Tryptophan is removed as its insoluble mercuric sulfate complex, since it gives an interfering colored product with Millon's reagent. The construction and operation of a visual colorimeter are described in the Appendix (see Photometry) and will be demonstrated by the instructor.

EXPERIMENTAL

Obtain approximately a 0.3-g. sample of an unknown casein and assignment to a visual colorimeter. Transfer 0.3 g. (weighed to ±1mg.) of the casein quantitatively to a 50-ml. conical flask, add 10 ml. of 5 *N* sodium hydroxide, attach a reflux condenser, place the flask in a melted hydrogenated-cottonseed-oil bath, heat the bath to 120°, and maintain this temperature for 5 hr.

Remove the flask and cool it to room temperature. Add 10 ml. of 5 *N* sulfuric acid and transfer the mixture quantitatively to a 500-ml. volumetric flask. Add distilled water to the mark and mix the liquids thoroughly. Pipette 10.0 ml. of this solution into a 50-ml. centrifuge tube (*A*) and 5.00 ml. into a 50-ml. centrifuge tube (*B*). Submit *B* to the instructor, who will add 5.00 ml. of a standard solution of pure L-tyrosine. Pipette into separate 8-in. test tubes 5.00 ml. of standard L-tyrosine solutions containing 0.500 mg. (*C*) and 0.800 mg. (*D*) of L-tyrosine, respectively. Add 5.0 ml. of distilled water to each tube.

Add (from a 10-ml. graduate) to each of the four tubes 10 ml. of distilled water and 5.0 ml. of Folin's reagent (mercuric sulfate in sulfuric acid). Place the tubes in a boiling water bath. After 10 min. remove the tubes and cool them to room temperature. Add about 15 mg. of filter aid to each of the centrifuge tubes *A* and *B*, and centrifuge the tubes at moderate speed for 5 min. to separate the insoluble tryptophan—mercuric sulfate complex. Carefully transfer the supernatant liquids containing the soluble tyrosine—mercuric sulfate complex to separate 50-ml. volumetric flasks. Wash each precipitate as follows: Add 5 ml. of a solution of 1.5 per cent mercuric sulfate in 6 *N* sulfuric acid to each centrifuge tube, stir the precipitates thoroughly, and centrifuge the suspensions for 5 min. Add each supernatant solution to its corresponding volumetric flask. Repeat the washing process using 3 ml. of the mercuric sulfate-sulfuric acid reagent. Add each wash liquid to its respective volumetric flask. Transfer the contents of tubes *C* and *D* to separate 50-ml. volumetric flasks and add 8 ml. of the mercuric sulfate—sulfuric acid reagent to each flask.

Pipette 1.0 ml. of 0.8 per cent sodium nitrate solution into each of the four volumetric flasks and add distilled water to the marks. Mix the liquids in each flask (stoppered the minimum time, since nitric oxide is evolved), and allow the solutions to stand for 10 min. Compare (within 30 min.) the intensities of the colors in the unknown solutions with that of the standard tyrosine which matches the unknown more closely.

EXPERIMENT 15

PREPARATION OF TYRAMINE HYDROCHLORIDE

Tyramine causes a rise in blood pressure, and it increases the force of the heart beat, although its action is less pronounced than that of adrenaline. That tyramine may originate in animal tissues from bacterial action is indicated by the observation that tyrosine is decarboxylated by *Escherichia coli* (Sasaki, 1914) and *Proteus vulgaris* (Kawai, 1916). Tyrosine decarboxylases are present in milk, blood, urine, yeast, and microorganisms (Gale and Epps, 1945).

Tyramine is to be prepared by thermal decarboxylation of tyrosine, essentially by Johnson and Daschavsky's (1924–1925) modification of Graziani's (1915) method. Tyrosine is heated in a mixture of high-boiling solvents until the evolution of carbon dioxide ceases. Solvents which have been employed, in addition to diphenylamine (Abderhalden and Gebelein, 1926) and diphenylmethane, include glycerol (Maillard, 1914a), paraffin, anthracene, and α-naphthylamine (Johnson and Daschavsky, 1924–1925). Satisfactory analogous procedures for other amines have not been reported.

EXPERIMENTAL

Place 10.0 g. of technical tyrosine, 60 g. of technical diphenylmethane, and 60 g. of technical diphenylamine in a 250-ml. conical flask. Place the flask in a sand bath and heat the bath while stirring the mixture (carefully, to avoid breaking the thermometer) with a 360° thermometer. Carbon dioxide is evolved at about 210°. Continue heating and stirring (for about 15 min.) until the evolution of gas ceases. Remove the flask and allow it to cool to room temperature. Add 100 ml. of diethyl ether, stir the mixture thoroughly, and filter the suspension of tyramine on a Buchner funnel. Transfer the filtrate to a bottle provided for that purpose. Repeat this extraction process twice, using 50-ml. portions of ether. Transfer the tan-colored precipitate to a 250-ml. conical flask, add 75 ml. of absolute ethanol, and heat the mixture on a water bath until the solid dissolves. Remove the flask and add 5 g. of decolorizing carbon. Place the flask on the water bath and heat the mixture for 5 min. while stirring it at intervals. Filter the hot suspension on a Buchner funnel and repeat the decolorizing process until the filtrate is colored light tan. Transfer the filtrate to a beaker, add 5 ml. of 12 N hydrochloric acid, stir the mixture thoroughly, and add 75 ml. of diethyl ether. Stir the mixture thoroughly and allow it to stand for 5 min. (on longer standing a blue or blue-green impurity forms which is difficult to remove). Filter the suspension of nearly white crystalline tyramine hydrochloride on a Buchner funnel and wash the precipitate twice with 10-ml. portions of diethyl ether. Redissolve the product in the minimum volume (about 35 ml.) of hot absolute ethanol, cool the solution for 30 min. in an ice-water bath, filter the suspension on a Buchner funnel, and wash the precipitate on the funnel with 15 ml. of diethyl ether. Transfer the product to a watch glass and allow it to dry in air. Submit the product to the instructor in a tared, labeled sample bottle.

EXPERIMENT 16

ISOLATION OF L-CYSTINE FROM HUMAN HAIR

L-Cystine has been isolated from hair and other keratins as its mercuric sulfate complex (Hopkins and Cole, 1901b), copper salt (Harris, 1922–1923), phosphotungstate (Winterstein, 1901–1902), hydrochloride (Toennies and Bennett, 1935–1936), and cuprous mercaptide derivative (Vickery and White, 1932; Lucas and Beveridge, 1940). Tyrosine, the principal impurity, has been removed from crude cystine by precipitating it at its isoelectric point (pH 5.7) (Greenbaum, 1935) and by extracting tyrosine ethyl ester from the esterified mixture (Plimmer, 1913).

The cystine content of keratins from different animals was determined by Wilson and Lewis (1927), who precipitated cystine at its isoelectric point and determined cystine in the crude product by the Folin and Looney (1922) photometric method and on the basis of the total sulfur content. Values by the two methods were in good agreement. The percentages of cystine found were human hair, 15.6 to 21.2; sheep wool, 8.0 to 19.0; feathers, 7.05 to 12.2; rabbit hair, 11.9 to 14.0; tortoise shell, 6.4 to 8.1; rat hair, 14.1; cat hair, 13.1; and dog hair, 19.0. Cystine has been isolated from hog hair (Greenbaum, 1935) and horsehair (Okabe, 1928). According to Clay, Cook, and Routh (1940), there is no constant relation between the age of the individual and the percentage of cystine in the hair. Dark hair was found to contain more cystine than light hair and hair of males more than that of females.

Vickery and Leavenworth (1929) obtained more than 10 per cent of analytically pure L-cystine from human hair, but yields usually are only about 5 per cent. Lucas and Beveridge (1940) reported 14.8 per cent, but the purity of the product was not established. Unless the product is carefully purified, considerable amounts of sulfate, sulfinic and sulfonic acids, DL-cystine, and mesocystine may be present.

L-Cystine is to be isolated from the hydrochloric acid hydrolysate of purified human hair, essentially by the method first described by Mörner (1899) and modified by Folin (1910), Gortner and Hoffman (1941), and Vickery and Leavenworth (1929). L-Cystine is precipitated at (or near) its isoelectric point (pH 5.0) and is purified by precipitating it with ethanol at the isoelectric point. The yield of analytically pure product is about 5 per cent of the weight of the dry purified hair. Because of its low solubility (about 0.1 g. per 100 ml. at 100°) it is impracticable to purify L-cystine by crystallization from water. Tyrosine may be removed by trituration with hot water, but this procedure is not entirely satisfactory since the solubility of tyrosine is only about five times that of cystine.

EXPERIMENTAL

Obtain about 600 g. of men's hair, remove the matches and other debris, and suspend the picked hair in 1.5 liters of commercial cleaning solvent (or petroleum ether, b.p. 60 to 100°). Stir the hair thoroughly at intervals for 30 min. Place a layer of cheesecloth in a funnel, transfer the hair to the funnel, and allow the solvent to drain. Resuspend the hair in 1.5 liters of the solvent, stir the hair at intervals for 10 min., and drain as before. Repeat this process until the hair appears to be thoroughly clean. Spread the clean hair on paper, preferably in the sun, until the solvent has evaporated.

Weigh 400 g. of the clean, dry hair and transfer the hair to a 2-liter round-bottomed flask. Add 1 liter of 8 N hydrochloric acid, attach a reflux condenser, and place the flask in a sand bath. Heat the sand sufficiently to cause gentle boiling and maintain this temperature for 8 hr. Longer heating may reduce the yield of L-cystine. Filter the hot suspension of humin on a Buchner funnel with the aid of celite. Wash the precipitate on the funnel with two 100-ml. portions of boiling distilled water.

Transfer the combined filtrate and washings to a 2-liter round-bottomed flask, set up the reduced-pressure apparatus shown in Fig. 7 (see Distillation in the Appendix), and distill the solution to a sirup under reduced pressure on a water bath. Add 700 ml. of boiling distilled water, stir the mixture, heat the solution to boiling, remove the flame, add 20 g. of decolorizing carbon in small portions while stirring, and allow the suspension to stand for 15 min. Filter the suspension on a Buchner funnel and wash the carbon residue on the funnel with two 20-ml. portions of boiling distilled water. If the filtrate is dark colored, repeat the decolorizing process, using 10 g. of decolorizing carbon. The final color of the filtrate should not be darker than light amber.

Transfer the filtrate to a beaker and add 6 N sodium hydroxide dropwise with constant stirring to pH 3.5[1] (tyrosine crystallization is minimum at this low pH). Determine the pH with congo red paper, which changes color from blue to purple over the pH range 3 to 4. Determine the shade of color to be expected by testing a buffer solution at pH 3.5. Allow the solution to stand for 30 min. in an ice-water bath or overnight in the refrigerator.

Filter the suspension and wash the gray-colored precipitate on the Buchner funnel with two 50-ml. portions of boiling distilled water. Discard the washings. Suspend the crude cystine in 100 ml. of boiling distilled water and add 12 N hydrochloric acid (about 40 ml.) until the precipitate dissolves. Heat the solution to boiling, remove the flame, add 15 g. of decolorizing carbon in small portions while stirring the mixture, and allow the suspension to stand for 10 min. Filter the hot suspension on a Buchner funnel and wash the carbon residue on the funnel with two 25-ml. portions of hot N hydrochloric acid. Filter the combined filtrate and washings to remove traces of carbon. Transfer the filtrate to a beaker and add 6 N sodium hydroxide dropwise to pH 3.5, determined as previously described. Allow the solution to stand for 30 min. in an ice-water bath or overnight in the refrigerator.

Filter the crystalline suspension on a Buchner funnel and wash the precipitate on the funnel with two 25-ml. portions of boiling distilled water. Test the final wash liquid with Millon's reagent (see Exp. 21, Step XI, Test 5), and if the test for tyrosine is positive, continue washing with additional portions of boiling distilled water until the test is negative.

Resuspend the cystine in 100 ml. of boiling distilled water and add 12 N hydrochloric acid dropwise with stirring until the solid dissolves. If the solution is colored, decolorize it with 10 g. of decolorizing carbon as previously described. Filter the suspension and wash the precipitate on the funnel with 25 ml. of hot N hydrochloric acid. Add 6 N sodium hydroxide dropwise to the combined filtrate and washings to pH 4.5 (tested as previously described), and add an equal volume of 95 per cent ethanol. Place the solution in an ice-water bath for 30 min. or overnight in the refrigerator.

Filter the suspension on a Buchner funnel and wash the crystals with distilled water until the test for chloride ion (white precipitate of silver chloride) is negative (1 ml. of the AgNO$_3$-HNO$_3$ reagent added to 1 ml. of the filtrate). Wash the crystals with two 25-ml. portions of 95 per cent ethanol and apply suction until the product is nearly dry. Dry the product in a covered evaporating dish overnight at 50°. Submit the product to the instructor in a tared, labeled sample bottle. Calculate the percentage yield and submit the calculations to the instructor.

NOTE

1. The pH should not increase beyond 7 at any time, since cystine is decomposed even in slightly alkaline solution. Sodium acetate, rather than sodium hydroxide, has been employed to avoid this danger.

EXPERIMENT 17

POLARIMETRIC ANALYSIS OF L-CYSTINE

The optical rotation of L-cystine prepared in Exp. 16 is to be determined, and the purity of the sample is to be calculated from the specific rotation,[1] which is a dependable criterion of purity for optically active amino acids. The construction and operation of a polarimeter are described in the Appendix (see Polarimetry) and will be demonstrated by the instructor. The measurement of optical rotation consists essentially in determining the number of angular degrees to which the plane of polarized light is rotated by a solution of an optically active substance.

EXPERIMENTAL

Obtain from the instructor three approximately 0.5-g. samples of L-cystine and one of analytically pure L-cystine. Obtain assignment to a polarimeter. Transfer 0.5 g. (weighed to ± 1 mg.) of each sample quantitatively to a 50-ml. volumetric flask, add 1.00 N hydrochloric acid to each flask, rotate the flasks until the samples dissolve, and add 1.00 N hydrochloric acid to the marks.

Turn on the sodium light and allow it to warm up for 10 min. Thoroughly rinse the polarimeter tube with distilled water and fill the tube with distilled water in such a manner that air bubbles are removed. Place the tube in the instrument, focus the eyepiece, and rotate the scale until the dark fields match. Record the scale reading to three figures. Repeat this matching process several times while approaching the matching point from both directions.

Empty the tube, rinse it thoroughly with the minimum volume of one of the unknown L-cystine solutions, and fill it with this solution. Match the fields as described and record the scale readings. Place a thermometer in the L-cystine solution and record the temperature. Repeat these operations using each of the remaining L-cystine solutions in turn.

NOTE

1. Specific rotation is calculated from the equation

$$[\alpha]_D^t = \frac{\alpha v}{w l}$$

where α = observed rotation, angular deg.
   t = temperature of the solution, $^\circ$C.
   D = D line of sodium light
   v = volume of solution, ml.
   w = weight of sample, g.
   l = length of polarimeter tube (light path), dm.
   $[\alpha]$ = specific rotation

Specific rotation and temperature are related (for L-cystine) by the equation $[\alpha]_D^t = [(2.061t) - 264.84]^\circ$, derived by Toennies and Lavine (1930).

EXPERIMENT 18

PHOTOMETRIC ANALYSIS OF CYSTINE BASED ON THE REACTION OF CYSTEINE WITH PHOSPHOTUNGSTIC ACID

The reaction of cysteine with phosphotungstic acid, first observed by Winterstein (1901–1902), was applied by Folin and Looney (1922) to the quantitative determination of cystine. Because the reagent was reduced by tyrosine and other substances, more specific reagents were devised by Folin and Marenzi (1929b) and Folin (1934). Further improvements were effected by substituting $NaHCO_3$ for Na_2CO_3 to prevent the turbidity caused by sodium phosphotungstate (Tompsett, 1931), introducing a buffer solution to maintain the pH at 5.0 to 6.5, over which range the colored complex is stable (Lugg, 1932a, 1932b; Schöberl and Rambacher, 1937–1938), and measuring the color intensities with a photoelectric, rather than a visual, colorimeter (Balint, 1938; Block and Bolling, 1940; Kassell and Brand, 1938).

Cysteine (formed by reduction of cystine) has been determined by (a) titration with standard iodine in the presence of starch (Mörner, 1901–1902), (b) titration with standard iodate in the presence of iodide and starch (Okuda, 1925), (c) reaction with standard iodine in potassium iodide solution and titration of the excess iodine with standard thiosulfate (Virtue and Lewis, 1934), (d) photometric determination of the colored complex formed with 1,2-naphthoquinone-4-sulfonate (Andrews and Andrews 1937; Bushill et al., 1934; Hess and Sullivan, 1943; Lugg, 1933; Sullivan et al., 1942) or with sodium nitroprusside (Shinohara and Kilpatrick, 1934), (e) determination of nitrogen or sulfur in cuprous mercaptide (Lucas and Beveridge, 1940; Vickery and White, 1932; Zittle and O'Dell, 1941), and (f) reaction with iodine and gasometric determination of the nitrogen formed by reaction of the excess iodine with hydrazine (Hess, 1933).

Cystine has been determined by (a) oxidation and gravimetric analysis of sulfate as barium sulfate (Callan and Toennies, 1941) and (b) polarographic analysis (Callan and Toennies, 1941; Stern et al., 1939).

The purity of unknown cystine samples is to be determined by reducing the cystine to cysteine and analyzing photometrically the blue-colored complex formed by reaction of the cysteine with phospho-18-tungstic acid. According to Clarke (1932) one molecule of cystine is reduced by sulfite to one molecule of cysteine sodium mercaptide $[NaSCH_2CH(NH_2)COOH]$ and one molecule of sodium S-cysteinesulfonate $[HOOCCH(NH_2)CH_2SO_3Na]$. Zinc, tin, sodium cyanide, sodium amalgam, cuprous chloride, and cuprous oxide have been employed as reducing agents.

EXPERIMENTAL

Obtain three L-cystine unknowns and assignment to a visual colorimeter. Transfer quantitative approximately 0.25 g. (weighed to ± 1 mg.) of each sample to a 250-ml. volumetric flask. Add 100 ml. of 0.5 N sulfuric acid to each flask and rotate the flasks until the solids dissolve. Add 0.5 N sulfuric acid to the marks and mix the liquids in each flask thoroughly.

Pipette 2.00-ml. aliquots of the three unknown solutions and the standard solution, containing 1.00 mg. per ml. of purified L-cystine, to four separate 100-ml. volumetric flasks. Add to each flask 10 ml. of saturated sodium bicarbonate solution and 2.0 ml. of Folin's improved phospho-18-tungstic acid reagent. Mix the liquids thoroughly and allow the mixtures to stand for 10 min. Dilute each solution to the mark with distilled water and mix the liquids in each flask thoroughly. Compare the color intensities of the unknown solutions with the standard which has been developed simultaneously

EXPERIMENT 19

ISOLATION OF ASPARAGINE MONOHYDRATE FROM LUPINE SPROUTS

Asparagine, the beta amide of aspartic acid, is a metabolic product of sprouted lupines (*Lupinus*), vetches (*Vicia*), beans (*Phaseolus*), soybean (*Glycine hispida*), and other members of the legume family. It is widely used as an essential component of media on which bacteria and yeasts are cultured.

Asparagine was first isolated from asparagus sprouts by Robiquet (1805) and Vacquelin and Robiquet (1806), but the first practicable isolation procedure was reported by Chibnall (1924). Asparagine has been isolated most commonly from lupine sprouts by modifications of the method of Piria (1848). The early literature has been reviewed by Schulze and Winterstein (1910), Vickery and Schmidt (1931), Murneek (1935), Vickery *et al.* (1937), and Chibnall (1939).

Asparagine is to be isolated from lupine sprouts by a modification of Vickery and Pucher's (1943) method. Lupine seeds are grown in the dark in tap water for 10 to 12 days (*Lupinus angustifolius*) or 15 to 20 days (*Lupinus albus*). The highest yield has been obtained from *Lupinus albus*. The etiolated seedlings are ground and extracted with water; the extract is heated to coagulate the proteins, the suspension is filtered, the filtrate is evaporated, and asparagine monohydrate is allowed to crystallize.

EXPERIMENTAL

Germination of Seeds. Obtain 100 g. of *Lupinus albus* seeds and assignment to a tray (or part of a tray) about 2 ft. square and approximately 6 in. deep which is provided with a drain tube at the bottom and near the side of the tray. Attach a rubber tube to the drain and close the tube with a screw clamp. Place the tray in a well-ventilated, lightproof room or cabinet. Fill the tray nearly full with clean sand, run in tap water sufficient to cover the sand, and allow the water to drain. Punch holes about 1/2 in. deep and as closely spaced as possible in the moist sand. Place one seed in each hole and cover the holes with sand. Resaturate the sand with tap water at 48-hr. intervals. After the sprouts appear, allow them to grow for an additional 18 or 19 days.

Extraction of Asparagine. Remove the entire mass of sprouts, roots, and residual seed substance. Remove the adhering sand by immersing and agitating the root mass in a pan of water. Blot the roots with cheesecloth to remove excess water. Fill the glass (or metal) bowl of a Waring Blendor about three-fourths full with the moist sprouts. Add 150 ml. of boiling distilled water, place the cover on the bowl, and turn on the motor. When the material has been thoroughly macerated, transfer the suspension to a 2-liter flask containing 500 ml. of boiling distilled water, and place the flask in a boiling water bath. Macerate the remainder of the sprouts similarly, add the suspensions to the 2-liter flask, and continue to heat the bath for 15 min.

Place a filter paper on a 6-in. Buchner funnel, add a suspension of filter aid, and apply suction until about 1/2 in. of well-packed filter aid has deposited. Place a perforated filter paper on the filter aid, disconnect the tube to the water pump, and discard the liquid in the filter flask. Transfer the hot suspension to the Buchner funnel, connect the tube to the water pump, and apply suction until the bulk of the water has been removed and the residual material on the funnel is nearly dry. Transfer enough residual material to fill halfway the bowl of the Waring Blendor, add 150 ml. of boiling distilled water, stir the material until it is thoroughly macerated, and transfer the mixture to a 2-liter flask containing 200 ml. of boiling distilled water. Place the flask on a boiling water bath. Repeat this procedure until all the residual material has been extracted. Filter the suspension on a Buchner funnel and wash the residual material on the funnel with 200 ml. of boiling distilled water. Combine the filtrate and washings. This solution should be preserved in the refrigerator in a stoppered, labeled flask if it is allowed to stand overnight. A few milliliters of toluene should be added as preservative if the solution is allowed to stand for a longer time.

Isolation of Asparagine Monohydrate. Transfer the solution to a 2-liter beaker and heat it on a wi gauze over a free flame until the volume is reduced (from about 1,200 ml.) to 500 ml. Remove the flame add 2 g. of decolorizing carbon slowly to avoid foaming, stir the mixture at intervals for 15 min. and filter the suspension. Transfer the filtrate to a 1-liter round-bottomed flask, set up the reduced pressu apparatus shown in Fig. 7 (see Distillation in the Appendix), and distill the liquid under reduced-pressure on a water bath to a thin sirup (about 40 ml.). Transfer the sirup to a 100-ml. beaker and rinse the sirup from the flask with two 15-ml. portions of boiling distilled water. Label the container, cover it with a watch glass, and allow it to stand in the refrigerator until the next laboratory period (but not longer than 48 hr. because of the danger of bacterial or mold contamination).

Decant the supernatant liquid to a Hirsch or small Buchner funnel, and after the liquid has filtere add the crystalline material. Filter the mixture and wash the crystals on the funnel with 5 ml. of ice-cold distilled water. Transfer the crystals to a 100-ml. beaker, add 30 ml. of distilled water, and heat the mixture on a water bath until the crystals dissolve. Add 0.5 g. of decolorizing carbon, heat the mixture for 5 min. on a water bath with frequent stirring, and filter the hot suspension on a Hirsch funne Reheat and refilter the filtrate if carbon particles are observed. Allow the filtrate to cool slowly to roo temperature with frequent shaking. Place the container in the refrigerator and allow it to stand overnig Filter the suspension and wash the crystals on the funnel with two 10-ml. portions of 95 per cent ethan Allow the crystals to dry in air in a covered, labeled evaporating dish. Submit the product[1] to the in-structor in a tared, labeled sample bottle. Calculate the percentage yield of asparagine monohydrate based on the weight of the seeds and submit the calculations to the instructor.

NOTE

1. A second crop may be obtained by evaporating the combined filtrates and washings to a small volume and recrystallizing the crude product from water.

EXPERIMENT 20

AMIDE-NITROGEN ANALYSIS OF ASPARAGINE MONOHYDRATE

The purity of an asparagine sample is to be determined by alkaline hydrolysis of the asparagine monohydrate, collection of the ammonia in standard boric acid solution, determination of the pH of the ammonium borate—boric acid solution, and estimation of the ammonia by interpolation of a curve relating pH and ammonia concentration of standard ammonium borate—boric acid solutions. This method is an adaptation of the Taylor and Smith (1942) modification of the Wagner (1940) method.[1] The theory and construction of a pH meter are explained in the Appendix (see pH). The instructor will demonstrate.

EXPERIMENTAL

Obtain a sample of asparagine monohydrate and assignment to a pH meter. Transfer about 0.25 g. (weighed to ±1 mg.) of the sample quantitatively to a 100-ml. volumetric flask. Add 25 ml. of distilled water and rotate the flask until the sample dissolves. Add distilled water to the mark and mix the liquids thoroughly. Pipette 25.0 ml. of the solution to a 50-ml. volumetric flask and submit the flask to the instructor, who will add a known quantity of pure asparagine monohydrate.

Standard Curve Relating pH and Ammonia Concentration of Ammonium Borate—Boric Acid Solutions. Pipette 10.0 ml. of 4.0 per cent boric acid solution into a 250-ml. beaker. Add 150 ml. of distilled water[2] from a graduate. Mix the solutions and measure the pH with a pH meter. Pipette into this mixture 1.00 ml. of a standard, approximately 0.01 M, ammonium hydroxide solution,[3] mix the liquids thoroughly, and determine the pH. Continue adding 1.00-ml. volumes of the standard ammonium hydroxide solution and measuring the pH until there is a total volume of 10 ml. of ammonium hydroxide.

Calculate the equivalents of ammonia in each mixture and plot on coordinate paper the points relating the ammonia and corresponding pH values. Draw a smooth curve, label the ordinates, and title the graph.

Determination of Amide Ammonia in Asparagine Monohydrate. Pipette 5.00 ml. of the unknown asparagine monohydrate solution into a 500-ml. distilling flask. Add 75 ml. of distilled water and a few boiling stones. Attach a Liebig condenser to the side arm of the flask. Pipette 10.0 ml. of 4.0 per cent boric acid solution into a 125-ml. conical flask and add about 25 ml. of distilled water. Insert the end of the condenser into the flask and incline the apparatus so that the tip of the condenser is below the surface of the boric acid solution. Add 10 ml. of 6 N sodium hydroxide to the distilling flask with the aid of a pipette, in such a manner that the alkali solution is introduced directly into the solution without coming in contact with the wall of the flask. Immediately stopper the distilling flask and heat it on a wire gauze over a small flame to gentle boiling. Continue heating for 20 min., remove the receiver, remove the burner, and rinse any boric acid solution from the condenser to the receiver. Transfer the boric acid solution quantitatively to a 250-ml. graduate, add distilled water to the mark, and mix the liquids thoroughly. Transfer the solution to a beaker and determine its pH with the pH meter. Estimate the equivalents of ammonia corresponding to the pH value by interpolating the standard curve.

Analyze the asparagine monohydrate recovery solution by the described procedure.

1. By the Wagner method the ammonia in the boric acid solution is titrated directly in the presence of methyl red indicator. Taylor and Smith titrated with the aid of the glass electrode. The present modification is more convenient, although somewhat less accurate, than electrometric titration.

2. Distilled water of uniform quality obtained from the container on the side shelf should be used throughout this experiment.

3. Determine the titer of the ammonium hydroxide solution on the day of the experiment by pipetting an aliquot into an excess of standard acid and back-titrating with standard sodium hydroxide solution using the mixed indicator employed in Exp. 9.

EXPERIMENT 21

IDENTIFICATION OF AMINO ACIDS IN A MIXTURE OF AMINO ACIDS

The amino acids in an unknown mixture of amino acids are to be identified by applying the group separations and specific tests described below.

SCHEME OF ANALYSIS

Step I. Detection of Amino Acids. *Ninhydrin Test.*

Step II. Detection of Pyrrolidine-containing Amino Acids. *Proline and Hydroxyproline. Lead Dioxide Oxidation Test.*

Step III. Detection of Sulfur-containing Amino Acids. *Cystine and Methionine. Sodium Fusion Test.*

Step IV. Detection of Aromatic Amino Acids. *Tryptophan, Tyrosine, and Phenylalanine. Xanthoproteic Test.*

Step V. Solubility Separation.

    1. *Proline. Extraction with Absolute Ethanol.*

    2. *Cystine and Tyrosine. Separation from Water-soluble Amino Acids.*

Step VI. Detection of Basic Amino Acids. *Arginine, Histidine, and Lysine. Phosphotungstic Acid Precipitation Test.*

Step VII. Detection and Separation of Acidic Amino Acids. *Glutamic Acid and Aspartic Acid. Lime-Ethanol Precipitation Test.*

Step VIII. Separation of Basic Amino Acids and Tryptophan.

    1. *Arginine, Histidine, and Lysine Phosphotungstates Precipitation.*

    2. *Tryptophan Phosphotungstate Precipitation.*

    3. *Phosphotungstic Acid Removal.*

Step IX. Detection of Amino Acids Containing Adjacent Amino and Hydroxy Groups. *Serine and Threonine. Periodic Acid Oxidation Test.*

Step X. Detection of Ketone-forming Amino Acids. *Valine, Leucine, and Isoleucine. Permanganate Oxidation Test.*

Step XI. Detection of Individual Amino Acids.

    1. *Proline. Isatin Test.*

    2. *Hydroxyproline. Pyrrole-Isatin Test.*

    3. *Cystine. β-Naphthoquinonesulfonic Acid Test.*

    4. *Methionine. Sodium Nitroprusside Test.*

    5. *Tyrosine. Mercuric Nitrite Test.*

    6. *Tryptophan. Glyoxylic Acid Test.*

    7. *Phenylalanine. Nitric Acid—Hydroxylamine Test.*

    8. *Arginine. Hypobromite—α-Naphthol Test.*

    9. *Histidine. Bromidazole-Ammonia Test.*

    10. *Lysine. Picrate Precipitation and Bromine—Phosphomolybdic Acid—Phosphotungstic Acid Tests.*

    11. *Glutamic Acid. Hydrochloride Precipitation Test.*

    12. *Aspartic Acid. Glyoxal—2,4-Dinitrophenylosazone and Cupric Aspartate Hydrate Precipitation Tests.*

    13. *Threonine. Periodic Acid—Acetaldehyde—p-Hydroxydiphenyl Test.*

    14. *Serine. Periodic Acid—Formaldehyde—Chromotropic Acid Test.*

15. *Leucine and Valine. Acetone-Salicylaldehyde Test.*
16. *Isoleucine. Methyl Ethyl Ketone—Salicylaldehyde Test.*
17. *Alanine. Ninhydrin—Acetaldehyde—p-Hydroxydiphenyl Test.*
18. *Glycine. Ninhydrin—Formaldehyde—Chromotropic Acid and o-Phthalaldehyde Tests.*

EXPERIMENTAL

Obtain a homogeneous mixture of unknown amino acids and identify each amino acid. Solid materials are to be weighed on a horn-pan balance or measured by comparison with the volumes of weighed sample in test tubes on the reagent shelf.

Make an accurate record of all experimental observations. If any result is inconclusive, repeat the test on a sample of the pure amino acid obtained from the instructor. After the group tests have been completed, prepare a flow sheet outlining the individual tests of Step XI applicable to the unknown mixture. Submit a written report summarizing the results of each test and the conclusions.

Step I. Detection of Amino Acids. *Ninhydrin Test.*[1] Transfer 5 mg. of the unknown to a 3-in. test tube. Add 3 ml. of distilled water and 1 ml. of 0.1 per cent ninhydrin solution. Heat the mixture in a boiling water bath for 3 min. Note the color of the solution. Add 1 drop of glacial acetic acid and 1 ml. of chloroform. Shake the tube vigorously. The appearance of a blue to violet or red color after heating and of an orange color entirely concentrated in the chloroform layer after acidification indicates the presence of at least one amino acid in the unknown.

Step II. Detection of Pyrrolidine-containing Amino Acids. *Proline and Hydroxyproline.*[2] *Lead Dioxide Oxidation Test.* Transfer 20 mg. of the unknown to a 125-ml. conical flask, add 5 ml. of distilled water, and stir the mixture until all, or almost all, the solid dissolves. Add 10 ml. of phosphate (Na_2HPO_4) buffer solution to maintain the pH at 8.7 and add 0.2 g. of lead dioxide. Stir the mixture, fit a Hopkins condenser into the neck of the flask, and heat the flask in a boiling water both for 20 min. Filter the suspension and transfer 5 ml. of the filtrate to a 6-in. test tube. Add 1 ml. of a 4 per cent solution of p-dimethylaminobenzaldehyde in 95 per cent ethanol and add 5 ml. of N hydrochloric acid. Mix the liquids thoroughly and heat the tube in a boiling water bath for 1 min. The immediate appearance of a red color indicates the presence of proline, hydroxyproline, or both these amino acids.

Step III. Detection of Sulfur-containing Amino Acids. *Cystine and Methionine. Sodium Fusion Test.* Place a clean 3-mm. cube of sodium metal (obtained from the instructor) in a clean, dry 3-in. test tube and add 15 mg. of the unknown. Suspend the tube through an asbestos board which is supported by an iron ring. Heat the tube with a flame until sodium vapors are visible in the lower part of the tube. Add 10 mg. of the unknown (*Cautiously*) to the tube. Heat the tube until the glass is red and continue heating for 1 min. Allow the tube to cool and add 0.5 ml. of 75 per cent ethanol to destroy the unreacted sodium. Remove the tube from the board, heat it with a flame, and immerse the hot tube in a 50-ml. beaker containing 10 ml. of distilled water. Shatter the cracked tube, pulverize (with glass rod) the glass and solid material, and filter the suspension. Transfer 5 ml. of the filtrate to a 6-in. test tube and add 6 N acetic acid until the solution is neutral to litmus paper. Add 1 drop of 2 N lead acetate solution. The formation of a black precipitate of lead sulfide indicates the presence of cystine or methionine or both these amino acids.

Step IV. Detection of Aromatic Amino Acids. *Tryptophan, Tyrosine, and Phenylalanine. Xanthoproteic Test.*[3] Transfer 20 mg. of the unknown to a 4-in. test tube. Add 1 ml. of concentrated nitric acid and 1 drop of concentrated sulfuric acid. Heat the tube for 5 min. in a boiling water bath. Cool the tube in running water and note the color of the solution. Add (*Carefully*) 2 ml. of saturated sodium hydroxide, mix the liquids, and note the color of the solution. A yellow-colored acid solution and an orange to orange-red alkaline solution indicates the presence of an aromatic amino acid. Disregard any white precipitate (sodium chloride) in the alkaline solution. Phenylalanine may give only a faint color in acid solution, but it yields a definite orange color in basic solution.

Step V. Solubility Separations. 1. *Proline. Extraction with Absolute Ethanol.*[4] Transfer all the unknown to a 6-in. test tube, add 10 ml. of absolute ethanol, and stopper and shake the tube vigorously for 2 min. Allow the mixture to stand, and decant most of the supernatant liquid to a dry gravity filter. Collect and preserve the filtrate in a 3-in. evaporating dish. Add 10 ml. of absolute ethanol to the test tube, stopper the tube, and shake it vigorously for 1 min. Transfer the mixture to the funnel and collect the filtrate. Evaporate the combined filtrates on a water bath and preserve the dry residue (principally proline) for the confirmatory test (Step XI, Test 1).

Transfer the dry residue in the test tube to a dry filter, using 25-ml. portions of diethyl ether as rinse fluid. Pour the ether filtrate into the sink and flush it into the drain with water. Preserve the residual material for use in Step V-2.

2. *Cystine and Tyrosine. Separation from Water-soluble Amino Acids.*[5] If cystine and tyrosine are absent (shown in Steps III and IV), transfer the proline-free residual material prepared in Step V-1 to a 50-ml. conical flask, add 20 ml. of distilled water, and rotate the flask (or heat it in a water bath) until the solid dissolves. Proceed to Step VI.

If undissolved solid remains (cystine or tyrosine present), continue to heat the flask in the water bath for 15 min. at 80°. Cool the flask for 15 min. in an ice-water bath, filter the mixture on a dry gravity filter, and transfer the filtrate to a labeled flask. When the solution is not in use, preserve it in the refrigerator for use in Step VI. If additional precipitate forms, filter the suspension and utilize the filtrate in Step VI. Wash the precipitate with two 5-ml. portions of methanol, dry it in air, and preserve it for the confirmatory cystine (Step XI, Test 3) and tyrosine (Step XI, Test 5) tests.

Step VI. Detection of Basic Amino Acids. *Arginine, Histidine, and Lysine. Phosphotungstic Acid Precipitation Test.*[6] Transfer 0.5 ml. of the solution of the soluble amino acids prepared in Step V-2 to a 6-in. test tube. Add 7 ml. of distilled water and 0.5 ml. of a 20 per cent solution of phosphotungstic acid. Stir the mixture vigorously for 1 min. The immediate appearance of a white precipitate indicates the presence of at least one of the basic amino acids.

Step VII. Detection and Separation of Acidic Amino Acids. *Glutamic Acid and Aspartic Acid. Lime-Ethanol Precipitation Test.*[7] Heat the remaining volume of the solution of the soluble amino acids prepared in Step V-2, remove the flame when the solution starts to boil, and add 0.7 g. of powdered, carbonate-free calcium hydroxide. Stopper the flask and shake it vigorously for 1 min. Cool the flask to 0° in an ice-water bath and shake it vigorously. Cool 50 ml. of 95 per cent ethanol to 0° in a 125-ml. flask, add the amino acid—lime mixture slowly while rotating the flask. stopper the flask, and shake it vigorously. Filter the mixture as quickly as possible, or centrifuge it if filtration is slow. Preserve the precipitate for later use in this test. Acidify the filtrate (or supernatant liquid) with 0.5 N sulfuric acid to pH 4 (test with congo red paper, which changes color from blue to purple over the pH range 3 to 4). Filter the calcium sulfate suspension, wash the solid on the funnel with 5 ml. of distilled water, and evaporate the combined filtrate and washing to 15 ml. Preserve this solution for use in Step VIII.

Transfer the lime-ethanol precipitate to a 50-ml. flask, add 10 ml. of boiling distilled water, stopper the flask, and shake it vigorously for 1 min. to dissolve the calcium glutamate and calcium aspartate. Heat the suspension to boiling and filter (or centrifuge) it to remove the excess calcium hydroxide and any calcium carbonate which may have formed. Add the filtrate to 30 ml. of 95 per cent ethanol while rotating the flask and cool the mixture in an ice-water bath for 15 min. with frequent stirring. If no precipitate forms in 15 min., allow the mixture to stand overnight in the refrigerator. If a precipitate forms, filter the suspension and preserve the precipitate for the glutamic acid (Step XI, Test 11) and aspartic acid (Step XI, Test 12) confirmatory tests.

Step VIII. Separation of Basic Amino Acids and Tryptophan. Test the solution of the soluble amino acids prepared in Step VII for tryptophan by the procedure given in Step XI, Test 6. If both the basic amino acids and tryptophan are absent, omit Step VIII. If basic amino acids are absent and tryptophan is present, omit Step VIII-1. If basic amino acids are present and tryptophan is absent, omit Step VIII-2.

1. *Precipitation of Arginine, Histidine, and Lysine Phosphotungstates.* The object of this procedure is to precipitate the basic amino acids but not tryptophan, which might interfere with the confirmatory tests for the basic amino acids. The quantity of phosphotungstic acid required to accomplish this purpose is variable, depending upon the number of basic amino acids present in the unknown.

Transfer the amino acid solution prepared in Step VII to a 125-ml. conical flask, add 37 ml. of a 20 per cent solution of phosphotungstic acid, add 1 ml. of 6 N hydrochloric acid, and stir the mixture at intervals for 5 min. Immediately filter the suspension with suction and preserve the precipitate

(A-1). Add 1 ml. of the phosphotungstic acid reagent to 5 ml. of the filtrate. If a precipitate forms, combine this suspension with the remaining filtrate and add 22 ml. of the phosphotungstic acid reagent. Stir the mixture at intervals for 10 min. and filter the suspension with suction. Preserve the precipitate (A-2).

If tryptophan was present in the unknown, test the filtrate (from which A-2 was removed) for tryptophan by the procedure given in Step XI, Test 6, to determine if tryptophan was removed in precipitate A-2. If this test is negative, preserve precipitate A-2, test A-2 for tryptophan, and (if the test is negative) omit Step VIII-2. If the test is positive, combine precipitates A-1 and A-2. Preserve the phosphotungstic acid precipitate (A-1 or A-1 plus A-2) for the removal of phosphotungstic acid in Step VIII-3. Preserve the filtrate from precipitate A-1 (if tryptophan was absent from the filtrate of A-2) or from A-1 plus A-2 for the precipitation of tryptophan phosphotungstate (Step VIII-2) (if tryptophan was present) or for the removal of phosphotungstic acid (Step VIII-3) (if tryptophan was absent).

2. *Precipitation of Tryptophan Phosphotungstate. Basic amino acids absent.* Add 10 ml. of the phosphotungstic acid reagent and 0.5 ml. of 6 N hydrochloric acid to the solution preserved from Step VII, stir the mixture, and place it in an ice-water bath for 1 hr. or in the refrigerator overnight. Filter the suspension and preserve the precipitate (containing some glycine if glycine is in the unknown) for use in Step VIII-3. If the filtrate is turbid, add 0.5 g. of decolorizing carbon, stir the mixture, and filter the suspension, using two thicknesses of filter paper. If necessary, repeat this process until the filtrate is clear. Preserve the filtrate for use in Step VIII-3.

Basic amino acids removed. Evaporate the filtrate from Step VIII-1 to 10 ml. and carry out the procedure described in this section.

3. *Removal of Phosphotungstic Acid.* Transfer the phosphotungstic acid precipitate (from Step VIII-1) to a separatory funnel. Add 10 ml. of distilled water, 5.0 ml. of N hydrochloric acid, and 25 ml. of a 1:1 mixture of amyl alcohol and diethyl ether.[8] Shake the funnel, while holding the stopper and stopcock firmly with the funnel in an inverted position, until the precipitate dissolves (turn the stopcock at intervals to release the pressure). Allow the layers to separate and draw off the lower, heavier water layer containing the amino acids. If the water layer does not settle, add additional 10-ml. portions of distilled water with shaking until the layers separate. Reextract the aqueous solution with 10 ml. of the alcohol-ether mixture to remove traces of phosphotungstic acid. Preserve the aqueous solution for the confirmatory tests in Step XI for arginine (Test 8), histidine (Test 9), and lysine (Test 10). Place the alcohol-ether solution of phosphotungstic acid in the container provided for that purpose.

Transfer the phosphotungstic acid filtrate from Step VIII-1 (or Step VIII-2) to a separatory funnel, add 20 ml. of the amyl alcohol—ether mixture, and shake the funnel as described. Remove the lower water layer and reextract it with 10 ml. of this solvent. Add N sodium hydroxide to pH 4 (test with congo red indicator, which changes color from blue to purple over the pH range 3 to 4), and preserve the solution for use in Step IX. Place the alcohol-ether solution of phosphotungstic acid in the special container.

Step IX. Detection of Amino Acids Containing Adjacent Amino and Hydroxy Groups. *Serine and Threonine. Periodic Acid Oxidation Test.*[9] Obtain the aeration assembly shown in Fig. 5 (see Aeration in the Appendix). Put 0.5 ml. of the unknown amino acid solution preserved in Step VII or VIII into the reaction tube; add 3 ml. of concentrated (50 g. per 100 ml.) potassium carbonate solution and 2 drops of antifoam agent (turkey red oil). Apply suction and aerate for 2 min. Disconnect the receiver, add 5 ml. of Nessler reagent (HgI_2 in an alkaline solution of KI) to the receiver, and add 2 ml. of 0.5 M periodic acid to the reaction tube. Immediately reassemble the apparatus and aerate for 5 min. The appearance of a red color in the Nessler solution indicates the presence of ammonia in the solution and of serine, threonine, or both these amino acids in the unknown.

Step X. Detection of Ketone-forming Amino Acids. *Valine, Leucine, and Isoleucine. Permanganate Oxidation Test.*[10] Transfer 2 ml. of the solution prepared in Step VII or VIII to a 50-ml. conical flask. Add 1 ml. of 6 N sulfuric acid and 1 ml. of 30 per cent aqueous sodium nitrite solution. Heat the flask for 15 min. in a boiling-water bath to deaminize the amino acids and destroy the excess nitrous acid. Add N sodium hydroxide to pH 4 (test with congo red indicator). Add 10 ml. of pH 6.8 buffer solution (KH_2PO_4 and K_2HPO_4), 1 g. of solid potassium permanganate, and a boiling stone. Insert a stopper fitted with a glass tube leading downward into a test tube containing 5 ml. of water. Immerse the receiver in an ice-water bath. Heat the flask with a small flame and continue heating until the volume of the liquid has been reduced to about 3 ml. Immediately remove the receiver to prevent the liquid from being sucked back as the reaction tube cools. Transfer 3 ml. of the solution in the receiver to another test tube. Add 3 ml. of water, 4 ml. of 95 per cent ethanol, and (*Cautiously*) 4 ml. of concentrated sulfuric acid. Cool the mixture to room temperature under running water. Add 2 ml. of a freshly prepared 6 per cent alcoholic solution of salicylaldehyde, and place the tube in a water bath at 60° for 20 min. The appearance of a red color indicates the presence of a ketone-forming amino acid. Preserve the remainder of the solution in the receiver for the leucine and valine (Step XI, Test 15) and isoleucine (Step XI, Test 16) confirmatory tests.

Step XI. Detection of Individual Amino Acids. 1. *Proline. Isatin Test.*[11] Transfer 20 mg. of the solid isolated in Step V-1 to a 6-in. test tube. Add 5 ml. of glacial acetic acid and 1 mg. of isatin. Heat the test tube for 5 min. in a boiling-water bath. The appearance of a blue color confirms the presence of proline.

2. *Hydroxyproline. Pyrrole-Isatin Test.*[12] Transfer 4 drops of the solution prepared in Step VIII to a test tube. Add 1 ml. of water, 1 ml. of 0.01 M cupric sulfate solution, 1 ml. of 3 N sodium hydroxide, and 1 ml. of 6 per cent hydrogen peroxide. Allow the solution to stand for 5 min. with frequent shaking. Heat the solution in a boiling-water bath for 5 min. and cool it to room temperature. Add N hydrochloric acid dropwise until the deep-blue color of cupric sulfate has been discharged. Add 0.3 ml. of N hydrochloric acid. Transfer 2 ml. of the solution to a 4-in. test tube and add 2 ml. of a freshly prepared 1 per cent aqueous solution of isatin. Add 2 ml. of N hydrochloric acid. Heat the tube for 5 min. in a boiling-water bath. The appearance of a red color confirms the presence of hydroxyproline.

3. *Cystine. β-Naphthoquinonesulfonate Test.*[13] Transfer 1 mg. of the precipitate obtained in Step V-2 to a 6-in. test tube. Add 5 ml. of 0.1 N sodium hydroxide, stir the mixture until the solid dissolves, and add 1 ml. of a freshly prepared 5 per cent solution of NaCN in N sodium hydroxide (obtain this solution from the instructor). Allow the solution to stand for 10 min., add 1 ml. of a freshly prepared 0.5 per cent solution of 1,2-naphthoquinone-4-sulfonate, and stir the mixture. Add immediately 5 ml. of a 10 per cent solution of sodium sulfite in 0.5 N sodium hydroxide. Stir the mixture, and after 10 min., add 1 ml. of a 2 per cent solution of sodium hydrosulfite in 0.5 N sodium hydroxide. If the deep-red color first formed persists after the addition of the hydrosulfite, the presence of cystine is confirmed. If the red color is discharged, cystine is absent.

4. *Methionine. Sodium Nitroprusside Test.*[14] Transfer 0.5 ml. of the solution prepared in Step VII or VIII to a 6-in. test tube. Add 2 ml. of water and 3 ml. of 3 N sodium hydroxide. Stir the mixture, add 1 ml. of a freshly prepared 1 per cent solution of sodium nitroprusside, and mix the solutions. (*Caution:* Sodium nitroprusside is highly poisonous.) Heat the tube for 5 min. in a water bath at 40°. Cool the tube in an ice-water bath for 5 min. and add 3 ml. of 6 N hydrochloric acid slowly, while shaking the cold solution. The appearance of a red color confirms the presence of methionine.

5. *Tyrosine. Mercuric Nitrite Test.*[15] Transfer 1 mg. of the precipitate obtained in Step V-2 to a 3-in. test tube. Add 1 ml. of water and 2 drops of Millon's reagent. Stir the mixture and heat the tube for 1 min. in a boiling-water bath. The appearance of a bright-red color confirms the presence of tyrosine.

6. *Tryptophan. Glyoxylic Acid Test.*[16] Transfer 1 drop of the filtrate from Step VII to a pyrex test tube. Add 2 ml. of distilled water, add 2 drops of the Hopkins-Cole-Benedict reagent (magnesium glyoxylate solution), and mix the liquids. Incline the tube and allow 2 ml. of concentrated sulfuric acid to flow down the side of the tube and form a layer beneath the aqueous solution. Heat the tube for 2 min. in a boiling-water bath. The appearance of a purple to black ring at the interface of the liquids confirms the presence of tryptophan. If the layers are mixed (*Cautiously*), the solution will be colored uniformly purple.

7. *Phenylalanine. Nitric Acid–Hydroxylamine Test.*[17] Transfer 2 ml. of the solution prepared in Step VII or VIII to a 6-in. pyrex test tube and evaporate the solution to dryness in a boiling-water bath. Cool the tube, add 2 ml. of the nitrating agent (KNO_3 in concentrated sulfuric acid), and heat the tube in a boiling-water bath for 20 min. with occasional (*Cautious*) stirring. Remove the tube, cool it under running water, and transfer the contents (*Cautiously*) to a 50-ml. flask containing 3 ml. of distilled water. Stir the mixture and cool the flask in an ice-water bath for 5 min. Add 4 ml. of 20 per cent hydroxylamine hydrochloride solution, allow the flask to stand for 1 min., and add (*Cautiously*) in small

– 36 –

portions 10 ml. of concentrated ammonium hydroxide. Remove the flask from the bath. The appearance of a violet color confirms the presence of phenylalanine.

8. *Arginine. Hypobromite—α-Naphthol Test.*[18] Transfer 0.1 ml. of the solution prepared in Step VIII-3 to a 6-in. test tube containing 10 ml. of distilled water. Mix the solutions thoroughly and transfer 0.1 ml. to a 6-in. test tube. Add 5 ml. of distilled water, 1 ml. of 6 N sodium hydroxide, and 1 ml. of a 0.02 per cent solution of α-naphthol in 20 per cent ethanol. Mix the liquids, place the tube in an ice-water bath for 3 min., add 2 (not more) drops of sodium hypobromite reagent (bromine in 1.5 N sodium hydroxide), and stir the liquids. The appearance of a red color confirms the presence of arginine.

9. *Histidine. Bromimidazole-Ammonia Test.*[19] Transfer 0.1 ml. of the solution prepared in Step VIII-3 to a 3-in. test tube, add 2 ml. of distilled water, and add a solution of bromine in 33 per cent acetic acid dropwise until a light-yellow color persists. Allow the solution to stand for 5 min. Add 2 ml. of an ammonia—ammonium carbonate solution and heat the tube for 5 min. in a boiling-water bath. The appearance of a dark blue-violet color confirms the presence of histidine.

10. *Lysine. Picrate Precipitation Test.*[20] Transfer 10 ml. of the solution of basic amino acids prepared in Step VIII-3 to a flask. Add 15 ml. of a saturated solution of picric acid (1.4 g. per 100 ml. of water). Stopper the flask and shake it vigorously. The appearance of yellow crystals of lysine picrate confirms the presence of lysine. If no crystals appear within a few minutes, allow the flask to stand overnight in the refrigerator.

Bromine—Phosphomolybdic Acid—Phosphotungstic Acid Test.[21] Transfer 0.5 ml. of the solution of basic amino acids prepared in Step VIII-3 (if histidine was absent) or 20 mg. of the lysine picrate preparation to a 6-in. test tube. Add 1 ml. of saturated bromine water, add 2 drops of 6 N hydrochloric acid, and allow the solution to stand for 5 min. Add a 5 per cent solution of sodium arsenite dropwise until the yellow bromine color is discharged. Add sodium carbonate solution to a basic reaction to litmus paper. Heat the solution for 2 min. in a boiling-water bath, add 0.5 ml. of the Folin-Ciocalteu reagent (phosphomolybdic acid—phosphotungstic acid), and heat the mixture for 5 min. in a boiling-water bath.

Lysine gives a green color which changes to a deep blue or blue green within 1 to 2 min. Histidine gives a purple color on the addition of sodium carbonate and obscures the color formed by lysine. Arginine yields a green color which deepens to blue on standing 20 min. Lysine and lysine picrate behave similarly, except that the yellow picric acid alters the shade of color to a pronounced greenish blue.

11. *Glutamic Acid. Hydrochloride Precipitation Test.*[22] Transfer the precipitate obtained in Step VII to a 125-ml. flask. Add 15 ml. of distilled water, rotate the flask until the solid dissolves, and add slowly, with stirring, M oxalic acid solution to pH 4 as tested with congo red indicator. Heat the suspension of calcium oxalate in a boiling-water bath for 15 min. with occasional stirring. Add additional oxalic acid solution until the pH is 4 and digest the suspension in a boiling-water bath for 10 min. Repeat this process until the pH is not lowered during the digestion process.

Filter the suspension and wash the precipitate thoroughly on the funnel with 10 ml. of cold water. Evaporate the clear filtrate and wash liquid on a boiling-water bath to 10 ml. Cool the solution in an ice-water bath and saturate it with hydrogen chloride from a generator in the fume hood. Stopper the flask tightly and allow it to stand in the refrigerator until the next laboratory period. The formation of colorless needle-like crystals indicates the presence of glutamic acid hydrochloride. Preserve the filtrate (or solution, if glutamic acid is absent) for use in Test 12. Dry the precipitate in air and determine its melting point.

12. *Aspartic Acid. Glyoxal-2,4-dinitrophenylosazone Test.*[23] Transfer 2 ml. of the solution prepared in Test 11 to a 50-ml. flask and heat the flask for 5 min. in a boiling-water bath to remove excess hydrochloric acid. Add 10 ml. of water, 1 ml. of concentrated sulfuric acid (*Caution*), and 1 ml. saturated bromine water. Heat the solution for 5 min. in a boiling-water bath. Cool the solution to room temperature. Add 1 ml. of M potassium bromide solution and 2.5 ml. of 1.5 N potassium permanganate solution. Stir the liquids and allow the mixture to stand for 10 min. at room temperature.

Add 6 per cent hydrogen peroxide dropwise until the solution is decolorized. Attach an aeration assembly as shown in Fig. 5 (see Aeration in the Appendix), and add to the receiving tube cooled in an ice-water bath 5 ml. of a clear (filter, if necessary) 0.5 per cent solution of 2,4-dinitrophenylhydrazine in 2.4 N hydrochloric acid. Immerse the reaction flask in a boiling-water bath and aerate the solution until the volume has decreased to 8 ml. Filter the orange-colored suspension (formed if aspartic acid was present) on a Hirsch funnel and wash the precipitate on the funnel with 2 ml. of water. Dissolve the precipitate by filtering 3 ml. of pyridine repeatedly through the funnel using suction. Add 20 ml. of distilled water to the pyridine solution, add 2 ml. of 6 N sodium hydroxide, and stir the mixture. The appearance of a blue color confirms the presence of aspartic acid.

Cupric Aspartate Hydrate Precipitation Test.[24] Evaporate the remainder of the solution prepared in Test 11 to a sirup on a boiling-water bath. Add 5 ml. of distilled water and repeat this process. Add 5 ml. of distilled water to the sirup and heat the mixture on a boiling-water bath until the sirup dissolves. Continue heating and add 0.3 g. of solid CuCO₃ in small portions with stirring. Filter the mixture after 5 min. and allow the filtrate to stand in the refrigerator until the next laboratory period. The formation of fine blue needles with a violet-colored tinge indicates the presence of aspartic acid.

13. *Threonine. Periodic Acid—Acetaldehyde—p-Hydroxydiphenyl Test.*[25] Transfer 0.1 ml. of the solution prepared in Step VII or VIII to a 6-in. test tube. Add 2 drops of an antifoam agent (turkey red oil), 5 ml. of 0.5 M sodium bicarbonate solution, and 7 ml. of 0.1 N sodium arsenite in 2 per cent sodium bicarbonate solution. Mix these liquids and add 1 ml. of 0.5 M periodic acid. Immediately connect the aeration assembly shown in Fig. 5 (see Aeration in the Appendix) to the receiving tube, to which 10 ml. of concentrated sulfuric acid and 10 mg. of purified solid p-hydroxydiphenyl have been added. Aerate for 20 min. The appearance of a violet color in the sulfuric acid confirms the presence of threonine. Preserve the periodic acid—oxidized solution in the reaction tube for use in Test 14.

14. *Serine. Periodic Acid—Formaldehyde—Chromotropic Acid Test.*[26] Add 2 drops of methyl red indicator solution to the reaction tube (preserved from Test 13) containing the periodic acid—oxidized solution. Add 6 N acetic acid dropwise to an acid reaction (red color). Add 10 ml. of distilled water to a clean receiving tube and attach the aerating assembly shown in Fig. 5 (see Aeration in the Appendix). Place the reaction tube and the trap in a boiling-water bath. Place the receiver in an ice-water bath and aerate until the volume of solution in the reaction tube is reduced to 5 ml. (about 20 min.). Transfer 3 ml. of this solution to a 6-in. test tube. Add 5 ml. of water, 3 ml. of concentrated sulfuric acid (*Caution*), and 10 mg. of solid chromotropic acid. Stir the mixture and heat it in a boiling-water bath. The appearance (within 20 min.) of a violet-rose color confirms the presence of serine.

15. *Leucine and Valine. Acetone-Salicylaldehyde Test.*[27] Transfer 1 ml. of the solution prepared in Step X to a 6-in. test tube. Add 10 ml. of 6 N sodium hydroxide and 1 ml. of a 6 per cent solution of salicylaldehyde in ethanol. Heat the tube for 15 min. in a boiling-water bath. The appearance of a red color confirms the presence of leucine, valine, or both these amino acids.

16. *Isoleucine. Methyl Ethyl Ketone—Salicylaldehyde Test.*[28] Transfer 5 ml. of the solution prepared in Step X to a 250-ml. flask. Add 100 ml. of distilled water, 5 ml. of concentrated sulfuric acid, and 35 ml. of Denigès reagent (15 per cent HgSO₄ in 6 N sulfuric acid). Attach a condenser and reflux the solution for 30 min. Cool and filter the suspension of the acetone—mercuric sulfate complex, using a Hirsch funnel and a smooth filter paper. Transfer a 5-ml. portion of the filtrate to a 6-in. test tube. Add 3 ml. of 95 per cent ethanol, 2 ml. of concentrated sulfuric acid (*Caution*), and 1 ml. of a 6 per cent solution of salicylaldehyde in ethanol. Heat the tube in a boiling-water bath. The appearance (within 15 min.) of a red color confirms the presence of methyl ethyl ketone in the solution and of isoleucine in the unknown.

17. *Alanine. Ninhydrin—Acetaldehyde—p-Hydroxydiphenyl Test.*[29] Transfer 0.5 of the solution prepared in Step VII or VIII to a 6-in. test tube. Add 3 ml. of water and add 0.1 N sodium hydroxide to pH 7 (test with bromthymol blue indicator). Add 2 ml. of a 1 per cent solution of ninhydrin and heat the tube for 3 min. in a boiling-water bath. Cool the solution and attach the aerating assembly shown in Fig. 5 (see Aeration in the Appendix). Add 5 ml. of concentrated sulfuric acid and 10 mg. of p-hydroxydiphenyl to the receiving tube. Allow the solution to aerate for 15 min. The appearance of a pink to violet color confirms the presence of alanine. Preserve the solution in the reaction tube for use in the confirmatory test for glycine.

18. *Glycine. Ninhydrin—Formaldehyde—Chromotropic Acid Test.*[30] Attach the reaction tube (containing the ninhydrin-reaction products preserved from Test 17) to the aeration assembly shown in Fig. 5 (see Aeration in the Appendix). Place the reaction tube and the trap in a boiling-water bath and the receiving tube containing 10 ml. of water in an ice-water bath. Aerate for 20 min. Transfer 3 ml. of the

solution in the receiver to a 6-in. test tube. Add 5 ml. of water and (*Caution*) 3 ml. of concentrated sulfuric acid. Add 10 mg. of chromotropic acid, stir the mixture, and heat the tube in a boiling-water bath. The appearance of a deep-violet color confirms the presence of glycine.

o-Phthalaldehyde Test.[31]   Transfer 1 ml. of the solution prepared in Step VII or VIII to a test tube. Add 2 ml. of a pH 8.0 buffer solution (Na$_2$HPO$_4$ and NaH$_2$PO$_4$) and 5 ml. of the *o*-phthalaldehyde reagent. Mix the solutions and allow the mixture to stand for 2 min. Add 5 ml. of a freshly prepared and cooled mixture of 6 ml. of ethanol and 1 ml. of concentrated sulfuric acid. Shake the tube vigorously for 30 sec. and add 15 ml. of chloroform. The appearance of a green color in the chloroform layer indicates the presence of glycine.

NOTES

1. The observation of Ruhemann (1910) that a blue-colored solution is formed by boiling an aqueous solution of ninhydrin and an alpha-amino acid was explained (Ruhemann, 1911) by the following postulated reactions:

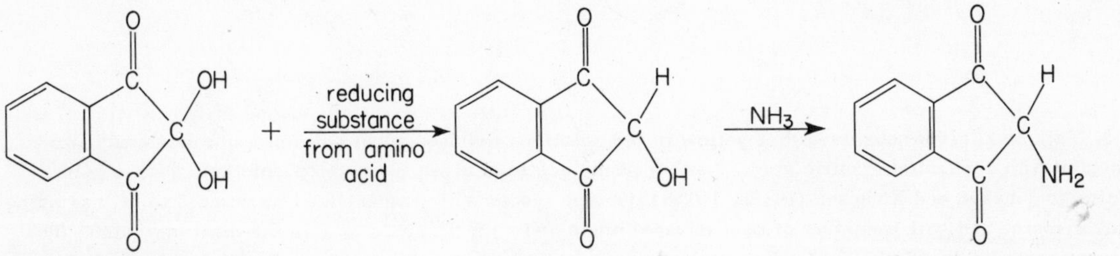

(A) ninhydrin
(triketohydrindine
hydrate)

1,3-diketohydrindole

(B)1,3-diketohydrindamine

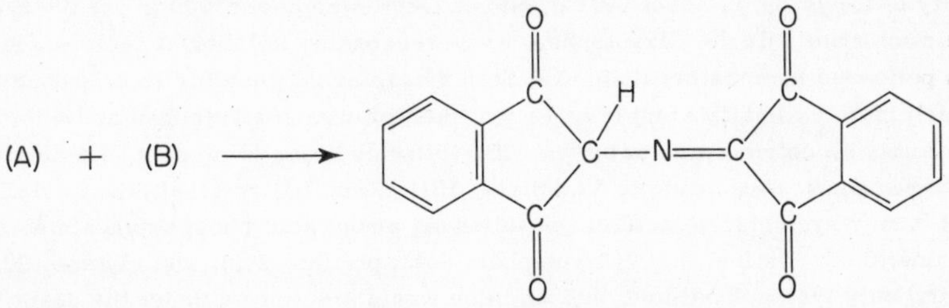

(A)   +   (B)   ⟶

diketohydrindylidene
diketohydrindamine

Retinger (1917) has presented objections to this mechanism.

Ammonium salts (Harding and Warneford, 1916) and amines (Harding and MacLean, 1916) give reddish-violet to blue colors with ninhydrin, but proline, hydroxyproline, diketopiperazine, urea, hippuric acid, purines, and β-, γ-, and δ-amino acids give little or no color. The sensitivity of nine amino acids tested by Abderhalden and Schmidt (1911, 1913) ranged from 1 part of histidine in 79,000 parts of water to 1 part of valine in 16,000 parts of water. Harding and MacLean (1915) found that 1 part of alanine and other amino acids could be detected in 1,500,000 parts of water.

The ninhydrin reaction has been applied to the analysis of amino acids (MacFadyen, 1944; Schott *et al.*, 1944) and to the determination of amino acids in proteins (Stein and Moore, 1949), blood (Hamilton, 1945; Hamilton and Van Slyke, 1943; MacFadyen, 1942; Van Slyke and Dillon, 1938; Van Slyke, Dillon, MacFadyen, and Hamilton, 1941; Van Slyke, MacFadyen, and Hamilton, 1942), and urine (Van Slyke, MacFadyen, and Hamilton, 1943). Analytical procedures based on the reaction of ninhydrin with alpha-amino acids to give ammonia (MacFadyen, 1944; Sobel, Hirschman, and Besman, 1945), carbon dioxide (Hamilton, 1945), and volatile aldehydes (see Step XI, Tests 17 and 18) have been reported. Virtanen and Rautanen (1947) have shown that of the amino acids in proteins only alanine, valine, leucine, isoleucine, phenylalanine, and methionine form volatile aldehydes. Moore and Stein (1949) have investigated the color yields from reactions of ninhydrin with amino acids.

Alpha-amino acids react with β-naphthoquinonesulfonate to give red-colored solutions (Folin, 1922a) and with p-nitrobenzoyl chloride and alkali to give 4-isobutyl-2-p-nitrophenyl-5-oxazolone (Waser and Brauchli, 1924), which forms a deep-violet-blue color with alkali salts (Karrer and Keller, 1943).

2. Proline, hydroxyproline, or both amino acids are determined usually by the reaction of isatin or p-dimethylaminobenzaldehyde with pyrrole or related product formed by oxidation with PbO_2 (Guest, 1939), Na_2O_2 (Morse, 1933), $CuSO_4$ and Na_2O_2 (McFarlane and Guest, 1939), or $NaOCl$ (Lang, 1933; Waldschmidt-Leitz and Akabori, 1934). According to Pratesi (1933), the isatin-pyrrole condensation product has the following structure:

3. Salkowski (1888) observed that yellow to red solutions resulted when some proteins and amino acids were heated with concentrated nitric acid. Neither phenylacetic acid nor phenylpropionic acid gave a color. According to Johnson and Kohmann (1915a, 1915b) tyrosine reacts with concentrated nitric acid to give principally 3-nitrotyrosine and with a mixture of concentrated nitric and sulfuric acids to give 3,5-dinitrotyrosine. The color reaction probably depends upon the nitration of the benzene and indole rings to form nitro derivatives which have resonating electronic structures. Tryptophan may undergo partial oxidation as well as nitration.

4. The solubility of L-proline is 1.5 g. per 100 g. of absolute ethanol (Kapfhammer and Eck, 1927). Other amino acids are only slightly soluble in this solvent.

5. The solubility of L-cystine is about 0.01 g. and of L-tyrosine about 0.05 g. per 100 g. of water at $25°$. All other amino acids are much more soluble. Tryptophan, while reasonably soluble, dissolves slowly.

6. This test is performed here, rather than after Step VII, to avoid possible interference from calcium phosphotungstate, which is only slightly soluble and might precipitate. If tryptophan and a basic amino acid are present, the precipitate may be colored pink or brown. If tryptophan alone is present, a precipitate may form which changes rapidly to a brown scum. According to Van Slyke, Hiller, and Dillon (1942) the solubilities at $22°$ in millimoles per liter of 0.25 N hydrochloric acid of the following amino acid phosphotungstates are lysine, 0.055; histidine, 0.390; arginine, 0.69; cystine, 0.507; tryptophan, 4.43; proline, 21.1, and glycine, 32.8. Since cystine was removed previously, only lysine, histidine, and arginine would precipitate under the described experimental conditions. The ratios of amino acid to phosphotungstic acid found by Van Slyke et al. for the complexes were cystine, 1:1; arginine, histidine, and lysine, 1.5:1; and glycine, proline, and tryptophan, 3:1.

Tungstic acid and phosphoric acid form a series of complex acids of the general formula $P_2O_5 \cdot nWO_3 \cdot mH_2O$ or $H_3PO_4 \cdot n/2(WO_3) \cdot m'H_2O$. According to Wu (1920) the complex acids are stable only if the values for n are 18 or larger. The degree of hydration varies, but the values for m (or m') commonly fall between 14 and 25. Commercial phosphotungstic acid consists principally of $P_2O_5 \cdot 24WO_3 \cdot mH_2O$ but may contain as much as 10 per cent of the "18" acid. The structure of phosphotungstic acid purified by ether extraction was reported by Van Slyke et al. to be $P_2O_5 \cdot 24WO_3 \cdot 17H_2O$.

7. The precipitation of glutamic acid and aspartic acid as their calcium salts was first described by Ritthausen (1869a). Ritthausen's procedure has been modified by Foreman (1914), Chibnall et al. (1940), and Bailey et al. (1943). Barium hydroxide has been used in place of calcium hydroxide (Dakin, 1920; Jones and Moeller, 1928). The acidic amino acids have been separated from other amino acids by adsorption on a synthetic anion-exchange (polyamine-formaldehyde) resin, Amberlite (Cannan, 1944).

8. The relatively high solubility of phosphotungstic acid in a mixture of amyl alcohol and diethyl ether was reported by Van Slyke (1915a).

9. Malaprade (1934) observed that carbon chains with adjacent hydroxyls are split by periodic acid, and Nicolet and Shinn (1939) and Shinn and Nicolet (1941) found that amino acids with adjacent amino and hydroxyl groups are split similarly. The rate of reduction of periodic acid by nonhydroxylated amino acids is only one-thousandth that by serine. The products ammonia, aldehydes, and iodate are yielded in the oxidation of

hydroxyamino acids. Glyoxylic acid (CHOCOOH) and formaldehyde are formed from serine; glyoxylic acid and acetaldehyde from threonine. Van Slyke, Hiller, and MacFadyen (1941) and Van Slyke, Hiller, MacFadyen, Hastings, and Klemperer (1940) analyzed serine, threonine, and hydroxylysine quantitatively by means of the periodic acid reaction.

10. Fromageot and Heitz (1939) reported that leucine and valine could be determined by deamination, oxidation of the hydroxy acids to acetone, and photometric analysis of the acetone-salicylaldehyde condensation product. Block, Bolling, and Kondritzer (1940) found that acetone (from valine and leucine) and methyl ethyl ketone (from isoleucine) could be separated by precipitating acetone as its $HgSO_4$ complex. Both acetone and methyl ethyl ketone react with salicylaldehyde in acid solution to give colored products, but only acetone gives a colored product in alkaline solution. According to Fabinyi (1900a, 1900b) the colored complex (A) is formed from two molecules of salicylaldehyde and one of acetone and (B) from two molecules of each substance. Analogous compounds are formed from methyl ethyl ketone.

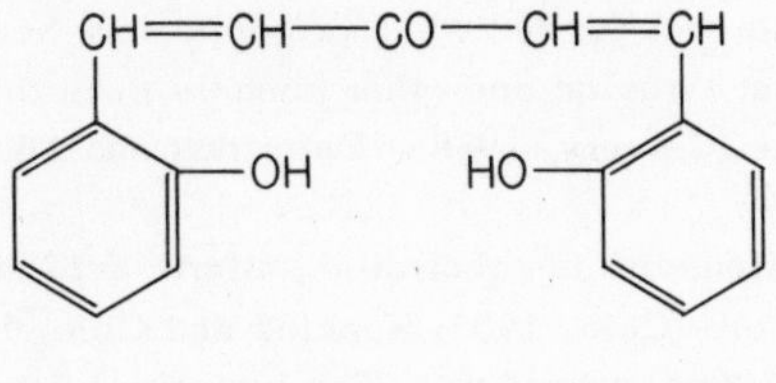

(A) di-*o*-hydroxydibenzalacetone

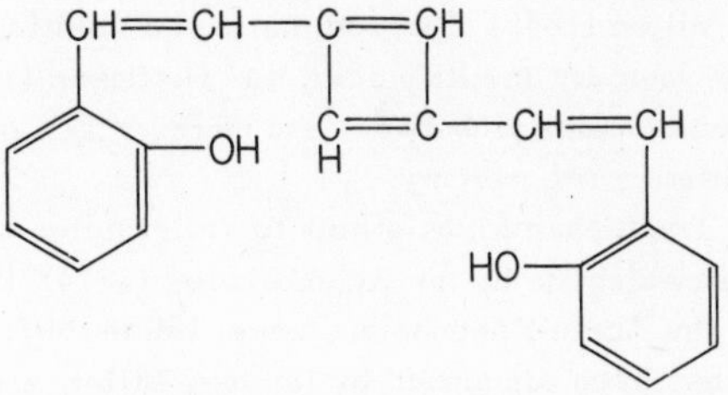

(B)

11. Pyridine, dihydropyrrole, and pyrrolidine give no color with isatin (Fromm, 1935). According to Grassman and von Arnim (1934, 1935) isatin (A) condenses with proline to yield the blue-colored complex (B) and with hydroxyproline to yield an analogous product. Only a red-colored solution has been observed with hydroxyproline under the authors' conditions of this test.

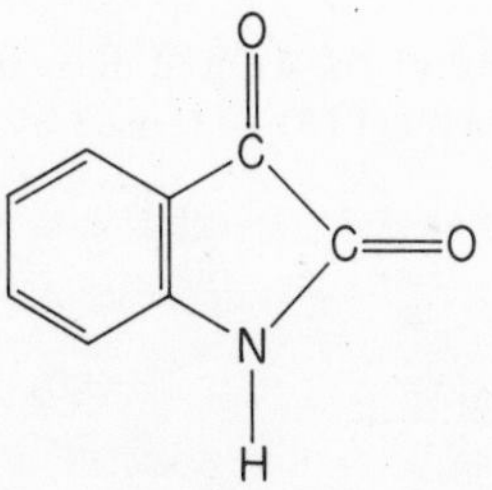

isatin

(A)

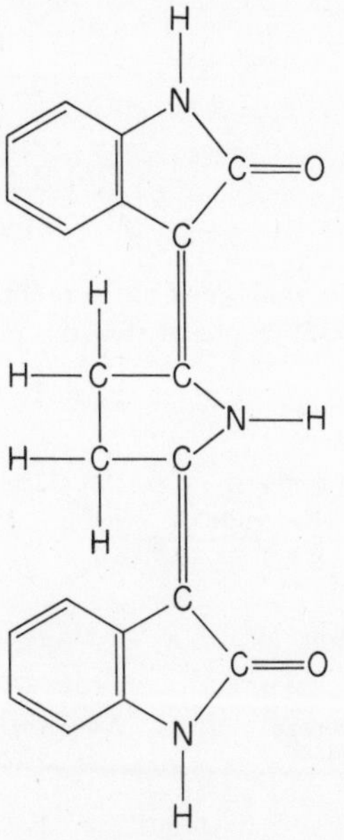

(B)

12. Proline is oxidized to give a colored product when tested with *p*-dimethylaminobenzaldehyde but not with isatin, according to Guest (1939). The yields of pyrrole from proline and hydroxyproline vary widely under different conditions (Guest and McFarlane, 1939).

13. This test for cystine (Sullivan, 1929a, 1929b; Sullivan and Hess, 1929) depends upon the reduction of cystine with sodium cyanide

$$R—S—S—R + NaCN \rightarrow R—S—Na + R—SCN$$

cystine   sodium   S-cyanocysteine
                                  cysteinate

and upon the condensation of cysteine with sodium 1,2-naphthoquinone-4-sulfonate to give a red-colored solution. Sodium hydrosulfite ($Na_2S_2O_4$) is added to intensify the color. Tin or zinc and hydrochloric acid, titanium chloride, sodium amalgam, and other reducing agents may be used, although the technique with sodium cyanide is most simple. Since reduction with sodium amalgam yields 2 moles of cysteine per mole of cystine, both cystine and cysteine can be determined by reducing different samples with NaCN and Na-Hg. The test for cysteine is highly specific since three functional groups (— SH, — NH₂, and — COOH) are required.

14. McCarthy and Sullivan (1941) have shown that a red-colored solution is formed when methionine is heated in an alkaline solution of sodium nitroprusside $[Na_2(NO)Fe(CN)_5]$ and the mixture is acidified. The sensitivity of the reaction is 20 to 50 parts of methionine per 1,000,000 parts of solution. Many common amino acids give no color, but histidine, histamine, and carnosine (β-alanylhistidine) give methionine-like reactions. Tryptophan yields a reddish-brown color which, unlike the red colors given by methionine and histidine, is extractable with butyl alcohol. Glycine has been added to the reagent to eliminate the interfering histidine color. There are no interfering substances in the present procedure, since both histidine and tryptophan have been removed previously in the solution tested. Modifications of this test have been proposed by Csonka and Denton (1946) and by Horn, Jones, and Blum (1946).

15. Millon (1849) observed that a red solution or precipitate was formed when proteins were heated with a solution of mercury in nitric acid, and Hoffmann (1853) found that tyrosine and other phenols gave this test. The red-colored complex probably is the mercury salt of nitrotyrosine (Calvery, 1938). Chlorides and alkali interfere by precipitating the mercury.

16. Tryptophan forms a pink to violet color when it is treated with concentrated sulfuric acid and glyoxylic acid or formaldehyde by the Adamkeiwiez (1874), the Hopkins-Cole (Cole, 1903; Hopkins and Cole, 1901a, 1901b, 1903), or the Acree-Rosenheim (Acree, 1906–1907; Rosenheim, 1906a) procedure. The historical development of this test has been discussed by Harvey, Miller, and Robson (1941), who suggested that a compound (A) first formed is oxidized to a blue pigment.

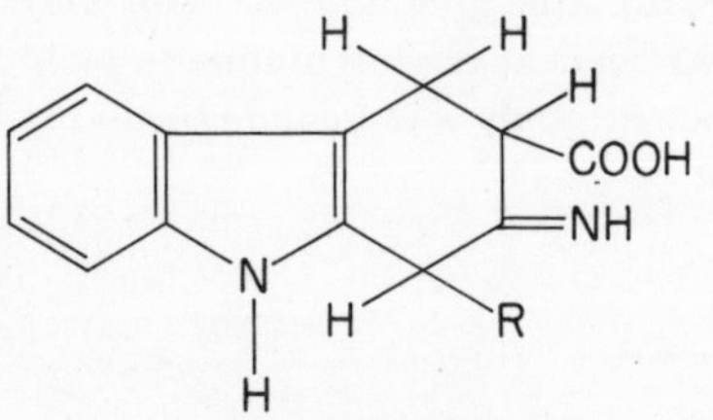

(A) 2,3,4,5-tetrahydro-
β-carboline-4-carboxylic acid

Rydon (1948) has studied the analogous color reactions of methyl-substituted derivatives of tryptophan.

17. Kapeller-Adler (1932) proposed that the colored compound (A) is formed by the indicated reactions:

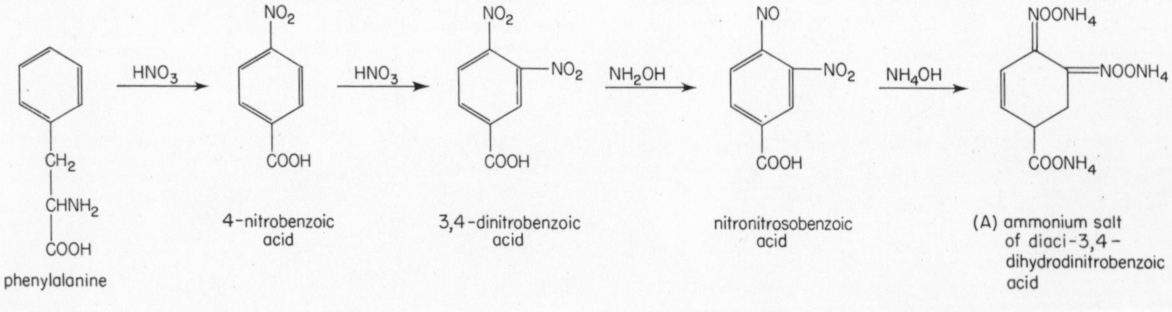

Support for this mechanism was presented by Block and Bolling (1939), who prepared diaci-3,4-dihydrodinitro-phenylalanine by these reactions. Modified procedures have been described by Kuhn and Desnuelle (1937) and Block and Bolling (1945). Of the amino acids yielding interfering colored nitration products, Kapeller-Adler removed tryptophan by acid hydrolysis, tyrosine by oxidation with permanganate, and histidine by precipitation with phosphotungstic acid. Knight and Stanley (1941) corrected for tryptophan, while Brown (1944) precipitated tryptophan with mercuric sulfate. In the present procedure these interfering amino acids are removed before applying the phenylalanine test.

18. Sakaguchi (1925a, 1925b) observed that arginine reacts in alkaline solution with sodium hypochlorite and α-naphthol to give a red-colored product assumed to have the structure shown on following page.

NH—C—N—O
| ‖ |
CH₂ NH O
|
CH₂
|
CH₂
|
CHNH₂
|
COOH

Sakaguchi and later workers (Poller, 1926; Weber, 1930) found that glycocyamine (guanidinoacetic acid), mono-methylguanidine, dimethylguanidine, and trimethylguanidine gave colored solutions with the Sakaguchi reagent, while guanidine, nitroarginine, creatinine, methylguanidinoacetic acid, and asymmetrical di-and trimethylguanidines did not. Substitution of hypobromite for hypochlorite simplifies the preparation of the reagent without reducing its specificity (Weber, 1930). The color formed by arginine is detectable in 1:2,500,000 dilution. In order to remove interfering substances, arginine has been separated by electrodialysis (Macpherson, 1942) and by adsorption on Permutit (Dubnoff, 1941).

19. Knoop (1908) observed that histidine and histamine but not imidazoleacetic acid, imidazolepropionic acid, or imidazolelactic acid gave a positive test with this reagent. According to Kapeller-Adler (1934) little or no color is produced with carnosine (β-alanylhistidine), α-amino-N-methylimidazolepropionic acid, or α-methyl-amino-β-imidazolepropionic acid. It has been reported that two (Plimmer and Phillips, 1924) or more (Lieben and Müller, 1928) bromine atoms react per molecule of histidine, but the nature of the reaction is unknown. Tryptophan, tyrosine, glycine, and some other amino acids alter the shade of color (Woolley and Peterson, 1937–1938), but these effects are minimized in the present test.

20. Kossel (1898) first identified lysine by precipitation as its picrate. Lysine picrate precipitates readily because of its low solubility [340 mg. at 0° (Tristram, 1939) and 540 mg. at 21 to 22° (Lawrow, 1899) per 100 ml. of water]. According to Block and Bolling (1945) lysine picrate decomposes (with a slight explosion) at 250° if impure and at 266° if pure. Picric acid melts at 121 to 122°.

21. This procedure is a modification of that given by Boulet, Nelson, and McFarlane (1947). These authors eliminated interfering amino acids by adsorbing lysine and arginine (which gives no color with the reagent) on an ion-exchange column (Decalso) and eluting them with sodium carbonate solution.

22. Glutamic acid hydrochloride (m.p. 210°) was first identified by Hlasiwetz and Habermann (1873). Waelsch and Prescott (1945) have detected glutamic acid by oxidizing it with ninhydrin to formylpropionic acid and coupling this product with 2,4-dinitrophenylhydrazine. On the addition of alkali a red-brown color is formed. Of the other amino acids tested, only aspartic acid gave an oxidation product which formed a hydrazone. Glutamic acid has been determined by oxidation with chloramine-T to succinic acid, enzymatic oxidation of the latter to carbon dioxide, and estimation of the carbon dioxide (Cohen, 1939).

23. Pucher, Vickery, and Wakeman (1934) observed that aspartic acid could be determined as a blue pigment, which was formed, according to Suomalainen and Arhimo (1947), by the indicated reactions:

COOH   COOH   Br
| | |
CHNH₂   HNO₂ CHOH   CHBr
| ────▶ | ────▶ | ────▶
CH₂   CH₂   CHO
| |
COOH   COOH
aspartic   malic   dibromo-
acid   acid   acetaldehyde

CH=N—NH—⟨NO₂,NO₂⟩
|
CH=N—NH—⟨NO₂,NO₂⟩
glyoxal–2,4–dinitrophenylosazone

──OH⁻──▶ blue pigment

Arhimo (1939) found that aspartic acid could be oxidized directly with bromine without prior treatment with nitrous acid and that tyrosine and dihydroxyphenylalanine were the only interfering amino acids.

24. Ritthausen (1869b) was the first to observe that aspartic acid may be readily isolated as its cupric hydrate. It has been reported that the hydrate contains two (Bergmann and Niemann, 1937), four and one-half (Bailey et al., 1943; Ritthausen, 1869b), and five (Abderhalden and Weil, 1911) molecules of water of hydration.

25. According to Shinn and Nicolet (1941), "the acetaldehyde which is produced almost immediately from the reaction of periodate on threonine can be quantitatively carried over (without important contamination by formaldehyde) by aeration at pH close to 7 and preferably at pH 7.0 to 7.2." Although Eegriwe (1933), Barker and Summerson (1941), and Miller and Muntz (1938) have shown that propionaldehyde, glyceric aldehyde, pyruvic acid, methylglyoxal, dihydroxyacetone, and other aldehydes and ketones react with p-hydroxydiphenyl in concentrated sulfuric acid to give red-purple colors, interfering substances of these types are not present. Formaldehyde gives a blue-green color which would obscure the color given by acetaldehyde.

26. Eegriwe (1937) observed that formaldehyde, but not other aldehydes, reacts with chromotropic acid (1,8-dihydroxynaphthalene-3,6-disulfonic acid) to give a violet-rose color detectable at a dilution of 1:360,000. This test was employed by Boyd and Logan (1942) for the quantitative determination of serine.

27. According to Block and Bolling (1945) methyl ethyl ketone (formed from isoleucine) gives no color with salicylaldehyde in alkaline solution.

28. The composition of the acetone-mercuric sulfate complex has been reported as $2HgSO_4 \cdot 3HgO \cdot (CH_3)_2CO$ (Denigès, 1898a, 1898b) and $3HgSO_4 \cdot 5HgO \cdot 2(CH_3)_2CO$ (Van Slyke, 1917). Methyl ethyl ketone is not precipitated in the concentrations present (Block and Bolling, 1945).

29. Alexander and Seligman (1945) determined alanine by oxidizing it with ninhydrin to acetaldehyde and estimating the latter by photometric analysis of its p-hydroxydiphenyl complex. Acetaldehyde may also be determined as its bisulfite complex (Virtanen and Rautanen, 1947). Only the volatile aldehydes from leucine, norleucine, and norvaline interfere with the former procedure, and their color intensities may be decreased by forming the chromogens at a higher temperature (37°). Aspartic acid yields acetaldehyde at pH 4 but does not react at pH 5.5. Alanine is quantitatively converted to acetaldehyde on boiling it with ninhydrin for 1 hr. at pH 5.5 (Alexander and Seligman, 1945). Glycine is quantitatively converted to formaldehyde by boiling it with ninhydrin for less than 1 hr. at pH 5.5 (Alexander, Landwehr, and Seligman, 1945) and 1.5 hr. at pH 1 (MacFadyen, 1945). The aeration procedure employed in the test (see Note 25) minimizes interference from glycine.

30. MacFadyen (1945) and Alexander, Landwehr, and Seligman (1945) determined glycine by oxidizing it with ninhydrin, condensing the formaldehyde with chromotropic acid, and estimating the color intensity of the product photometrically.

31. According to Zimmerman (1930) and Klein and Linser (1932a) the o-phthalaldehyde test is given by glycine, tryptophan, cystine, arginine, alanine, asparagine, and ammonium salts, although only the colored products from glycine, tryptophan, and ammonium ion are extracted by chloroform. Since tryptophan, cystine, and arginine have been removed, they do not interfere in the present test. This color reaction has been utilized by Patton (1935) for the determination of glycine in proteins.

EXPERIMENT 22

PREPARATION OF CASEIN FROM MILK

Casein, first recognized by Scheele (1780) as a protein in milk, has been most commonly prepared by Hammarsten's (1873–1874) method. Dilute acetic acid is added to skim milk, the precipitate is dissolved in dilute sodium hydroxide, this process is repeated several times, and the product is washed with ethanol and dried. Van Slyke and Bosworth (1913) modified the Hammarsten procedure by dissolving the casein in ammonium hydroxide and adding ammonium oxalate to precipitate traces of calcium as calcium oxalate. Van Slyke and Baker (1918) avoided possible decomposition by alkali by precipitating casein with lactic acid and centrifuging at pH 7.0 to remove calcium and magnesium phosphates. To prevent denaturation of the casein, Cohn and Hendry (1943) avoided the use of hot organic solvents and a pH more alkaline than 6.3. Clark, Zoller, and Dahlberg (1920), Zoller (1921), and Northrop (1923) precipitated casein at pH 4.6 with a mixture of hydrochloric and citric acids. According to Van Slyke and Carpenter (1924) a high-purity product free from inorganic salts is obtained by electrodialyzing casein suspensions.

Most casein preparations are mixtures of proteins, according to the solubility studies of Linderstrom-Lang and Kodoma (1925) and the electrophoretic experiments of Warner (1944). Casein is used widely for animal and microbiological experimentation. The industrial importance of casein in the manufacture of glue, adhesives, plastics, textile fibers, and coated papers has been reviewed by Sutermeister and Brown (1939).

Casein is to be prepared essentially by Dunn's (1949) method. Hydrochloric acid is added to skim milk to pH 4.6 (isoelectric point), the suspension is centrifuged, and the precipitate is washed with water, ethanol, and ether. The product is not an entity, but it has reasonably constant composition and properties.

EXPERIMENTAL[1]

Transfer 100 ml. of skim milk from a graduate to a 250-ml. beaker. Add a sufficient volume (about 56 ml.) of 0.10 N hydrochloric acid from a 50-ml. burette at the rate of 5 ml. per min., with constant stirring, until the pH is 4.6 (measured with a pH meter). The principle and operation of the pH meter are explained in the Appendix (see pH) and will be demonstrated by the instructor. Allow the suspension to stand until the casein settles. Decant and discard the supernatant liquid.

Filter the residual material on a Buchner funnel and transfer the moist casein to a 200-ml. centrifuge bottle containing 50 ml. of distilled water. Stir the mixture until it becomes homogeneous. Centrifuge the suspension, decant the supernatant liquid, and test it for phosphate ion by the following procedure: Transfer 2 ml. of the liquid to a test tube containing 2 ml. of clear 9 per cent ammonium molybdate $[(NH_4)_6Mo_7O_{24} \cdot 4H_2O]$ and 2 ml. of 6 N nitric acid. A yellow precipitate of ammonium phosphomolybdate $|[(NH_4)_3PO_4 \cdot 12MoO_3 \cdot 3H_2O]$ indicates the presence of phosphate ion. If this test is positive, repeat the purification procedure and continue purification until the test is negative. The sensitivity of this test is about 0.4 mg. per cent of phosphate ion.

Add 50 ml. of methanol to the centrifuge bottle, stir the mixture thoroughly, and decant the supernatant liquid. Repeat this process twice, using 25-ml. portions of methanol. Add 25 ml. of ether, stir the mixture thoroughly, and transfer the suspension to an evaporating dish. Cover the dish with filter paper and allow the precipitate to dry overnight in air. Submit the product to the instructor in a tared, labeled sample bottle. Calculate the percentage yield and submit the data to the instructor.

NOTE

1. Contamination of the milk or the casein with dirt or other insoluble impurities should be avoided, since they will be retained in the final product. The casein should not be allowed to dry at any time prior to the final step, since it will turn to a dark-colored, hard, lumpy mass. If any of the solutions are stored during the course of the experiment, they should be preserved in the refrigerator, but not longer than 24 hr. to avoid bacterial or mold contamination.

EXPERIMENT 23

DETERMINATION OF PHOSPHORUS IN PURIFIED CASEIN

The literature on methods for the gravimetric, titrimetric, and photometric determination of phosphorus has been reviewed by Peters and Van Slyke (1946). Phosphorus is determined gravimetrically as strychnine phosphomolybdate, ammonium phosphomolybdate, magnesium ammonium phosphate, or magnesium pyrophosphate and volumetrically by titrating these compounds with standard acid, alkali, or permanganate. Phosphate in urine and fertilizers is determined by precipitating phosphate as $Ur_2O_3(PO_4)_2$ with an excess of a standard solution of a soluble uranium salt. Photometric methods have been described based on the color intensities of molybdivanadophosphate (Kitson and Mellon, 1944a, 1944b) and other molybdenum complexes.

Hammarsten (1883) reported that casein contained from 0.83 to 0.88 per cent of phosphorus, and, 30 years later, values ranging from 0.71 to 0.85 per cent were found by Van Slyke and Bosworth (1913) and Van Slyke and Baker (1918). It has become evident, however, from the work of Berggren (1932), Cherbuliez and Schneider (1932), and Linderstrom-Lang (1928, 1929) that purified casein fractions contain from 0.15 to 2.3 per cent of phosphorus.

The phosphorus content of purified casein, prepared in Exp. 22 and ashed by the wet method of Neumann (1902–1903), as modified by King (1932), is to be determined by Brigg's (1922) modification of the Bell-Doisy (1920) photometric method.

EXPERIMENTAL

Obtain approximately 0.5 g. of purified casein and assignment to a visual colorimeter.

Transfer 0.5 g. (weighed to ±1 mg.) of the casein quantitatively to an 8-in. pyrex test tube, using the minimum volume of distilled water as rinse fluid. Place a glass bead in the tube and in one additional tube to be used only for reagents. Transfer to each tube from a 10-ml. graduate 5 ml. of a 1:1 mixture of concentrated sulfuric acid and nitric acid. Heat each tube in a fume hood (or under an inverted funnel connected to a water aspirator) with a microburner (Tirrill burner with the barrel top removed) until the brown fumes of nitrogen oxides initially formed are replaced by the dense fumes of sulfur trioxide. (Heating time required is about 20 min.) Heat each tube for an additional 10 min., regulating the flame so that the mixtures boil smoothly. Cool the tubes (unknown solution is brown-colored) under running water. Add 5 drops (*Cautiously*) of 60 per cent perchloric acid to each tube. Heat each tube until white fumes appear and for an additional 5 min. Both solutions should be colorless at this point. If not, repeat the perchloric acid treatment.

Cool the tubes to room temperature. Add to each tube 10 ml. of distilled water, 3 drops of phenolphthalein indicator solution, and sufficient concentrated ammonium hydroxide (about 12 ml.) to produce a faint-pink color. Add 6 N sulfuric acid dropwise to each tube until the color is discharged.

Transfer the contents of each tube quantitatively to separate 250-ml. volumetric flasks and fill each flask to the mark with distilled water. Mix the contents of each flask thoroughly. Pipette into separate 50-ml. volumetric flasks (*a*) 10 ml. of the blank solution, (*b*) 10 ml. of the unknown solution, (*c*) 5 ml. of the unknown solution, (*d*) 10 ml. of a standard phosphate solution containing 0.015 mg. per ml. of phosphorus, and (*e*) 10 ml. of a standard phosphate solution containing 0.025 mg. of phosphorus per milliliter. Submit flask (*c*) to the instructor, who will add a known amount of phosphate.

Pipette into each of the five 50-ml. volumetric flasks 5 ml. of each of the following solutions in the order given: molybdic acid—sulfuric acid reagent, 1 per cent hydroquinone solution, and freshly prepared 20 per cent sodium sulfite solution. Fill each flask to the mark with distilled water, mix the contents of each flask thoroughly, and allow the solutions to stand for 30 min. Compare the color intensity of each blue-colored unknown solution in turn (visual colorimeter) with that of the standard phosphate solution which matches the unknown more closely. The blank solution should not be colored detectably.

EXPERIMENT 24

DETERMINATION OF ACID NUMBER OF UNKNOWN LIPID

"Acid number" is defined as the milligrams of potassium hydroxide required to titrate the free fatty acids in 1.00 g. of lipid. Acid numbers provide a basis for estimating the quality of fats and oils, even though they vary widely for samples differing in source, age, and storage conditions. According to Lewkowitsch (1922), the acid numbers of 27 types of semidrying oils (see the table facing page 246 in Lewkowitsch) varied from 0.53 to 57.4 and of 15 fish oils (see the table facing page 435 in Lewkowitsch) (from 0.18 to 21.6.

Increase in acid number and rancidity may occur simultaneously, owing to the liberation of butyric, oleic, and other fatty acids from the triglycerides and aldehydes, ketones, and other types of products by oxidation. Aromatic amines, cysteine, ascorbic acid, pyrogallol, carotene, α-tocopherol, and other antioxidants have been employed to retard oxidation of fats in lard, milk, and other food products.

The acid number of an unknown lipid is to be determined in this experiment.

EXPERIMENTAL

Obtain approximately 8 g. of an unknown lipid (oil). Transfer the oil to a sample bottle fitted with a bored cork and medicine dropper. Weigh the bottle and cork assembly to 1 mg. Transfer about 2 g. (80 drops) of the oil to a 125-ml. conical flask, replace the cork assembly, and weigh the sample bottle with cork assembly. Transfer a 2-g. quantity of the oil to each of two additional flasks in the manner described.

Pipette a 25-ml. aliquot of 95 per cent ethanol to each of two clean, dry 125-ml. conical flasks and to each of the three flasks containing the unknown oil. Add 8 drops of phenolphthalein indicator solution (from a dropping bottle) to one of the five flasks, and heat the mixture to boiling over a wire gauze, using a small flame. Titrate the hot solution with standard approximately 0.1 N potassium hydroxide delivered from a 10-ml. microburette. During the titration rotate the flask held by means of a clamp. The end point is a faint-pink color which persists for 30 sec. Titrate the solution in each of the four remaining flasks similarly.

EXPERIMENT 25

DETERMINATION OF SAPONIFICATION NUMBER OF UNKNOWN LIPID

The "saponification number" is defined as the milligrams of potassium hydroxide to saponify (hydrolyze) 1.00 g. of lipid. It is often referred to as the Koettstorfer (1879) number. Lewkowitsch (1921) has described the early methods. During saponification the triglycerides of the lipid are converted to glycerol and the potassium salts of the constituent fatty acids. Three moles of potassium hydroxide are required to saponify one mole of neutral triglyceride, but the grams of potassium hydroxide required per gram of triglyceride varies according to the molecular weights of the constituent fatty acids.

The saponification numbers of pure triglycerides are 557 for tributyrin, 303.6 for tricaprin, 208.6 for tripalmitin, 188.9 for tristearin, and 190.2 for triolein. For tributyrin the saponification-number calculation is $(168/1,000) \times (1/302.2) = 557$, where 168 is the molecular weight of potassium hydroxide and 302.2 the molecular weight of tributyrin. According to Elsdon (1926) the saponification numbers of lipids range from about 170 for oils from rapeseed, paradise nut, and other seeds to about 240 for oils from the palm, coconut, and other sources. Lewkowitsch (1901) and Jamieson (1943) have listed the saponification numbers of numerous natural fats and oils.

Saponification-equivalent (grams of fat saponified per equivalent of base) values are preferred because they are identical to the average molecular weights of the fatty acids, although saponification-number values are usually recorded.

The saponification number of an unknown lipid is to be determined in this experiment.

EXPERIMENTAL

Obtain approximately 2 g. of an unknown lipid. Transfer about 0.4 g. (weighed to ±1 mg.) (about 16 drops) to each of three clean, dry conical flasks by the technique described in Exp. 24. Pipette into each flask 25 ml. of 95 per cent ethanol and 25.0 ml. of standard, approximately 0.5 N potassium hydroxide in 95 per cent ethanol.

Clamp each flask in a water bath, insert a Hopkins condenser (see Distillation in the Appendix) in each flask, heat the bath sufficiently to reflux the alcohol gently, and continue heating for 30 min. Remove the flasks and rinse the alcoholic liquid from the condensers into their respective flasks with distilled water from a wash bottle. Add 3 drops of 0.1 per cent phenolphthalein indicator solution (from a dropping bottle) to each flask, and titrate the excess alkali in each flask with standard approximately 0.5 N sulfuric acid delivered from a 50-ml. burette.

EXPERIMENT 26

DETERMINATION OF IODINE NUMBER OF UNKNOWN LIPID

The "iodine number" of a lipid is defined as the grams of iodine absorbed per 100 g. of the lipid. Historical studies on the determination of degree of unsaturation of lipids have been reviewed by Lewkowitsch (1921). In 1857 Cailletet added a solution of the lipid in alcohol to a mixture of bromine and potassium hydroxide until the bromine color was discharged. Since this solution was unstable, Mills and coworkers added an excess of a solution of bromine in carbon tetrachloride and determined the excess bromine by adding iodide and titrating the liberated iodine with thiosulfate in the presence of starch. Since bromine was substituted, as well as added, under these conditions, it was necessary to correct for the former.

The now-classical procedures were proposed by Hübl (1884), Wijs (1898), and Hanus (1901). By the Hübl procedure a solution of the lipid in chloroform is mixed with a solution of iodine and $HgCl_2$ in ethanol, the mixture is allowed to stand for 2 hr. in the dark, iodide is added, and the liberated iodine is titrated with thiosulfate in the presence of starch. According to the Wijs method a solution of the lipid in chloroform or carbon tetrachloride is mixed with a solution of iodine and an equivalent quantity of chlorine in glacial acetic acid, the mixture is allowed to stand for 10 min. in the dark, iodide is added, and the liberated iodine is titrated with thiosulfate in the presence of starch. The Hanus method is essentially the same as that of Wijs except that the iodinating solution contains bromine in place of chlorine.

Nearly theoretical iodine numbers of pure unsaturated fatty acids are obtained by each of these methods. On the other hand the iodine numbers found for lipids vary considerably, as shown by reports referred to by Lewkowitsch (1921) and Elsdon (1926). Iodine numbers by the Hanus method usually are from 2 to 4 per cent lower than by the Wijs method. The Wijs method has been widely used in England and Europe, and it is the official method of the American Oil Chemists' Society. The Hanus method is used extensively in the United States, and it is the official method of the American Association of Official Agricultural Chemists.

Iodine numbers vary from 120 (tobacco seed) to 200 (linseed) for drying lipids, 95 (radish seed) to 140 (grape seed) for semidrying lipids, 70 (paradise nut) to 115 (cherry seed) for nondrying oils, 35 (porpoise) to 180 (cod liver) for marine-animal oils, 70 (horse's foot) to 130 (chrysalis) for terrestrial-animal oils, 5 (myrtle wax) to 95 (chaulmoogra) for vegetable lipids, and 25 (butter) to 110 (rattlesnake) for animal fats, according to data given by Lewkowitsch (1901, 1921), Elsdon (1926), and Jamieson (1943).

According to Scotti (1938) iodination proceeds by the reactions shown in the equations below.

$$2I_2 + 2Hg(OAc)_2 + 2H_2O \rightarrow HgIOI + HIO + 3HOAc + HgIOAc$$

$$-CH = CH- \; + HgIOAc \rightarrow \; -CHI-CHHgOAc-$$

$$-CHI-CHHgOAc- \; + HIO \rightarrow \; -CHI-CHHgOI- \; + HOAc$$

$$-CHI-CHHgOI- \; + HgIOI + 4AcOH + 4KI \rightarrow I_2 + 2HgI_2 + \; -CHI-CHI- \; + 2H_2O + 4KOAc$$

The Winkler and the Aschmann modified iodine methods, the Kaufman bromine method, and the Rosemund and Kuhnhenn pyridine sulfate dibromide method have been discussed by Elsdon (1926) and Jamieson (1943).

The iodine number of an unknown lipid is to be determined in the present experiment by the Norris and Buswell (1943) rapid modification of the Hanus (1901) method. Equations for the reactions are given below.

$$I_2 + Br_2 \rightarrow 2IBr$$
$$\text{Hanus solution}$$

$$IBr + - CH = CH - \rightarrow - CHI - CHBr -$$

$$KI + CH_3COOH \rightarrow HI + CH_3COOK$$

$$HI + IBr \rightarrow HBr + I_2$$

$$I_2 + 2Na_2S_2O_3 \rightarrow 2NaI + Na_2S_4O_6$$
$$\text{sodium tetra-}$$
$$\text{thionate}$$

EXPERIMENTAL

Obtain about 1.2 g. of an unknown lipid (oil). Transfer 0.2 g. (weighed to ±1 mg.) (about 8 drops) to each of three thoroughly dried 250-ml. glass-stoppered flasks by the technique described in Exp. 24. Add 10 ml. of chloroform to each of the three flasks and to two other (empty) flasks. Rotate the flasks until the samples dissolve. Draw up Hanus solution (iodine and bromine in glacial acetic acid) above the mark in a 25-ml. pipette, using the house vacuum or a water aspirator (*Caution*: never by mouth, since the liquid and vapors are extremely corrosive). Disconnect the rubber tubing attached to the pipette, allow the solution to fall to the mark, and deliver 25.0 ml. to one of the five glass-stoppered flasks. Pipette 10.0 ml. of a 2.5 per cent solution of mercuric acetate in glacial acetic acid into the flask by the described technique. Stopper and shake the flask. Allow the solution to stand for 3 min. During this time fill a 50-ml. burette with standard 0.1 N sodium thiosulfate solution. Immediately transfer 10 ml. (10-ml. graduate) of 15 per cent potassium iodide solution and 100 ml. (100-ml. graduate) of distilled water to the flask. Immediately (since potassium iodide is appreciably oxidized in a few minutes by dissolved oxygen) titrate the liberated iodine with the standard thiosulfate solution to a pale yellow-colored end point, add 2 ml. of 0.5 per cent soluble starch solution, and continue the titration to the disappearance of the blue color. Near the end of the titration, stopper and shake the flask between additions of thiosulfate.

EXPERIMENT 27

ISOLATION OF CHOLESTEROL FROM BEEF SPINAL CORDS

Accounts of the discovery, the early history, the chemistry, and the physiological properties of cholesterol and other sterols have been given by Bills (1935), Heilbron (1936), Butenandt (1936a–1936c), Callow (1938), Strain (1943), Fieser (1949), Sobotka (1938), and Friedmann (1937).

The sterols occur free and combined as fatty acid esters in animals (zoosterols), plants (phytosterols), and yeasts and fungi (mycosterols). Cholesterol, originally called "cholestrine" from the Greek words "chole" (bile) and "stereos" (solid), was first isolated from gallstones by Poulletier de la Salle in 1782. Cholesterol is abundant in brain and nerves, where it may have a special function. Okey (1945) has shown that egg yolk and brain are the only common foods containing more than 1 per cent cholesterol. Both plants and animals synthesize cholesterol, but, according to Schoenheimer (1932), mammals utilize plant sterols with difficulty, if at all.

Examples of sterols occurring in natural products are coprosterol ($C_{27}H_{48}O$) in feces, ergosterol ($C_{28}H_{44}O$) in yeast, and stigmasterol ($C_{29}H_{48}O$) in soybean. Types of natural sterols are the bile acids, sex hormones, toad poisons, cardiac glycosides, sapogenins, and adrenal hormones. Examples are cholic acid ($C_{24}H_{40}O_5$) in bile, testosterone ($C_{19}H_{28}O_2$) in urine of males, estrone or theelin ($C_{18}H_{22}O_4$) in urine of pregnant females, bufotalin ($C_{26}H_{37}O_6$) in the parotid secretion of the toad, digitoxigenin ($C_{23}H_{34}O_4$) in cardiac glycoside from foxglove (*Digitalis purpurea*), digitogenin ($C_{27}H_{44}O_5$) in noncardiac glycoside from foxglove, and corticosterone ($C_{20}H_{29}O_4$) in the adrenal cortex. Cholesterol may be the parent substance of some, if not all, of these sterols.

The sterols are derivatives of the hydrocarbon cyclopentanoperhydrophenanthrene. The structural formula of cholesterol ($C_{27}H_{46}O$) containing this nucleus is shown below.

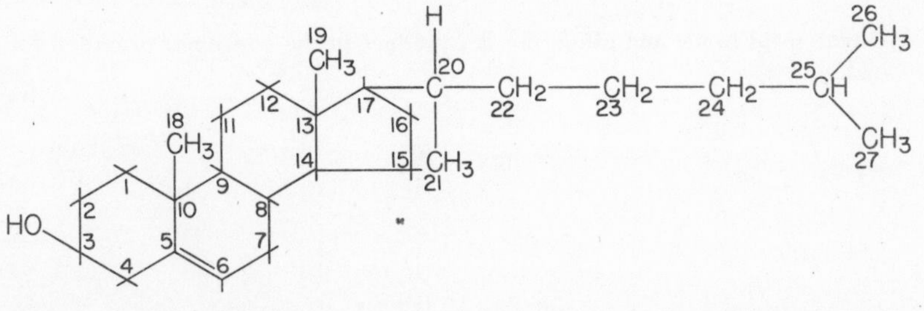

Cholesterol is readily prepared crystalline from organic-solvent extracts of brain from sheep or other animals (Baumstarck, 1885; Rosenheim, 1906a; Tebb, 1906), although it is prepared commercially from beef spinal cords. Ether was first employed as the solvent, but acetone and ethylene dichloride (Porsche, 1945) are used commonly because lecithin and other phospholipids are less soluble in these solvents than in ether.

In the present experiment cholesterol is to be isolated from acetone extracts of beef spinal cords essentially by the method of Giesy (1920).

EXPERIMENTAL[1]

Transfer about 400 g. of beef spinal cords, preserved in the refrigerator, to a meat grinder. Grind this material as fine as possible. Transfer the ground material (including the adhering material) to a tared evaporating dish or pyrex plate. Add 400 g. of filter aid and knead the mixture to a homogeneous, nearly dry powder. Dry the powder at 75 to 80° for 40 hr. or longer. Cool the dish (and contents) to room temperature and weigh the dish (and contents).

Transfer the dry material to a 2-liter beaker. Add 750 ml. of acetone and stir the mixture at intervals for 10 min. Decant and filter the supernatant liquid. Collect the filtrate in a 2-liter round-bottomed flask. Add 500 ml. of acetone to the residual material in the beaker, stir the mixture for 10 min., and filter the supernatant liquid. Repeat the extraction process using 500 ml. of acetone.[2]

Set up the distillation apparatus shown in Fig. 6 (see Distillation in the Appendix) and distill the combined acetone filtrates until 1 liter of acetone distillate has collected. Repeat the described extraction process twice, using 500-ml. portions of the recovered acetone as solvent. Distill the combined acetone filtrates from a 2-liter round-bottomed flask until crystals appear in the flask. Immediately transfer the hot acetone suspension to a beaker, allow the mixture to cool to room temperature, and filter the suspension on a Buchner funnel. Distill the filtrate until crystals appear in the hot liquid and collect the (second) crop of crystals as previously described. Transfer the acetone filtrate to the special container.

Transfer the first and second crops of crystals to a 250-ml. flask. Add 50 ml. of 0.5 N KOH in 95 per cent ethanol, attach a reflux condenser, and reflux the mixture (water bath) while adding sufficient ethanol through the condenser to keep the solid in solution. Continue refluxing for 40 min. to saponify the cholesterol palmitate present as impurity. Remove the condenser, allow the solution to cool, and add glacial acetic acid (about 1.5 ml.) dropwise until the solution is neutral to litmus paper. Allow the mixture to cool for 30 min. in an ice-water bath, filter the suspension on a Buchner funnel, and recrystallize the moist product from the minimum volume (about 10 ml. per g. of crude cholesterol) of 95 per cent ethanol. Filter the suspension on a Buchner funnel and apply suction until the solid is nearly dry. Transfer the product to a watch glass, cover the watch glass with a filter paper, and dry the product overnight at 50°. Submit the product to the instructor in a tared, labeled sample bottle. Determine the melting point (see Melting Point in the Appendix) of the samples furnished by the instructor.

NOTES

1. The authors are indebted to Dr. Sven Lassen, Van Camp Laboratories, Terminal Island, Calif., for helpful suggestions.

2. Dry the residual solid in air and place the dry product in the container provided for that purpose.

EXPERIMENT 28

PREPARATION OF STARCH FROM POTATOES

The early history of starch has been reviewed by Herstein (1911). The constitution and properties of starch have been discussed by Meyer (1942), Hassid (1943, 1945a, 1945b), Brimhall and Hixon (1943), Hixon and Rundle (1944), Haworth (1946), and Kermack (1946).

Ancient people used starch in cosmetics, in medicines, and for stiffening fabrics. The preparation of starch from grain was described by Cato in 184 B.C. In the nineteenth century it was found that starch is converted to sugar (glucose) during malting and by acid hydrolysis. Amylose and amylopectin were recognized as constituents of starch by Nägeli in 1858 and were separated by Maquenne and Roux (1903). By current procedures the relatively soluble amylose is extracted from starch with hot water and is precipitated from the solution with methanol (McCready and Hassid, 1943), butanol (Schock, 1942), or thymol (Haworth, Peat, and Sagrett, 1946). Starches prepared from tapioca, rice, corn, potato, wheat, bean, and Easter lily contain from 20 to 30 per cent amylose (Bates, French, and Rundle, 1943). Waxy-corn starch consists entirely of amylopectin (Schopmeyer, 1945).

It was first proposed by Meyer (1942) that the amylose fraction of starch consists of linear molecules, while amylopectin is made up of branched molecules. Amylose contains from 250 to 500 and amylopectin about 20 to 30 glucose residues per chain, as determined by the "end-group" assay method. By this procedure the starch is completely methylated, the methylated product is hydrolyzed, and the resulting 2,3,6-trimethylglucose and 2,3,4,6-tetramethylglucose are separated. Since the glucose residue at the nonreducing end of the chain has four hydroxyl groups which can form stable methyl derivatives, compared with three such groups within or at the reducing end of the chain, the length of the chain (or branch) can be estimated from the percentage of the tetramethylglucose obtained. Haworth has shown that starch chains consist of α-glucopyranose units joined by an oxygen atom (glucosidic linkage) through the first carbon atom (the reducing group) and the fourth carbon atom of the adjacent glucose unit. Formulas for starch and for these derivatives are shown below (Hassid, 1945b).

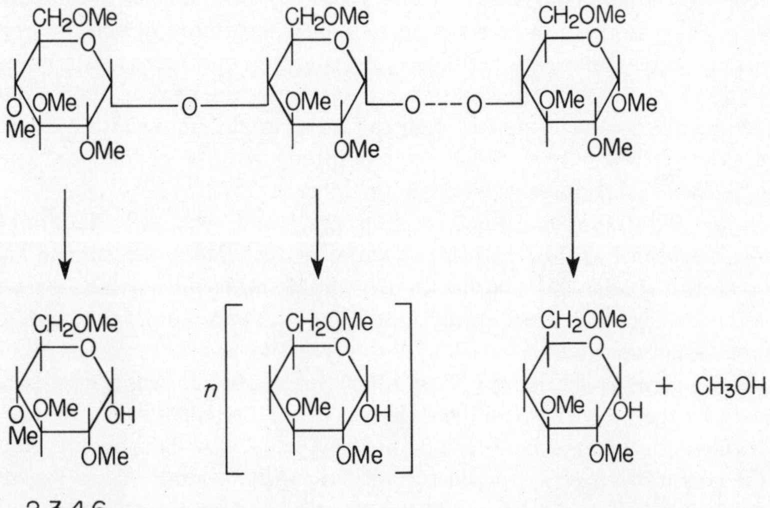

2,3,4,6-tetramethylglucose   2,3,6-trimethylglucose   2,3,6-trimethylglucose

According to Meyer's modification of Nägeli's micellar theory of starch structure, starch granules are built up of crystalline dendritic units (trichites) consisting of alternate layers of amylose and amylopectin (Sjostrom, 1936). Starch granules are striated concentrically, owing to the nonuniform distri-

– 55 –

bution of water in the layers. Canna starch granules are oyster-shaped and are among the largest known. The chemical and physical properties of starches from more than 30 different plants have been investigated (Barham, Wagoner, Campbell, and Harclerode, 1946; Bear, 1942; Kreger, 1946; Speich, 1942; Harris and Jesperson, 1946a, 1946b; Briant, Personius, and Cassel, 1945; Armitage, 1943; and Lampitt, Fuller, and Goldenberg, 1948).

The influence of place, season, soil, variety of plant, and other factors on the starch content of wheat (Barham, Kramer, and Reed, 1943; McCalla and Corns, 1943), sweet potatoes (Boswell *et al.*, 1944), and other plants has been studied. Starch has been manufactured from sweet potatoes (Kimbrough, 1942), wheat (Dimler, Davis, Rist, and Hilbert, 1944), corn (Kelling, 1944), peas (Hilbert and MacMasters, 1946), Easter lily bulbs (Stuart and Brimhall, 1943), water chestnut (Shafee and Sarin, 1937), and other plants. Waxy (glutinous) starch (stains iodine red brown rather than the usual blue) is obtained from rice, sorghum, millet, barley, and corn (Hixon and Sprague, 1942; MacMasters and Hilbert, 1944).

Starch contains about 0.1 per cent of phosphorus compounds (probably amylose phosphate) (Briggs and Hanig, 1946). Fatty acids embedded in the starch layers are difficult to remove with fat solvents (ether) but are easily extracted with hydrophilic solvents (methanol). Fatty materials interfere with the fractionation of starch, and they modify the iodine absorption, gelling power, and other properties.

Thick-boiling and thin-boiling starches, oxidized starch, gelatinized starch, and other products are manufactured from corn, kaffir, rice, potato, tapioca, and other plants for use in coating paper (Bullard *et al.*, 1947), impregnating textiles, color printing, cold-water pastes, adhesives, and other uses. Large quantities of starch are converted to glucose for use as food and as a source of poly-alcohols and organic acids (Kennedy, 1946).

Starch is to be prepared by macerating potatoes, mixing the macerated product with water, draining the suspension, and allowing the starch particles to settle.

EXPERIMENTAL

Preparation of Purified Starch. Wash, peel, and slice about 600 g. of potato tubers. Thoroughly macerate 500 g. of the slices by grating them with a metal grater. Collect all the product including the expressed liquid as well as the pulp. Thoroughly mix the ground material in a suitable container (enameled pan) with 500 ml. of distilled water. Drain the suspension on a double layer of cheesecloth, remove as much as possible of the fluid, and repeat this extraction process until nearly all the starch has been removed. Use separate beakers for the extracts. Discard the insoluble residue.

Allow the separate beakers to stand (for 1 hr.) until the finely divided starch particles have settled. Carefully pour the supernatant fluids into separate containers and preserve them for the tests described below. Collect the several starch precipitates in one beaker, using 100 ml. of distilled water as rinse fluid. Allow the starch to settle, pour the supernatant liquid into a beaker, and preserve this liquid for the tests described below. Wash the precipitate with two additional portions of distilled water and preserve the wash liquids separately for later tests.

Color Changes in Potatoes and Aqueous Extracts from Potatoes.[1] Macerate about 20 g. of sliced potatoes and permit one half of this material to stand in air. Place the second half in a beaker, add 50 ml. of distilled water, and heat the mixture for 15 min. at the boiling point. Allow the mixture to stand in air. Observe the color changes occurring over 24 hr. in the supernatant liquids and products obtained in this and the preceding section.

Reducing Substances in Potatoes. Test all the extracts and wash liquids obtained in the two preceding sections by the following method: Heat 5 ml. of Benedict's qualitative sugar reagent to boiling in a test tube. No change in color and no precipitation should occur. Add 5 drops of one of the extracts, heat the mixture to boiling, and maintain boiling for 1 min. Allow the mixture to cool to room temperature. Observe any changes. Discard the solutions containing the reducing substances, since they will putrefy if allowed to stand.

Nitrogeneous Substances in Potatoes. Heat to boiling 100 ml. of the first aqueous extract obtained in the first experimental section. Add 50 ml. of 6 *N* acetic acid and allow the mixture to cool to room temperature. Filter (or centifuge) the coagulum, wash the precipitate with 95 per cent ethanol and diethyl ether, and dry the precipitate in air. Weigh the dried material. Decompose it and a sample of purified starch by the procedure given in Exp. 21, Step III, using about 0.5 g. of test material.

Perform the following test for nitrogen: Add to the filtrate 2 ml. of potassium fluoride solution and 1 ml. of saturated ferrous sulfate solution. Allow the mixture to stand for 5 min. and then add concentrated hydrochloric acid dropwise until the mixture is slightly acid to litmus paper. The appearance of a brilliant-blue color or a blue precipitate of Prussian blue $\{Fe_4[Fe(CN)_6]_3\}$ confirms the presence of nitrogen.

NOTE

1. A dark-colored product, called melanin, is formed by the action of tyrosinase on tyrosine and the condensation of the intermediate quinones (Dulière and Raper, 1930; Raper, 1927).

EXPERIMENT 29

DETERMINATION OF STARCH FACTOR AND STARCH IN A STARCH-PROTEIN MIXTURE

The determination of starch is of interest to scientific workers and agencies concerned with botanical, horticultural, and other types of problems. Analyses are complicated by the presence of cellulose, hemicelluloses, pentosans, gums, mucilages, glucosides, pectins, tannins, and varying proportions of amylose and amylopectin.

It has been proposed (Krocker, 1846; Polit and Dhar, 1925) that starch may be determined by hydrolyzing it to sugar, fermenting the sugar, and measuring the loss in weight due to carbon dioxide. A more practicable procedure is to solubilize the starch with hydrochloric acid, precipitate the starch with ethanol, and weigh the (dried) product (Sullivan, 1935a). Solubilizing and extracting agents employed by other workers include $MgCl_2$ (Jirak, 1935), $CaCl_2$ (Mannich and Lenz, 1920), malt amylase (Hanes, 1936), salivary amylase (Hassid, McCready, and Rosenfels, 1940), takadiastase (Denny, 1934a, 1934b), NaClO (Balch, 1941), and $HClO_4$ (Nielsen and Gleason, 1945).

Litner (1907) and other workers (Mannich and Lenz, 1920; Hopkins, 1934; Clendenning and Wright, 1945) have determined starch on the basis of its optical rotation. Although it has been assumed that all starches have a specific rotation of 200 (Association of Official Agricultural Chemists, 1945, page 251), Earle and Milner (1944) have shown that it varies from 201 to 204 for different plants.

Several types of procedures have been proposed for the determination of starch as its starch-iodide complex (Bates, French, and Rundle, 1943; Kerr and Trubell, 1943; Pucher, Leavenworth, and Vickery, 1948). Plant tissues are extracted first with dilute ethanol, to remove glucosides and other substances which yield colored products with iodine, and then with cold hydrochloric acid or hot calcium chloride solution. Starch, but not other polysaccharides, is precipitated with iodine, and the concentration of the resulting blue starch-iodide complex held in colloidal solution is determined spectrophotometrically using purified potato starch as standard (see Exp. 36, Note 3, for discussion of the starch-iodide reaction).

Starch has been determined most commonly on the basis of the glucose liberated on hydrolysis. The literature on the starch factor published prior to 1896 has been reviewed by Fresenius and Grünhut (1896). The value 0.936 was established by Noyes, Crawford, Juniper, Flory, and Arnold (1904) and Pucher and Vickery (1936) confirmed this factor. Factors ranging from 0.92 to 1.01 have been reported (Earle and Milner, 1944; Etheredge, 1944; Sullivan, 1935a). As shown by Sullivan (1935b) and indicated in Fig. 4, the theoretical starch factor $[(C_6H_{10}O_5)_n \cdot H_2O / nC_6H_{12}O_6]$ approaches the limiting value 0.900 as the number of anhydroglucose residues per molecule of starch increases. This approximate value would be found experimentally in the absence of any decomposition during hydrolysis, since most starches contain about 80 per cent of branched-chain amylopectin (molecular weight about 500,000) and 20 per cent of straight-chain amylose (molecular weight about 60,000) (Stuart and Brimhall, 1943).

Modifications of Fehling (1849, 1858) procedure have been employed by Fraps (1932), Hartmann and Hillig (1931), Bish (1929), Hassid, McCready, and Rosenfels (1940), and Yemm (1935) for the determination of glucose in hydrolyzed starch. Whitmore (1934) combined the ferricyanide procedure of Gentele (1859), as modified by Hagedorn and Jensen (1923a), with the titrimetric determination of ferrocyanide by ceric sulfate. The last reaction was shown to be quantitative by Furman and Evans (1929). Because the end point in the titration was not sharp, Whitmoyer employed the internal indicator α-zurine G, which is extremely sensitive in acid solution to amounts of ceric sulfate. Hassid (1936, 193? substituted the internal indicators o-phenanthroline, ferrous sulfate, and setopaline C. The latter indicator is especially useful in the analysis of plant extracts. Hassid's method has been found applicable to quantities of reducing sugars ranging from 0.3 to 3.5 mg.

The *starch factor* is the number by which glucose is multiplied to give the quantity of starch from which the glucose was derived. Starch is to be determined in this experiment by hydrolyzing it with hydrochloric acid, oxidizing the liberated glucose with alkaline ferricyanide, and oxidizing the resulting ferrocyanide with standard ceric sulfate solution.

$$C_6H_{12}O_6 + Fe(CN)_6^{3-} \rightarrow Fe(CN)_6^{4-} + \text{oxidation products}$$

$$Fe(CN)_6^{4-} + Ce^{4+} \rightarrow Fe(CN)_6^{3-} + Ce^{3+}$$

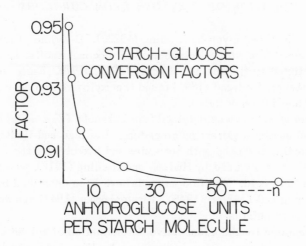

Fig. 4.

EXPERIMENTAL

Obtain a 0.5-g. sample of purified potato starch and a 0.5-g. sample of a mixture containing purified potato starch and protein. Transfer 0.4 g. (weighed to ±1 mg.) of the purified starch and 0.4 g. (weighed to ±1 mg.) of the starch-protein mixture to separate 250-ml. flasks. Pipette 50 ml. of N hydrochloric acid into each flask, attach a reflux condenser (10-in.) to each flask, and immerse both flasks in the same boiling-water bath for 180 min.

Remove the flasks and immerse them in an ice-water bath. Rinse each condenser with distilled water into its respective flask. When the solutions have cooled to room temperature,[1] transfer the contents of each flask quantitatively to separate 1-liter volumetric flasks. Add N sodium hydroxide to each flask until the solution is neutral to bromthymol blue indicator (olive-green color). Mix the contents of each flask thoroughly, add distilled water to the marks, mix the solutions thoroughly, and transfer a 100-ml. aliquot of each solution to separate conical flasks. Label and stopper the flasks. Store them in the refrigerator. As soon as possible, but no later than 24 hr., analyze the hydrolysates for glucose.

Pipette 5.00 ml. of one of the solutions into a 50-ml. conical flask. Add 5 ml. of the special alkaline potassium ferricyanide solution (preserved in a dark bottle in the refrigerator), mix the solutions, place the flask in a boiling-water bath, and maintain this temperature for exactly 15 min. Cool the flask to room temperature, add 5 ml. of 5 N sulfuric acid, and mix the solutions. Add 7 drops of setopaline C indicator solution (freshly prepared each day) and titrate the solution with standard, approximately 0.02 M ceric sulfate solution (10-ml. microburette). The solution turns a golden-brown color at the end point.

Repeat this process with additional aliquots of the same solution until consecutive titrations agree within 0.01 ml. Repeat these manipulations using 5-ml. aliquots of the other starch solution.

NOTE

1. At this point the solutions may be stored for several days if desired.

EXPERIMENT 30

ISOLATION OF D-XYLOSE FROM CORNCOBS

The history of xylose has been given by Harding (1923a). D-Xylose, first isolated from wood by Koch (1886), has been obtained from straw, corncobs, flax, coconut shells, apricot shells, cottonseed hulls, and other materials listed by Hudson and Harding (1917, 1918). Early workers obtained xylose from the polymer xylan; however, Bertrand (1891) found that xylose could be isolated directly from plants without preliminary separation of xylan.

About 3 per cent yield of xylose was obtained from corncobs (*Zea mays*) by Stone and Lotz (1891), who employed the classical ammonia extraction procedure. LaForge and Hudson (1918) increased the yield to 5 per cent by extracting corncobs with hot water and hydrolyzing the xylan with sulfuric acid. From 10 to 12 per cent yield was obtained by Hudson and Harding (1918), who hydrolyzed corncobs directly with 7 per cent sulfuric acid. Modified methods have been described by Monroe (1919), Ling and Nanji (1923), and Dunning and Lathrop (1945). Firstenberger (1943) has described the large-scale preparation of D-xylose from cornstalks.

Methods have been reported for the quantitative determination of xylose by selective fermentation with the microorganism (*Hansenula suaveolens*) (Wise and Appling, 1945) and by precipitation as its benzylidine dimethylacetal derivative (Breddy and Jones, 1945) (see Exp. 36, Test 13, for the latter test).

D-Xylose is not readily assimilated by man (Blatherwick *et al.*, 1936), but it is an essential nutrient for some microorganisms (Camien, Dunn, and Salle, 1947). Administered to rats, D-xylose leads to increase in nonfermentable reducing substances in the liver and other organs (Blatherwick *et al.*, 1936) and to cataracts (Darby and Day, 1940). Fermentation of xylose by *Clostridium acetobutylicum* yields butanol, acetone, and ethanol in quantities varying from 20, 26, and 46 per cent, respectively, in the early stages to 60, 30, and 10 per cent after 118 hr. (Underkofler, Christensen, and Fulmer, 1936).

D-Xylose is to be isolated by crystallizing it from a sulfuric acid hydrolysate of corncobs.

EXPERIMENTAL

Weigh 100 g. of corncobs, break the cobs into small pieces, and grind them to a coarse powder in a food grinder. Transfer the powder to a 2-liter round-bottomed flask and add 600 ml. of N sulfuric acid. Reflux the mixture on a sand bath for 2 hr.

Allow the suspension to settle, decant the orange-colored supernatant liquid to a Buchner funnel, transfer the precipitate to the funnel, and wash the precipitate on the funnel with 100 ml. of distilled water. Transfer the filtrate to a flask and add 85 g. (0.54 equivalent) of powdered $Ba(OH)_2 \cdot 8H_2O$ in 10-g. portions, with frequent vigorous stirring to minimize coating the barium hydroxide particles with barium sulfate. Place the flask in a boiling-water bath. Add 15 g. (0.15 equivalent) of powdered barium carbonate slowly enough to prevent foaming[1] while stirring and heating the mixture. Continue heating and stirring for 15 min. Transfer 1 drop of the mixture to a spot plate containing congo red indicator solution. If the mixture is acid (blue color), add 10 g. of the barium carbonate powder and repeat the described procedure. Continue this process until the indicator solution is colored red (pH 4 to 5).

Filter the hot suspension on a Buchner funnel fitted with a filter paper covered with 1/2 in. of filter aid. Wash the precipitate thoroughly with two 100-ml. portions of boiling distilled water. Add N sulfuric acid slowly to the filtrate until it appears that all the barium ions have been converted to insoluble barium sulfate. Allow the precipitate to settle, transfer 10 ml. of the supernatant liquid to a test tube, and add N sulfuric acid dropwise. If a precipitate is formed, return the test solution to the flask and add a volume of N sulfuric acid calculated to precipitate the barium ions in the entire solution. Test the supernatant liquid as described and continue this treatment until all the barium ions have been removed. Test a drop of the final supernatant liquid with congo red indicator. The color should be red, indicating that the solution has not been acidified beyond pH 4.

Add 1 ml. of glacial acetic acid and 15 g. of decolorizing carbon to the suspension and allow the mixture to stand at room temperature for 15 min. with frequent stirring. Filter the suspension, wash the precipitate with hot distilled water, and transfer the filtrate and washings to a 2-liter flask. Set up the reduced-pressure apparatus shown in Fig. 7 (see Distillation in the Appendix) and distill the pale-yellow-colored filtrate[2] under reduced pressure on a boiling-water bath to a thin sirup (about 50-ml. volume). Pour the sirup with continuous stirring into 3 volumes of methanol and allow the mixture to stand in the refrigerator overnight or until the next laboratory period. Filter the mixture to remove any impurities which may have precipitated.

Distill the filtrate[3] under reduced pressure on a boiling-water bath to a thick sirup (10 to 15 ml.). Add 30 ml. of hot methanol to the warm sirup with stirring, transfer the mixture to a beaker, and add several seed crystals of D-xylose. Allow the (covered) beaker to stand in the refrigerator overnight or until the next laboratory period. Filter the suspension and wash the precipitate with 20 ml. of 75 per cent methanol.

Dissolve the crude D-xylose in distilled water (0.5 ml. per g.) and add a drop of glacial acetic acid and 0.5 g. of decolorizing carbon. Allow the mixture to stand for 10 min. with frequent stirring. Filter the suspension and pour the clear filtrate into 3 volumes of methanol with vigorous stirring. Seed the solution with a few crystals of D-xylose and allow it to stand in the refrigerator overnight or until the next laboratory period.

Filter the suspension and wash the crystals with 75 per cent methanol and with absolute methanol. Allow the recrystallized product[4] to dry in air in a covered evaporating dish. Submit the product to the instructor in a tared, labeled sample bottle. Calculate the percentage yield and submit the calculations to the instructor.

NOTES

1. A few drops of butyl alcohol may aid in dispersing the foam.

2. Repeat the decolorizing procedure with 5 g. of decolorizing carbon if the color of the filtrate is darker than pale yellow.

3. If the liquid is dark-colored when the volume has been reduced to 40 ml., decolorize it with 1 g. of decolorizing carbon.

4. α-D-Xylose melts at $145°$ and $[\alpha]_D^{20} = +93.6$ deg. in 4 per cent aqueous solution. The equilibrium value after mutarotation is +18.8 deg. (Bates and associates, 1942).

EXPERIMENT 31

ISOLATION OF L-ARABINOSE FROM MESQUITE GUM

L-Arabinose has been isolated from beet pulp, cherry gum, wheat, rye bran, peach gum, Australian black wattle gum, and other plant materials (Bates and associates, 1942; Harding, 1922). Mesquite gum is the most convenient source, and the methods described by Anderson and Sands (1925, 1926, 1941), Anderson, Sands, and Sturgis (1925), and Isbell (referred to by Bates and associates, 1942) are most commonly employed. According to Anderson and coauthors, mesquite gum is the exudate of *Prosopis juliflora* and other species of the mesquite tree native to various parts of Texas, New Mexico, Arizona, and northern Mexico.

Mesquite gum exudes from the stem and branches of the tree in irregular pieces weighing 5 to 25 g. When the gum first appears, it is soft and sticky and may run down the branch, but it gradually dries to a hard, brittle mass. The gum is a pectin-like material which, according to Ehrlich (1917), is the calcium salt of anhydrogalactomethoxytetragalacturonic acid. Anderson and Otis (1930, concluded that the organic acid consists of arabinose, galactose, and 3-methoxyglucuronic acid ($CHOCHOHCHOCH_3CHOHCHOHCOOH$) residues in the ratio 4:3:1, respectively. White (1946, 1947) has suggested that the ratio probably is 4:2:1. He has shown that the uronic acid component and part of the arabinose occupy terminal positions in the complex, that arabinose occurs in the furanose configuration, linked in the polysaccharide by glycosidic oxygen bridges at the first and second carbon atoms, and that galactose occurs in the pyranose configuration, linked by oxygen bridges at the first, third, and sixth carbon atoms. It appears that mesquite gum has a branched-chain structure concerned only with galactose units, that the four arabinose units form a branch or tail attached to the remainder of the polysaccharide and terminated by a residue of arabofuranose, and that the araban fraction of the gum is attached at the three position of a galactose anhydride unit. The position of the methoxy group in the glucuronic acid and the exact structural relations of the various monosaccharide units have not been determined.

L-Arabinose is an essential nutrient for some microorganisms (Camien, Dunn, and Salle, 1947) and L- and D-arabinose are utilized equally well by some microorganisms (Nicolle, 1944) and the rabbit (Corley, 1929). *Clostridium acetobutylicum* ferments arabinose to butanol, acetone, and ethanol in the ratio 50:40:10, respectively (Underkofler and Hunter, 1938).

L-Arabinose is to be isolated by crystallizing it from a sulfuric acid hydrolysate of mesquite gum. The gum is partially hydrolyzed by this treatment to L-arabinose and a residual polysaccharide (galactose-methoxyglucuronic acid), since the latter contains ether linkages more resistant to hydrolysis than the glycosidic linkages of araban (polymer of anhydroarabinose).

EXPERIMENTAL

Weigh 100 g. of coarsely powdered mesquite gum and suspend this material in 600 ml. of distilled water. Allow the suspension to stand at room temperature with occasional stirring until the gum dissolves completely except for insoluble impurities. It may be necessary to allow the mixture to stand overnight or longer time to dissolve the gum. Strain the suspension using several thicknesses of cheese cloth, add to the strained liquid 30 ml. of 18 N sulfuric acid, slowly with stirring, and heat the mixture for 3 hr. in a water bath at about 90°, with occasional stirring.

Add to the cooled solution 80 g. (0.5 equivalent) of powdered $Ba(OH)_2 \cdot 8H_2O$ in 10-g. portions, with frequent vigorous stirring to avoid incomplete reaction due to coating of the barium hydroxide particles with barium sulfate. Place the flask in a boiling-water bath and add 10 g. (0.1 equivalent) of powdered barium carbonate slowly to minimize foaming[1] while stirring and heating the mixture. Continue heating and stirring for 10 min. Test a drop of the mixture on a spot plate with congo red indicator solution. If the solution is acid (blue color), add 10 g. of barium carbonate and repeat the described process. Continue to add barium carbonate in this manner until the acid is neutralized (pH 4 to 5), as shown by the color (red) of the indicator.

Allow the precipitate to settle and decant the hot supernatant liquid to a Buchner funnel fitted with a filter paper covered with a 1/2-in. layer of filter aid. Wash the precipitate thoroughly with two 100-ml. portions of boiling distilled water. Precipitate the excess barium ions from the combined filtrate and washings as described in Exp. 30 (the final pH may be somewhat less than 4). Add 30 g. of decolorizing carbon to the suspension, heat the mixture in a water bath at 80° for 30 min., with occasional stirring, and filter the suspension. Refilter the filtrate if necessary to remove traces of carbon.

Transfer the filtrate to a 2-liter round-bottomed flask, add about 1 g. of antifoam agent (turkey red oil), and distill the solution to a volume of about 130 ml., using the apparatus shown in Fig. 6 (see Distillation in the Appendix) and a water bath. Add 400 ml. of 95 per cent ethanol (heated nearly to boiling on a water bath) and mix the liquids thoroughly. Allow the mixture to stand until the gummy material has settled and a clear supernatant liquid forms. Decant the latter and add 200 ml. of methanol (heated to 60° on a water bath) to the residual material. Allow the gum to settle and decant the clear supernatant liquid. Extract the gum with another 200-ml. portion of hot methanol. Distill the combined ethanol and methanol extracts to a sirup (volume about 40 ml.), add 2 ml. of distilled water, and stir the mixture thoroughly. Add several seed crystals of L-arabinose and allow the mixture to stand in the refrigerator overnight or until the next laboratory period.

Filter the suspension, wash the L-arabinose crystals with methanol, and apply suction until the crystals are nearly dry.[2] Weigh the crude product.

Dissolve the crude product in distilled water (0.3 ml. per g.), add 95 per cent ethanol (2.5 ml. per g.) heated nearly to boiling on a water bath, and add decolorizing carbon (0.05 g. per g.). Stir the mixture thoroughly, filter the hot suspension, and wash the carbon on the funnel with hot 95 per cent ethanol. Allow the filtrate to cool spontaneously to room temperature without shaking or seeding. Decant the upper layer, add hot methanol to the sirupy lower layer, stir the mixture thoroughly, and allow it to stand until the suspended material settles. Decant the supernatant liquid, reextract the lower layer with hot methanol, combine the methanol extracts, and distill the solution *in vacuo* to about 6 ml., using the reduced-pressure apparatus shown in Fig. 7 (see Distillation in the Appendix). Seed the solution with a few crystals of L-arabinose and place the mixture in the refrigerator overnight or until the next laboratory period.

Filter the suspension and wash the crystals twice with methanol. Allow the crystals to dry in air in a covered evaporating dish. Submit the product to the instructor in a tared, labeled sample bottle. Calculate the percentage yields of the crude and the purified L-arabinose[3] and submit the calculations to the instructor.

NOTES

1. A few drops of butyl alcohol may aid in dispersing the foam.
2. An additional crop of crystals may be obtained by evaporating the filtrate and treating it as described.
3. β-L-Arabinose melts at 155 to 157° (Anderson and Sands, 1941) and $[\alpha]_D^{20} = +190.6$ deg. in 4 per cent aqueous solution (Bates and associates, 1942). The mutarotation value is +104.5 deg. (Bates and associates, 1942).

EXPERIMENT 32

ISOLATION OF D-MANNOSE FROM IVORY-NUT WASTE

The most convenient source of D-mannose is vegetable-ivory (endosperm of the seed of the tagua palm, *Phytelephas macrocarpa*) turnings from button factories, although it occurs in the fruit of the snowberry, *Symphoricarpus racemosus* (von Lippmann, 1921), the seeds of *Daubentonia drummondii* (shrub of the pea family which grows in the coastal plain from Florida to Texas) (Curl and Nelson, 1944), and other plant and animal materials (Bailey and Roe, 1944; Fischer and Hirschberger, 1888, 1889a, 1889b).

D-Mannose has been isolated by crystallization from the sulfuric acid hydrolysate of ivory-nut waste (Bates and associates, 1942; Clark, 1922; Horton, 1921; Hudson and Sawyer, 1917; Isbell, 1941; Levene, 1923, 1924, 1935) and through the intermediate phenylhydrazone (Fischer and Hirschberger, 1888, 1889a, 1889b) and methylmannoside (Hudson and Jackson, 1934; Sheehan and Freudenberg, 1942). It has been reported that α-D-mannose, which first crystallizes, is transformed on recrystallization to β-D-mannose. Wise, Ratliff, and Browning (1948) have determined mannose in hardwoods.

Mannose is absorbed slowly from the intestinal tract of the rabbit (Bailey and Roe, 1944), and it is readily fermented by yeasts (Bailey and Roe, 1944) and lactic acid bacteria (Camien, Dunn, and Salle, 1947). The history of mannose has been given by Harding (1923b).

D-Mannose is to be isolated by crystallizing it from a sulfuric acid hydrolysate of ivory-nut meal.

EXPERIMENTAL

Transfer 100 g. of ivory-nut meal (ivory-nut waste sieved through a 20-mesh sieve) to a 500-ml. flask and add 60 ml. (1.44 equivalents) of 24 N sulfuric acid. Stir the mixture thoroughly and allow it to stand at room temperature overnight or until the next laboratory period. Rinse the mass from the flask to a 2-liter beaker, add distilled water to a total volume of solution of 1 liter, and stir the mixture thoroughly. Filter the mixture on a Buchner funnel fitted with several thicknesses of cheesecloth, allow the liquid to drain, add 50 ml. of distilled water, and allow the liquid to drain as completely as possible while pressing the mass with an inverted glass stopper.

Transfer the suspension to a 2-liter beaker and add 25 g. (0.25 equivalent) of powdered barium carbonate slowly to minimize foaming,[1] while stirring and heating the mixture. Continue heating and stirring for 15 min. Test a drop of the mixture on a spot plate with congo red indicator solution. If the mixture is acid (blue color), add 10 g. of powdered barium carbonate and repeat the described procedure. Continue this process until the solution is neutral (red color) to congo red (pH 4 to 5).

Filter the hot suspension on a Buchner funnel fitted with a filter paper and 1/2 in. of filter aid. Wash the precipitate thoroughly with two 100-ml. portions of boiling distilled water. Add N sulfuric acid to the combined filtrate and washings as described in Exp. 31 until all the barium ions have been converted to insoluble barium sulfate. Add 30 g. of decolorizing carbon and stir the mixture thoroughly at intervals for 15 min. Filter the suspension, and if particles of carbon are observed, refilter the filtrate, using a fluted gravity filter. Transfer the filtrate to a 2-liter round-bottomed flask and distill it to a thick sirup (20 to 25 ml.) under reduced pressure, using the apparatus shown in Fig. 7 (see Distillation in the Appendix) and a water bath.[2]

Add 100 ml. of methanol (heated to 60°) while continuously stirring the mixture. Add 200 ml. of isopropyl alcohol while stirring and allow the mixture to stand until the gummy impurities settle. Decant the supernatant liquid, add 30 ml. of hot methanol to the gummy residue with stirring, and add 60 ml. of isopropyl alcohol with stirring. Allow the gum to settle, decant the alcoholic supernatant liquid, and reextract the gummy residue with 30 ml. of hot methanol. Distill the combined solutions under reduced pressure on a water bath to a thin sirup (25 to 30 ml.). Add 25 ml. of glacial acetic acid, stir the mixture, add several crystals of D-mannose, and allow the mixture to stand overnight or for longer time at room temperature until crystals are observed. Place the mixture in a refrigerator for 24 hr. and filter the suspension (on longer standing the crystals may become gummy). Wash the crystals with a solution containing 1 part of methanol and 3 parts of 95 per cent ethanol. Apply suction until excess solvent has been removed (10 min.). Weigh the product.

Recrystallize the crude mannose using the indicated quantities of materials per 5 g. of mannose. Dissolve the product in water (5 ml.), add glacial acetic acid (1/2 drop) and decolorizing carbon (0.25 g.), and allow the mixture to stand for 15 min. in a boiling-water bath with frequent stirring. Add methanol (10 ml.), stir the mixture, and add isopropyl alcohol (20 ml.). Allow the gummy impurities to settle and decant the supernatant liquid to a Buchner funnel. Add a few crystals of D-mannose to the filtrate and stir the mixture vigorously at intervals until crystals are observed. Place the mixture in the refrigerator for 1 day. Filter the suspension and wash the crystals with 95 per cent ethanol until the washings are neutral to litmus paper.[3] Wash the crystals with 10 ml. of absolute ethanol and allow the crystals to dry in air in a covered evaporating dish. Submit the product to the instructor in a tared, labeled sample bottle. Calculate the percentage yields of the crude and the purified mannose[4] and submit the calculations to the instructor.

NOTES

1. A few drops of butanol may aid in dispersing the foam.

2. If the filtrate is dark-colored when the volume has been reduced to 200 ml., decolorize it with 5 g. of decolorizing carbon.

3. An additional crop of crystals may be obtained by evaporating the filtrate and treating it as described.

4. α-D-Mannose melts at 131 to 132° (Sheehan and Freudenberg, 1942). $[\alpha]_D^{20} = +29.3$ deg. in 4 per cent aqueous solution, and the equilibrium value after mutarotation is +14.2 deg. (Bates and associates, 1942).

EXPERIMENT 33

ISOLATION OF α-D-LACTOSE MONOHYDRATE FROM WHEY POWDER

The history of lactose has been reviewed by Whittier (1925–1926, 1944). Lactose was manufactured from whey as early as the seventeenth century because of its supposed value as a remedy for gout, distemper, and other disorders. It occurs in the milk of all mammals (except, possibly, the whale), although the percentages range from about 1.8 per cent for the rabbit to 8 per cent for the human. Cow's milk contains about 4.5 per cent lactose.

The large quantities of lactose manufactured at the present time in connection with cheese production find use in medicinal tablets, infant food, and bacteriological media. Lactose is usually prepared by crystallization from extracts of whey powder (Leviton, 1949; Leviton and Leighton, 1938; Pederson, 1913; Webb and Ramsdell, 1944).

It has been reported that excess lactose in the diet changes the intestinal flora from the putrefactive to the fermentative type (Rettger and Cheplin, 1923; Kulp and Rettger, 1924). On the other hand it has been found that excess lactose causes rats to develop alopecia (loss of hair), fail to grow, and die in 3 to 17 days (Ershoff, 1946; Handler, 1947a; Riggs and Beaty, 1947). Lactose is employed to differentiate the lactose-fermenting colon group of organisms from the nonfermenting typhoid-dysentary bacteria.

α-D-Lactose monohydrate is to be isolated by crystallizing it from an aqueous-ethanol extract of whey powder essentially by the procedure of Leviton and Leighton (1938).

EXPERIMENTAL

Obtain 25 g. of finely powdered, spray-dried, "sweet" whey powder[1] and assignment to a Waring Blendor. Transfer the powder and 300 ml. of 95 per cent ethanol to the bowl of the Blendor. Add 155 ml. of hot (90 to 95°) distilled water and stir the mixture for 10 (not more) min. Add 5 g. of filter aid and stir for 10 sec. Immediately filter the suspension on a dry Buchner funnel as rapidly as possible, since the lactose may start to crystallize. Transfer the filtrate to a 2-liter round-bottomed flask, add 5 ml. of concentrated hydrochloric acid and 150 ml. of 95 per cent ethanol, and mix the solutions thoroughly. The reduction in pH (from about 6 to 4) increases the solubility of the proteins, while the increased concentration of alcohol decreases the solubility of lactose. Add several crystals of α-D-lactose monohydrate and place the mixture in the refrigerator until crystallization appears to be complete (about 4 days). Shake the flask at intervals to accelerate crystallization. Filter the suspension on a Buchner funnel, wash the crystals with 25 ml. of 95 per cent ethanol, apply suction until the product is nearly dry (10 min.), and weigh the crude material.

Suspend the crude lactose monohydrate in distilled water (0.8 ml. per g.) at about 90° and stir the mixture until most of the solid dissolves (5 min.). If the mixture is colored, add decolorizing carbon (0.05 g. per g.) and heat the mixture for 10 min. in a boiling-water bath with occasional stirring. Filter the hot suspension on a Buchner funnel. If traces of carbon are observed, filter the filtrate on a fluted filter. Add several crystals of α-D-lactose monohydrate, stir the mixture, and place it in the refrigerator overnight or until the next laboratory period. Filter the suspension on a Buchner funnel and wash the crystals twice with 20-ml. portions of 95 per cent ethanol. Allow the product to dry in air in a covered evaporating dish. Submit the product to the instructor in a tared, labeled sample bottle. Calculate the percentage yields of the crude and the purified α-D-lactose monohydrate[2] and submit the calculations to the instructor.

NOTES

1. "Sweet" whey is the product obtained after rennet coagulation of the casein in skim milk during the manufacture of cheese. It contains about 60 to 70 per cent lactose, 10 to 15 per cent protein (lactalbumin and lactoglobulin), and 5 to 10 per cent minerals.

2. α-D-Lactose monohydrate gives $[\alpha]_D^{20} = +85.0$ deg. in 7.6 per cent aqueous solution, and the equilibrium value after mutarotation is +52.6 deg. (Bates and associates, 1942).

EXPERIMENT 34

POLARIMETRIC ANALYSIS OF α-D-LACTOSE MONOHYDRATE

The optical rotation of the α-D-lactose monohydrate prepared in Exp. 33 is to be determined, and the purity of the sample is to be calculated on the basis of its specific rotation. The procedure to be followed is essentially the same as that described in Exp. 17.

EXPERIMENTAL

Obtain from the instructor three 2.5-g. samples of α-D-lactose monohydrate. Weigh each 2.5-g. sample quantitatively to 1 mg. and transfer each sample quantitatively to a clean, dry 50-ml. volumetric flask.

Turn on the sodium lamp and allow it to warm up for about 10 min. Observe the zero reading of the scale with the polarimeter tube filled with distilled water, as described in Exp. 17. The following manipulations *must* be performed rapidly if the analytical results are to be satisfactory.

Simultaneously add about 40 ml. of distilled water (at room temperature) to one of the flasks and start the time clock. Immediately stopper the flask and shake it vigorously. Record the time (less than 2 min.) required to dissolve most of the lactose as indicated by a pronounced decrease in turbidity of the suspension. Continue to shake the flask until all but traces of the lactose dissolve. Add distilled water rapidly to the mark, stopper the flask, and mix the contents of the flask thoroughly. Rinse the polarimeter tube with two small portions of the lactose solution and fill the tube with this solution. Determine the rotation of the solution and record the time of this observation. Determine the rotation at 1-min. intervals, recording the time of each observation, until 10 readings have been made. The time required for the 10 readings should be approximately the same as that which elapsed prior to the first reading. Record the final temperature of the solution. Repeat this procedure using the second and third samples.

Correct each rotation value for the zero reading and determine the logarithm of each corrected rotation. Plot the logarithmic values as ordinates and time in minutes as abscissas on coordinate paper. Draw the best straight line through (or as close as possible to) the points and extrapolate this line to the time at which most of the lactose dissolved. Estimate the observed rotation at this time and calculate the specific rotation $[\alpha]_D^t$ for each sample. Calculate the percentage purity of each sample from the specific rotation determined experimentally and that of pure α-D-lactose monohydrate (+85.0 deg. at 20°C.). The temperature coefficient is small and may be neglected.

EXPERIMENT 35

DETERMINATION OF FREE AND COMBINED GLUCOSE IN CORN SIRUP

Corn (maize) was first cultivated extensively by the natives of the Americas, and today about 70 per cent of the world's corn is produced in the United States. Corn contains (dry basis) 67 per cent starch, 13 per cent fiber, 8 per cent protein, 7 per cent soluble materials (protein and minerals), 3.5 per cent oil, and 1.5 per cent ash and miscellaneous substances.

Corn sirup is prepared by digesting starch with dilute hydrochloric acid, neutralizing the excess acid with sodium carbonate, adsorbing the colored and other impurities on carbon, and evaporating the eluate to the desired consistency. Approximately 2 billion pounds of corn sirup are consumed annually in the United States as table sirup and in making candy and bakery products. Corn sirups contain 22 to 43 per cent glucose, 21 to 34 per cent maltose, 0 to 7.5 per cent levulose, and 6 to 20 per cent higher sugars (Bishop, 1944).

Free and combined glucose in corn sirup are to be determined by Somogyi's (1945) method. Glucose (free or liberated by hydrolysis of maltose, dextrin, and other combined forms) is oxidized with cupric ion to gluconic acid, and the resulting cuprous ion is converted to a colored complex with Nelson's (1944) chromogenic (arsenomolybdic acid) reagent. The intensity of the color is determined by comparing it with that formed by a standard glucose solution.

EXPERIMENTAL

Obtain a sample of commercial corn sirup. Transfer about 0.5 g. of the sirup to a 500-ml. volumetric flask by the technique described in Exp. 24. Add about 300-ml. of distilled water, thoroughly mix the liquids, fill the flask to the mark with distilled water, and thoroughly mix the liquids. Pipette 50.0 ml. of this solution (A) into a 250-ml. volumetric flask. Add 100-ml. of distilled water, mix the liquids thoroughly, fill the flask to the mark with distilled water, and mix the liquids thoroughly (solution B). Pipette 25.0 ml. of solution A into a 250-ml. volumetric flask and submit the flask to the instructor, who will add a known quantity of pure glucose. Add 200 ml. of distilled water to the flask, mix the liquids thoroughly, fill the flask to the mark with distilled water, and mix the liquids thoroughly (solution C).

Pipette 25.0 ml. of solution A and 25.0 ml. of 1.0 N hydrochloric acid into a 125-ml. flask. Attach a small condenser (Hopkins or 10-in. Liebig) to the flask, immerse the flask in a boiling-water bath, and maintain boiling for 2.5 hr. Remove the flask and detach and rinse the condenser into the flask. Add 25.0 ml. of 1.0 N sodium hydroxide[1] and transfer the mixture to a 250-ml. volumetric flask. Add 150 ml. of distilled water, mix the liquids thoroughly, fill the flask to the mark with distilled water, and mix the liquids thoroughly (solution D).

Determine the apparent free glucose in the unhydrolyzed corn sirup (solutions B and C) by the following procedure: Transfer (10-ml. graduate) 2.0 ml. of the cupric-ion reagent (Na_2HPO_4, NaOH, Rochelle salt, cupric sulfate, and sodium sulfate) to each of six 6-in. test tubes.[2] Pipette into each tube 2.00 ml. of one of the following solutions: (a) unknown sugar solution, (b) unknown sugar solution containing added pure glucose, (c) standard solution containing 0.035 mg. per ml. of glucose, (d) standard solution containing 0.060 mg. per ml. of glucose, (e) standard solution containing 0.10 mg. per ml. of glucose, and (f) standard solution containing 0.15 mg. per ml. of glucose. Cover the mouth of each tube with a marble. Immerse the tubes in a boiling-water bath for 10 min., remove the tubes, and cool them under running water. Transfer (10-ml. graduate) 1.0 ml. of the chromogenic reagent (ammonium molybdate, sulfuric acid, and disodium arsenate) to each of the tubes. Transfer quantitatively the colored solution in one of the tubes to a 25-ml. volumetric flask, rinse the tube into the volumetric flask, add distilled water to the mark, and mix the liquids thoroughly. Repeat this procedure with each of the other five solutions. Compare (visual colorimeter) the intensity of the color of the unknown solution with that of the standard which matches it most closely.

Determine the glucose in the hydrolyzed corn sirup (solutions D and E) by the described procedure, using freshly prepared standard solutions.

OPTIONAL (PHOTOELECTRIC COLORIMETER) PROCEDURE

Determine the intensities of all the solutions with a photoelectric colorimeter (Lumetron, Model 400A, with yellow-orange filter). Adjust the instrument so that the optical density reading of the blank is zero. Plot the data with optical density as the ordinate and glucose concentrations of the standard solutions as abscissa and draw a smooth curve. Determine the values of the unknown solutions by interpolating the standard curve.

NOTES

1. Do not add the alkali until ready to carry out the analysis, since a neutral solution of glucose may be decomposed by bacteria or molds within a few hours.

2. If a photoelectric colorimeter is to be used, add 2 ml. of the cupric-ion reagent to an additional test tube containing 2.0 ml. of distilled water.

EXPERIMENT 36

IDENTIFICATION OF CARBOHYDRATES IN A MIXTURE OF CARBOHYDRATES

Carbohydrates occurring in plant and animal materials are difficult to identify and determine because of the similarity of their structures and reactions. This probably accounts for the multiplicity of tests, including several hundred for glucose, which have been proposed. It is of interest that there are at least 6 modifications of Seliwanoff's reagent, 10 of Nylander's reagent, and 90 of Fehling's reagent (Dehn, Jackson, and Ballard, 1932).

Carbohydrate tests are of three types: (a) form and optical properties of crystals isolated from aqueous or organoaqueous solutions, (b) characteristic colors and precipitates formed with iodine, phenols, amines, alkaline or slightly acid solutions of heavy-metal ions (copper, bismuth, mercury, and iron), or phenylhydrazine (or derivative), and (c) fermentations by the action of yeasts, molds, or bacteria.

The carbohydrates in an unknown mixture of carbohydrates are to be identified by applying the group separations and specific tests described below.

SCHEME OF ANALYSIS

Step I. Detection of Carbohydrates. *Thymol Test.*

Step II. Detection of Glucopolysaccharides. *Dextrin, Glycogen, and Starch. Iodine Test.*

Step III. Detection of Monosaccharides and Oligosaccharides. *Monosaccharides: Arabinose, Fructose, Galactose, Glucose, Mannose, Rhamnose, and Xylose. Oligosaccharides: Lactose, Maltose, Raffinose, and Sucrose. Nitrochromic Acid Test.*

Step IV. Detection of Ketosaccharides. *Fructose, Inulin, Raffinose, and Sucrose. Phosphoric Acid Test.*

Step V. Detection of Reducing Saccharides. *Arabinose, Fructose, Galactose, Glucose, Lactose, Maltose, Mannose, Rhamnose, and Xylose. Basic Cupric Citrate Test.*

Step VI. Detection of Reducing Disaccharides. *Lactose and Maltose. Methylamine Test.*

Step VII. Detection of Reducing Monosaccharides. *Arabinose, Fructose, Galactose, Glucose, Mannose, Rhamnose, and Xylose. Acid Cupric Acetate Test.*

Step VIII. Detection of Pentoses. *Arabinose and Xylose. Orcinol Test.*

Step IX. Detection of Desoxysaccharides. *Rhamnose. Periodic Acid—p-Hydroxydiphenyl Test.*

Step X. Solubility Separations.

   1. *Fructose, Raffinose, and Rhamnose. Extraction with Absolute Methanol.*
   2. *Arabinose and Xylose. Extraction with 95 Per Cent Ethanol.*
   3. *Polysaccharides. Precipitation by 75 Per Cent Ethanol.*
   4. *Lactose. Precipitation by 85 Per Cent Ethanol.*
   5. *Inulin. Extraction with Water.*
   6. *Glycogen. Precipitation by Saturated Ammonium Sulfate Solution.*

Step XI. Detection of Individual Carbohydrates.

   1. *Starch, Dextrin, and Glycogen. Iodine Test.*
   2. *Inulin, Raffinose, Sucrose, and Fructose. Resorcinol Test.*
   3. *Raffinose and Sucrose. Basic Cupric Citrate Test.*
   4. *Raffinose and Sucrose. Diazouracil Test.*
   5. *Rhamnose. Periodic Acid—p-Hydroxydiphenyl Test.*

6. *Fructose. Cobaltous Chloride Test.*
7. *Arabinose and Xylose. Benzidine Test.*
8. *Lactose and Maltose. Acidic Cupric Acetate Test.*
9. *Lactose. Fermentation Test.*
10. √ *Galactose, Lactose, and Raffinose. Mucic Acid Test.*
11. *Reducing Sugars. Phenylhydrazine Test.*
12. *Arabinose. Benzhydrazide Test.*
13. *Xylose. Benzaldehyde—Methanolic Hydrochloric Acid Test.*

EXPERIMENTAL

Obtain from the instructor an unknown sample of a dry homogenous mixture containing two or more carbohydrates. Determine which carbohydrates are present on the basis of the group tests (Steps I to IX), prepare a flow sheet indicating the procedures to be followed in separating and identifying the carbohydrates in the unknown, and submit the flow sheet for the approval of the instructor. When the confirmatory tests have been completed, submit a written report summarizing the experimental results and conclusions. If any of the results are inconclusive, repeat the test on a sample of pure carbohydrate obtained from the instructor.

Step I. Detection of Carbohydrates.[1] *Thymol Test.* Transfer 5 mg.[2] of the unknown to a 3-in. test tube, add 2 ml. of distilled water, add 3 drops of 5 per cent thymol in 95 per cent ethanol, and stir the mixture. Incline the tube and introduce concentrated sulfuric acid in a manner such that the acid forms a layer below the aqueous solution. If a carbohydrate is present a rose-colored ring will appear at the interface of the liquids in a few seconds. The color will deepen on standing and will spread throughout the solution when the liquids are mixed.

Step II. Detection of Glucopolysaccharides. *Dextrin, Glycogen, and Starch. Iodine Test.*[3] Transfer 30 mg. of the unknown to a 3-in. test tube, add 2 ml. of water, add 2 drops of 0.01 N iodine in 0.01 N potassium iodide solution, stopper the tube, and shake it vigorously for 10 sec. The appearance of a color ranging from deep blue to magenta or reddish brown indicates the presence of at least one glucopolysaccharide. Other saccharides give no reaction.

Step III. Detection of Monosaccharides and Oligosaccharides. *Monosaccharides: Arabinose, Fructose, Galactose, Glucose, Mannose, Rhamnose, and Xylose. Oliogosaccharides: Lactose, Maltose, Raffinose, and Sucrose. Nitrochromic Acid Test.*[4] Transfer 30 mg. of the unknown to a 6-in. test tube, add 2 ml. of distilled water, and stir the mixture. Add 4 ml. of concentrated nitric acid, add 5 drops of 5 per cent potassium chromate solution, and stir the mixture. The appearance of a blue color within a minute or two indicates the presence of at least one low molecular-weight carbohydrate.

Step IV. Detection of Ketosaccharides. *Fructose, Inulin, Raffinose, and Sucrose. Phosphoric Acid Test.*[5] Transfer 20 mg. of the unknown to a dry 3-in. test tube, add 1 ml. of 85 per cent phosphoric acid, and stir the mixture. Heat the tube in a boiling-water bath for 1 min., remove the tube immediately, and observe the color. A brown or brownish-black solution indicates the presence of fructose or of a saccharide containing fructose. Other sugars give little or no color under these conditions.

Step V. Detection of Reducing Saccharides. *Arabinose, Fructose, Galactose, Glucose, Lactose, Maltose, Mannose, Rhamnose, and Xylose. Basic Cupric Citrate Test.*[6] Transfer 50 mg. of the unknown to a 6-in. test tube, add 5 ml. of Benedict's reagent (cupric sulfate, sodium citrate, and sodium carbonate), and stir the mixture. Heat the tube for 3 min. in a boiling-water bath. Allow the tube to cool to room temperature. The formation of a red-rust precipitate indicates the presence of at least one reducing sugar in the unknown. Traces of nonsugar impurities may form a small amount of cuprous oxide and color the solution green.

Step VI. Detection of Reducing Disaccharides. *Lactose and Maltose. Methylamine Test.*[7] Transfer 30 mg. of the unknown to a 6-in. pyrex test tube, add 4 ml. of distilled water, and stir the mixture. Add 3 drops of 5 per cent aqueous methylamine hydrochloride solution, heat the mixture to boiling over a free flame, and continue boiling for 30 sec. Remove the tube and add immediately 3 drops of 6 N sodium hydroxide. The appearance of a yellow color which changes on standing to a carmine red indicates the presence of at least one reducing disaccharide. Fructose gives a brown color and other sugars a yellow color.

Step VII. Detection of Reducing Monosaccharides. *Arabinose, Fructose, Galactose, Glucose, Mannose, Rhamnose, and Xylose. Acid Cupric Acetate Test.*[8] Transfer 30 mg. of the unknown to a 6-in. test tube, add 2 ml. of distilled water, and stir the mixture. Add 5 ml. of the modified Barfoed's reagent (cupric acetate and lactic acid) and heat the tube in a boiling-water bath for 5 min. Cool the tube to room temperature. The appearance of a brick-red precipitate indicates the presence of at least one reducing monosaccharide. Traces of impurities or small amounts of monosaccharide formed by hydrolysis of an oligosaccharide may cause the formation of a slight precipitate. If the results are inconclusive, repeat the test using 10 mg. of a monosaccharide.

Step VIII. Detection of Pentoses. *Arabinose and Xylose. Orcinol Test.*[9] Transfer 10 mg. of the unknown to a 6-in. test tube, add 3 ml. of modified Bial's reagent (orcinol and ferric chloride in hydrochloric acid), stir the mixture, and heat the tube for 3 min. in a boiling-water bath. Cool the solution to room temperature, add 10 ml. of butyl alcohol, and shake the mixture. In the presence of a pentose the heated solution turns green and darkens to a deep greenish-blue color. Addition of butyl alcohol intensifies the blueness of the solution, which may have a greenish cast if other carbohydrates are present. The sensitivity of the test may be decreased if other saccharides are present. If the results are inconclusive, carry out the confirmatory procedure (Step X-2).

Step IX. Detection of Desoxysaccharides. *Rhamnose. Periodic Acid–p-Hydroxydiphenyl Test.*[10] Obtain an aeration assembly, shown in Fig. 5 (see Aeration in the Appendix). Transfer 30 mg. of the unknown to the test tube (8-in.), add 0.3 g. of alanine, add 10 ml. of *N* sodium bicarbonate solution, add 10 ml. of 0.1 *N* sodium arsenite in 2 per cent sodium bicarbonate solution, and stir the mixture. Transfer 10 ml. of concentrated sulfuric acid and 20 mg. of purified (solid) *p*-hydroxydiphenyl to the receiving tube. Add 1 ml. of 0.5 *M* periodic acid solution to the reaction tube and immediately attach the aeration apparatus. Aerate the mixture for 20 min. The appearance of a violet color in the sulfuric acid indicates the presence of acetaldehyde in the solution and rhamnose in the unknown.

Step X. Solubility Separations.[11] 1. *Fructose, Raffinose, and Rhamnose. Extraction with Absolute Methanol.*[12] Assuming that the unknown contains 1 g. of each expected carbohydrate, add sufficient absolute methanol to the unknown (*P*-1) to dissolve the least soluble component. Stopper the container and shake it vigorously for 2 min. Allow the solid to settle and carefully decant the supernatant liquid as completely as possible onto a dry gravity filter. Collect the filtrate (*S*-1) in a labeled container, add 0.5 ml. of carbon disulfide, and preserve it for use in Step XI, Tests 2 to 5. Extract the residual material with 5 ml. of absolute methanol, shake the mixture for 2 min., allow the solid to settle, and discard the supernatant liquid. Extract the residual material with two 2-ml. portions of methanol similarly and discard the supernatant liquids. Pass air over the solid in the container until it is nearly free of methanol and preserve the solid (*P*-2) for later tests.[13]

2. *Arabinose and Xylose. Extraction with 95 Per Cent Ethanol.* If the group test for the pentoses (Step VIII) was uncertain, prepare a solution of the pentoses essentially free from other sugars by the following procedure: Add 5 ml. of 95 per cent ethanol to *P*-1 (if raffinose, rhamnose, and fructose absent) or to *P*-2; stopper the tube, shake it vigorously for 2 min., and decant the supernatant liquid onto a dry gravity filter. Test 3 drops of the filtrate (*S*-2) for pentoses by the orcinol test (Step VIII) and 1 drop by the benzidine test (Step XI, Test 7). Pass air over the solid in the container until it is nearly free from excess ethanol and preserve the solid (*P*-3) for later tests.

3. *Polysaccharides. Precipitation by 75 Per Cent Ethanol.* If the test for polyglucosaccharides (Step II) was positive or if inulin may be present (Step IV), add 10 ml. of distilled water to the unknown (*P*-1, *P*-2, or *P*-3), stir the mixture thoroughly at 30-sec. intervals for 5 min., and if any undissolved solid remains, filter the suspension with suction. Wash the precipitate thoroughly with two 5-ml. portions of distilled water and preserve the washings (*S*-3) for the test (Step XI, Test 1) for dextrin. Preserve the precipitate (*P*-4) for the tests in Step X-5. If the presence of lactose (Step VI) is suspected, preserve 3 ml. of the filtrate (*S*-4) for the tests in Step X-4 (*a*).

To the remaining filtrate (7 or 10 ml.) add a threefold volume (21 or 30 ml.) of 95 per cent ethanol, stir vigorously, and continue stirring at 30-sec. intervals for 5 min. Allow the solid to settle for 15 min., decant the supernatant liquid onto a dry gravity filter, and collect the filtrate in an evaporating dish. Transfer the remaining residual material to the filter with the aid of 95 per cent ethanol as rinse fluid and evaporate the combined filtrates in the evaporating dish on a boiling-water bath until the volume has been reduced to 10 ml. Add 0.5 ml. of carbon disulfide to this solution (S-5) and preserve the solution for the tests in Step XI. Pass air over the residue (P-5) on the filter and preserve it for use in Step X-5.

4. *Lactose. Precipitation by 85 Per Cent Ethanol. (a) Polysaccharides absent.* Dissolve the unknown (P-1, P-2, or P-3) in 10 ml. of distilled water. Add 0.5 ml. of carbon disulfide to 7 ml. of this solution (S-5) for use in Step XI. Add 30 ml. of 95 per cent ethanol to the remaining 3 ml. of S-5, shake the mixture thoroughly, and allow the solution to stand at room temperature for 30 min. or longer.

When precipitation of lactose (if present) appears to be complete, decant the supernatant liquid, evaporate it to dryness on a boiling-water bath, and preserve the residue (P-6) for later use. Wash the lactose precipitate twice with 5-ml. portions of 95 per cent ethanol and discard the washings. Dry the lactose by passing air through the flask and collect the lactose (P-7) by scraping the sides of the flask with a rubber policeman. Preserve the lactose (P-7) for use in Step XI, Tests 8, 10, and 11.

(*b*) *Polysaccharides present.* Add 30 ml. of 95 per cent ethanol to the solution S-4 prepared in Step X-3, shake the mixture vigorously until the precipitate (if any forms) coagulates, filter the suspension on a dry gravity filter, collect the filtrate in a dry 50-ml. flask, and allow the flask to stand for 30 min. or longer. If lactose is present, treat it as described in part (*a*).

5. *Inulin. Extraction with Water.* Transfer the solid P-4 from Step X-3, consisting principally of starch and inulin, to a 6-in. test tube, add 10 ml. of boiling distilled water, stir the mixture thoroughly, and place the tube in a hot-water bath. Allow the solid to settle and filter the supernatant liquid with suction. Transfer the residual material to the filter and apply suction until the solid is nearly dry. Preserve the solid (P-8) for use in Step XI, Test 1. Cool the filtrate in an ice-water bath until a precipitate [14] forms (10 to 30 min.), filter the suspension with suction, wash the precipitate (P-9) with 3 ml. of distilled water and with 5 ml. of 95 per cent ethanol, apply suction until the precipitate is nearly dry, and preserve the product for use in Step XI, Test 2.

6. *Glycogen. Precipitation by Saturated Ammonium Sulfate Solution.* Transfer the precipitate P-5 prepared in Step X-3 to a 50-ml. conical flask. Add 10 ml. of distilled water and stir the mixture until the solid dissolves. If any undissolved saccharide remains, filter the suspension. Add 7.5 g. of powdered ammonium sulfate and shake the mixture vigorously at intervals for 15 min. Filter the mixture, wash the precipitate (P-10) with 5 ml. of 95 per cent ethanol, allow the solid to dry in air, and preserve it for use in Step XI, Test. 1. Starch, but not dextrin, is precipitated by saturating the solution with ammonium sulfate. Starch, but not dextrin or glycogen, is precipitated by half saturating the solution with ammonium sulfate.

Step XI. Detection of Individual Carbohydrates.[15] 1. *Starch, Dextrin and Glycogen. Iodine Test.* Transfer to a 3-in. test tube 10 mg. of the precipitate P-4 prepared in Step X-3 or P-8 prepared in Step X-5. Transfer 20 mg. of the precipitate P-10 prepared in Step X-6 to another 3-in. test tube. Add 2 ml. of distilled water to each tube and stir the mixtures. Transfer 2 ml. of each of the solutions S-3, from Step X-3, and S-7, from Step X-6, to separate 3-in. test tubes. Add 2 ml. of distilled water to a fifth 3-in. test tube. Add 2 drops of 0.01 N iodine (in 0.01 N potassium iodide solution) to each tube and note the colors formed in the five tubes. Add 0.5 g. of sodium chloride to the tube containing the precipitate P-10 and to the tube containing the solution S-7. Stir the mixtures until the salt dissolves. Note any increase in the intensity of the iodine color. Any opalescence of either solution prior to the addition of iodine is caused by glycogen. Neither dextrin nor glycogen interferes with the formation of starch iodine blue color. In the absence of other polysaccharides, dextrin gives a blue-violet or violet-red color with iodine, while glycogen gives a brown-red color, which is intensified by sodium chloride.

2. *Inulin, Raffinose, Sucrose, and Fructose. Resorcinol Test.*[16] Transfer to separate 6-in. test tubes 0.5 ml. of the solution S-1[17] prepared in Step X-1, 5 mg. of the solid P-9 or 0.5 ml. of the solution S-6 prepared in Step X-5, and 0.2 ml. of the solution S-5 prepared in Step X-3 (or X-4 or Step XI, Note 15). Add to each tube 1 ml. of distilled water and 5 ml. of an ethanol—sulfuric acid mixture (40 ml. of acid in 150 ml. of 95 per cent ethanol) and stir the mixtures. Add to each tube 5 ml. of a 0.2 per cent solution of resorcinol in 95 per cent ethanol and heat the tubes for 2 min. in a boiling-water bath. The appearance of an intense red color confirms the presence of fructose or fructose-containing saccharide.

3. *Raffinose and Sucrose. Basic Cupric Citrate Test.* Omit this test if raffinose and sucrose were shown to be absent by the resorcinol test (Test 2). If reducing sugars are present, it is advantageous to destroy them with Benedict's reagent before testing for raffinose and sucrose.

Transfer to separate 6-in. test tubes 1.0 ml. of the solution S-1 prepared in Step X-1 and 0.5 ml. of the solution S-5 prepared in Step X-3. Treat each solution as follows: Add 5 ml. of Benedict's reagent, stir the mixture, and heat the tube in a boiling-water bath for 5 min. Filter the suspension of cuprous oxide, and if it appears that the cupric ion in the solution has been almost depleted, repeat this procedure. Remove the excess cupric ions by saturating the solution with hydrogen sulfide (fume hood) and filtering the suspension of cupric sulfide. Add 6 N sulfuric acid dropwise to the filtrate until the solution is acid to litmus paper and heat the mixture until the volume has been reduced to 4 ml. Test 0.5 ml. of this solution for raffinose and sucrose by the resorcinol test (Test 2) and preserve the remaining 3.5 ml. of solution for the diazouracil test (Test 4).

4. *Raffinose and Sucrose. Diazouracil Test.*[18] Omit this test if raffinose and sucrose were shown to be absent by the resorcinol test (Test 2).

Transfer to separate 4-in. test tubes 1.0 ml. of the solution S-1 prepared in Step X-1 and 0.5 ml. of the solution S-5 prepared in Step X-3. Dilute each solution with distilled water to a final volume of 3.5 ml. Transfer the 3.5 ml. of solution prepared in Test 3 and 3.5 ml. of distilled water to separate 4-in. test tubes. Add 1 ml. of 2 N sodium hydroxide to each tube, stir each mixture, and cool the tubes to 5° in an ice-water bath. Add 7 mg. of diazouracil (obtain from the instructor) to each tube and shake each mixture until a clear solution is formed. Allow each solution to stand at 5 to 10° for 20 min., add 2 drops of M magnesium chloride solution, and shake each mixture. The appearance of a green to blue-green to brown-green color within 20 min., followed by intensification of the color adsorbed on the precipitated magnesium hydroxide confirms the presence of raffinose, sucrose, or both these sugars. Sucrose is more sensitive to the test than raffinose and gives a more intense color. Other saccharides form a yellow to brown-red color which interferes markedly with the test.

5. *Rhamnose. Periodic Acid–p-Hydroxydiphenyl Test.* Transfer 1.0 ml. of the solution S-1 prepared in Step X-1 to an 8-in. test tube and carry out the procedure described in Step IX. The appearance of a violet color in the sulfuric acid confirms the presence of rhamnose.

6. *Fructose. Cobaltous Chloride Test.*[19] Transfer 0.5 ml. of the solution S-1 prepared in Step X-1 to a 3-in. test tube, add 2 ml. of a 1 per cent aqueous solution of cobaltous chloride, and stir the mixture. Heat the tube in a boiling-water bath for 2 min., cool the tube to room temperature, add 4 drops of concentrated ammonium hydroxide, and allow the mixture to stand for 20 min. The appearance of a violet color confirms the presence of fructose. Green cobaltous hydroxide precipitates in the absence of fructose. In the presence of another carbohydrate, fructose may form a violet-colored supernatant liquid discernible after the cobaltous hydroxide has settled.

7. *Arabinose and Xylose. Benzidine Test.*[20] Transfer 1 drop of the solution prepared in Step X-2 to a 3-in. test tube to which 0.5 ml. of a 4 per cent solution of benzidine in glacial acetic acid has been added. Heat the mixture to vigorous boiling over a flame and immerse the tube in an ice-water bath. The appearance of a red color confirms the presence of a pentose. Hexoses give yellow to brown colors which do not interfere with the test unless present in relatively high concentrations.

8. *Lactose and Maltose. Acidic Cupric Acetate Test.* Omit this test if reducing disaccharides (Step VI) and monosaccharides (Step VII) were shown to be absent.

Transfer to separate 6-in. test tubes 1 ml. of the solution S-5 prepared in Step X-4 and (if lactose was isolated) one-third of the solid P-6 prepared in Step X-4. Add 5 ml. of Barfoed's reagent to each tube, heat the tube in a boiling-water bath for 5 min., and cool the tube to room temperature. If little or no brick-red precipitate forms, the absence of reducing monosaccharides is confirmed. If an abundant precipitate of cuprous oxide forms, filter the suspension. If the copper reagent has been used up, as shown by the color of the filtrate, repeat the described procedure until reducing monosaccharides have been destroyed. Saturate the filtrate with hydrogen sulfide, filter the suspension of cupric sulfide, and add 6 N sulfuric acid dropwise to the filtrate until it is just acid to litmus paper. Heat the solution for 15 min. in a boiling-water bath to remove excess hydrogen sulfide, evaporate the solution to 1 ml., and preserve it for use in Test.9.

9. *Lactose. Fermentation Test.*[21] Transfer 1 g. of active dehydrated yeast to a mortar, add 10 ml. of distilled water, and grind the mixture to a uniform suspension. Transfer the suspension to a centrifuge tube, centrifuge the mixture, decant the supernatant liquid, resuspend the residual material in 10 ml. of distilled water, centrifuge the mixture, decant the supernatant liquid, and suspend the residual yeast in 30 ml. of distilled water.[22]

Add to separate Einhorn saccharometers (fermentation tubes) 20 mg. of lactose dissolved in 1 ml. of distilled water, 20 mg. of maltose dissolved in 1 ml. of water, 0.5 ml. of the solution S-5 prepared in Step X-4, and 1 ml. of the solution prepared in Test 8. Add 10 ml. of the prepared yeast suspension to each tube, stir the mixture in each tube to a uniform suspension, and fill the long arm of each saccharometer with the yeast suspension. Incubate the tubes at room temperature overnight or at 35° for 6 hr. Compare the volumes of carbon dioxide formed. The production of gas in amounts significantly greater than that from the blank (lactose) and comparable to the control (maltose) indicates the presence of at least one yeast-fermentable saccharide (glucose, mannose, sucrose, or maltose).

10. *Galactose, Lactose, and Raffinose. Mucic Acid Test.*[23] Transfer to separate 50-ml. flasks 3 ml. of the solution S-1 prepared in Step X-1, 100 mg. of the precipitate P-7 prepared in Step X-4, and one-third of the solid P-6 prepared in Step X-4. Dilute each solution to 10 ml. with distilled water, add 4 ml. of concentrated nitric acid to each flask, stir each mixture, and heat the flask in a boiling-water bath for a sufficient time to reduce the volume in each flask to about 5 ml. (about 3 hr.). Add 3 ml. of distilled water to each flask and allow the mixture to stand overnight (or longer) at room temperature in in a stoppered flask. If any crystals form, examine them under a microscope and compare them with photomicrographs of crystals provided by the instructor. Determine the melting point of the water-washed and dried crystals. The formation of mucic acid (m.p. 213 to 214°) confirms the presence of galactose or galactose-containing compound (raffinose or lactose).

11. *Reducing Sugars. Phenylhydrazine Test.*[24] Transfer 0.2 g. of phenylhydrazine hydrochloride and 0.3 g. of powdered sodium acetate to a test tube, add 2 ml. of distilled water, and stir the mixture until the solid dissolves. Only freshly prepared reagent should be used.

Transfer to a 4-in. test tube 0.5 ml. of the solution S-5 prepared in Step X-3 (or Step X-4 or Step XI, Note 15), add 2 ml. of distilled water, and cool the tube in an ice-water bath. Add 2 ml. of (freshly prepared) phenylhydrazine reagent, stir the mixture, and allow it to stand in an ice-water bath for 1 hr. with occasional stirring. If a precipitate forms, filter the suspension with suction and wash the solid with two 3-ml. portions of distilled water.[25] Discard the washings. The formation of mannose phenylhydrazone (m.p. 188°) confirms the presence of mannose.

Add 2 ml. of the phenylhydrazine reagent to the filtrate (or 0.5 ml. of solution S-5, if no mannose phenylhydrazone formed), stir the mixture, and heat the tube in a boiling-water bath for 30' min. Filter the hot suspension on a small suction filter which has been heated by immersion in hot distilled water. Wash the precipitate with two 2-ml. portions of hot distilled water and discard the washings.[25]

Allow the filtrate to cool to room temperature, and if a precipitate forms, filter the suspension. Add 5 ml. of acetone to the precipitate on the filter paper, return the filtrate to the paper, and continue this process until no more precipitate dissolves. Evaporate the acetone on a boiling-water bath and recrystallize the residue from hot water.[25] Recrystallize the precipitate remaining on the filter paper.[25]

Add 2 ml. of the phenylhydrazine reagent to 0.5 ml. of the solution S-1 prepared in Step X-1, heat the solution to boiling in a water bath, allow the mixture to cool to room temperature, filter the suspension, wash the precipitate with distilled water, and discard the washing.[25] This test is confirmatory for rhamnose or fructose but not both sugars.

Although separation of individual osazones from a mixture of osazones is not readily accomplished, advantage may be taken of the following solubility relations: The osazones of the monosaccharides (except galactose) are slightly soluble, while those of the disaccharides are readily soluble in hot water. Maltosazone, but not lactosazone, is soluble in acetone.

12. *Arabinose. Benzhydrazide Test.*[26] Transfer 2 ml. of the solution S-5 prepared in Step X-3 (or Step X-4 or Step XI, Note 15) to a 6-in. test tube, add 10 ml. of a solution of benzhydrazide in 57 per cent ethanol, stopper the tube, and shake it vigorously. Allow the tube to stand at room temperature with occasional shaking until the next laboratory period. If no crystals form, allow the tube to stand until the following period. Filter the suspension, wash the crystals with 5 ml. of ice-cold 95 per cent ethanol, and recrystallize the product from the minimum volume of hot 95 per cent ethanol. The formation of arabinose benzhydrazone (m.p. 210 to 212°) confirms the presence of arabinose.

13. *Xylose. Benzaldehyde–Methanolic Hydrochloric Acid Test.*[27] Transfer 3 ml. of the solution S-5 prepared in Step X-3 (or Step X-4 or Step XI, Note 15) to a 50-ml. conical flask and evaporate the solution to dryness (thick sirup) on a boiling-water bath. Add 1 ml. of absolute methanol, stir the mixture.

and heat the solution until the solvent evaporates. Place the flask in an oven at 100° and allow it to stand until moisture has been removed (15 to 20 min.). Add 6 ml. of absolute methanol, 1 ml of 1.4 N methanolic hydrochloric acid, and 2 ml. of redistilled benzaldehyde. Stir the mixture thoroughly, add a seed crystal of dibenzylidinexylose dimethyl acetal, stopper the flask, and allow the flask to stand at room temperature for a week with occasional vigorous shaking. Filter the suspension (fine intertwining needles), wash the precipitate with 5 ml. of water and with 5 ml. of methanol, and dry the product in air. Recrystallize the derivative by dissolving it in the minimum volume of chloroform and adding petroleum ether (b.p. 30 to 60°) to a faintly cloudy solution. Add sufficient chloroform to form a clear solution, allow the solution to stand in the refrigerator overnight or longer, filter the suspension, and dry the product in air. The formation of dibenzylidinexylose dimethyl acetal (m.p. 211°) confirms the presence of xylose.

NOTES

1. Ihl and Pechmann (1884), Ihl (1885, 1887), and Molisch (1886a, 1886b) discovered that sugars (treated with concentrated sulfuric or hydrochloric acid) react with phenols (types shown below) to give chromogenic con-

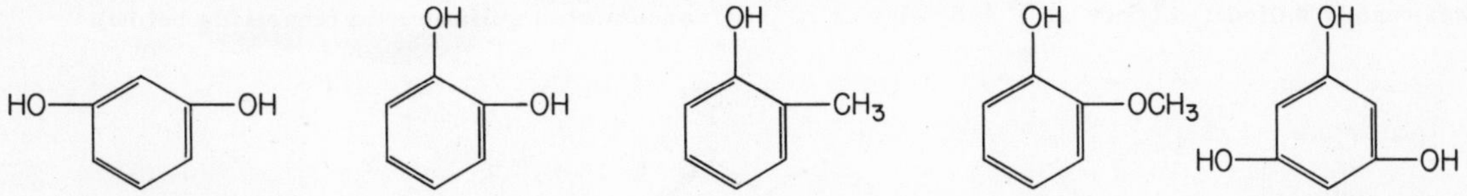

| catechol | pyrogallol | cresol | guaiacol | phloroglucinol |

| resorcinol | orcinol | thymol | α-naphthol | β-naphthol |

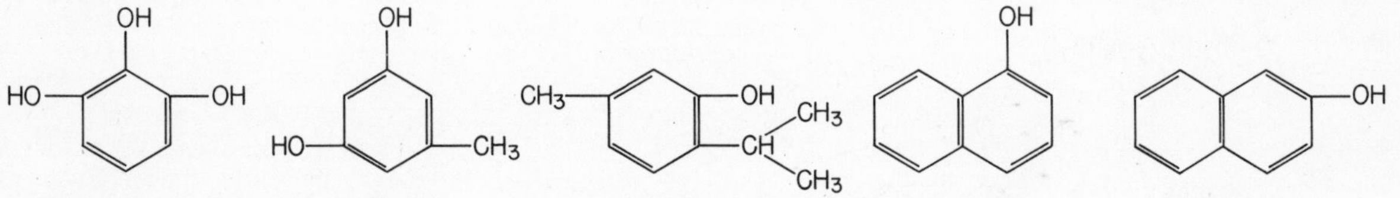

densation products. The specific absorption spectra of the hydrolysis and dehydration products formed by the reaction of carbohydrates and sulfuric acid have been determined by Ikawa and Niemann (1949), and the absorption spectra of the products formed by the condensation of acid-treated carbohydrates with phenols have been reported by Foulger (1931), Militzer (1946), and Pinoff (1905). These products include furfural from arabinose and xylose (pentoses) (equation below),

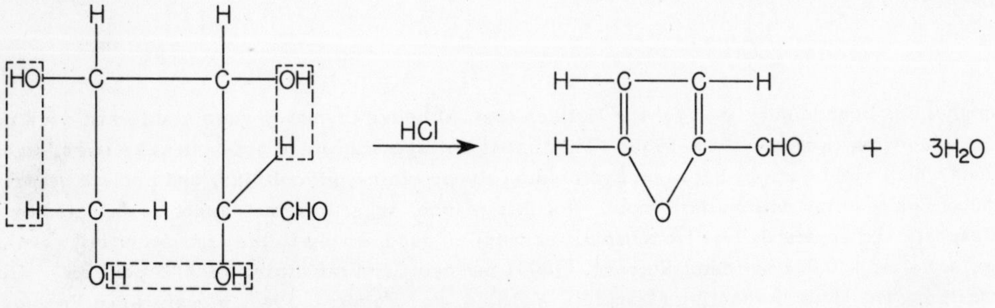

5-methylfurfural from rhamnose (methylpentose), and 5-(ω-hydroxymethyl) furfural in 20 to 25 per cent yield from fructose (ketohexose). Glucose, galactose, and mannose (aldohexoses) give only about 1 per cent of 5-(ω-hydroxymethyl) furfural, since this substance is converted nearly quantitatively to levulinic acid and formic acid (equations on following page) (Blanksma, 1909; van Ekenstein and Blanksma, 1910; Kiermayer, 1895; Wheeler and Tollens, 1889.

Düll, 1895; Pummerer and Gump, 1923; and Pummerer, Guyot, and Birkofer, 1935).

Hexose $\xrightarrow{-3H_2O}$ [structure] $\xrightarrow{H_2O}$

5-(hydroxymethyl) furfural

[structure] $\xrightarrow[-HCOOH]{H_2O}$ $HOCH_2COCH_2CH_2CHO \longrightarrow CH_3COCH_2CH_2COOH$

5-hydroxylevulinaldehyde   levulinic acid

v. Udránkszky (1888) was the first to consider the α-naphthol (Molisch) reaction to be a condensation with furfural. Bredereck (1931, 1932) obtained a condensation product from 5-(hydroxymethyl) furfural and α-naphthol which was readily sulfonated (once at 0° and twice at 30°) by concentrated sulfuric acid (equations below).

[structure] 5-(hydroxymethyl) furfural + 2 [structure] α-naphthol $\longrightarrow$

[structure] $\xrightarrow{H_2SO_4}$ [structure]

α-Naphthol has been widely used for the Molisch test, although thymol is more stable and does not become colored on long standing (Levine, 1929–1930). The test is not specific since aldehydes, ketones, organic acids, and compounds which yield carbohydrates on hydrolysis (glycoproteins, glycolipids, and nucleic acids) give chromogenic products on reaction with sulfuric acid. For this reason, sugar in urine cannot be detected by the Molisch reaction. Reagents and apparatus free from impurities must be used, owing to the high sensitivity of the Molisch test (glucose and starch, 0.001 per cent; sucrose, 0.0001 per cent; and raffinose, 0.00005 per cent). Quantitative procedures utilizing the Molisch reaction (Yamafuji, Yoshida, and Fukuura, 1941; Yamafuji and Yoshida, 1939) and the thymol test (Bollinger, 1944) for the determination of sugar have been described.

2. Weigh the material in this (or subsequent) test on a horn-pan balance, or estimate the weight by comparison with the volumes of weighed samples in test tubes on the reagent shelf.

3. The formation of a blue-colored substance by the action of iodine was observed in 1814, soon after the discovery of iodine, according to Barger (1930), who has reviewed the literature prior to 1930. The stable blue

color is formed by reaction with amylose, while amylopectin gives a less stable red complex (Bates, French, and Rundle, 1943). Branching of chains and iodine affinity are related, since amylopectin from potato starch has less affinity for iodine than the less highly branched amylopectin from cornstarch (Meyer, Wertheim, and Bernfeld, 1941). Glycogen, which is even more highly branched than amylopectin from potato starch, forms an unstable iodine complex (Bates, French, and Rundle, 1943). Molecular size and iodine affinity are also related, since amylodextrin has a lower iodine affinity than amylose. Concentrations of iodine as low as 10^{-6} N give a detectable color with 0.06 per cent starch solution and 0.01 to 0.1 per cent potassium iodide. The sensitivity depends also on the temperature, pH, salts, type of illumination, and nature of the starch (Koreman, 1934; Woodard, 1934).

Although the nature of the bonding between starch and iodine is not known, it has been suggested that a compound or solid solution is formed. It has been proposed (Rundle, Foster, and Baldwin, 1944; Stein and Rundle, 1948) that iodine molecules lie within the amylose matrix of the complex. Analogous complex formation between starch and organic substances (such as alcohols, ketones, and organic acids) (Bear, 1944; Whistler and Hilbert, 1944) and between iodine (and other halogens) and organic polymers (such as polyvinyl alcohols and polyamides) has been observed, although these complexes do not absorb in the visible spectrum (West, 1947). Iodine forms blue-colored complexes with colloidal metallic hydroxides and basic acetates as well as with compounds containing the α-pyrone or γ-pyrone ring (Barger, 1930).

α-pyrone γ-pyrone

According to Turner (1943) iodine is not required to maintain the blue color once it is formed from iodine and starch.

4. Agulhon's (1911) nitrochromic acid test, as modified by Fearon and Mitchell (1932), is given by all organic compounds containing the — CHOH group, but the reaction is less rapid with polysaccharides than with simpler sugars. Tertiary alcohols, aldehydes (other than formaldehyde), ketones, amino acids, and fatty acids give no reaction. Nitrites, peroxides, and hypohalites also form a blue-colored pigment, which is thought to be the anhydride of nitrous acid.

5. Only fructose solutions darken in 24 hr. at room temperature. The higher specificity of ketoses and ketosaccharides in acid solution was reported by Dehn, Jackson, and Ballard (1932). It has been observed that glucose, maltose, starch, and glycogen do not form a colored product when heated with 85 per cent phosphoric acid for 30 min. (Hestrin and Mager, 1947).

6. In the copper reagent, introduced by Fehling (1849, 1858), cupric ion is maintained in alkaline solution through complex formation with Rochelle salt (sodium potassium tartrate). The copper solution and the base are mixed shortly before use, owing to the instability of the reagent. Copper complex-forming substances which have been employed in place of Rochelle salt include glycerol (Löwe, 1870; Haines, Pond, and Webster, 1920); phosphate (Folin and McElroy, 1918), citric acid (Rosenthaler, 1904; Benedict, 1908—1909), ammonia (Pavy, 1880), potassium cyanide (Gerrard, 1893), and potassium sulfocyanide (Bang, 1906; Rudisch and Celler, 1907).

The reactions of carbohydrates in basic solution are exceedingly complex, according to Nef (1908, 1914), who isolated 93 different products. Evans (1929, 1942) has investigated the types and proportions of the substances formed by enolization, epimerization, polymerization, rearrangement, and oxidative degradation. Fischer and Hooker (1918 suggested that the yellow and green colors which are observed at low levels of glucose and in the intermediate stages of the reaction are explained by the colloidal properties of the cuprous oxide. By substituting sodium carbonate for potassium hydroxide and citrate for tartrate, Benedict (1907, 1908—1909) prepared a reagent which was more stable, more sensitive, and more suitable for the detection of glucose in urine (since it was not reduced by uric acid) than Fehling's solution.

7. Lactose, maltose, other disaccharides containing the 1,4-glycosidic linkage, and low molecular-weight dextrins respond to this test (Fearon, 1942; Malpress and Morrison, 1949). Methylamine, ethylamine, and ethanolamines (but not higher homologues) are satisfactory reagents. A red color is formed which turns yellow on acidification but is restored in basic solution. Color formation is inhibited by an excess of a hexose or amine. The reagent is sensitive to 0.05 per cent lactose.

8. The observation in 1815 that cuprous oxide is produced by the oxidation of honey with cupric acetate solution formed the basis of methods for the detection of reducing sugars with this reagent (Bates and associates, 1942). Barfoed (1873) found that glucose, but not dextrin, was reduced by cupric acetate in 1 per cent acetic acid. It was noted later that the rate of oxidation of reducing sugars decreased as the acidity increased and that monosaccharides, but not disaccharides (Hinkel and Sherman, 1907; McGuigan, 1907), are oxidized (fructose > galactose > glucose). All disaccharides give the test after sufficient reaction time (Bunzel, 1908; Mathews and McGuigan, 1907). von Fellenberg (1947) reported the following activities of the listed disaccharides compared to glucose : sucrose, 1:75; lactose, 1:45; and maltose, 1:26. Products which have been isolated after cupric acetate oxidation of fructose, glucose, and galactose include glucosone and formic, carbonic, glyoxylic, oxalic, and glycolic acids (Evans, Nicoll, Strouse, and Waring, 1928).

By replacing the acetic acid with lactic acid, Tauber and Kleiner (1932–1933) found that the cuprous oxide was proportional to the glucose concentration and that monosaccharides and disaccharides could be distinguished on the basis of their rates of reactions. A precipitate is produced by 0.1 per cent or higher concentration of a monosaccharide in the presence of 2 per cent maltose, 4 per cent lactose, or 10 per cent sucrose. Chlorides interfere in tests by the modified as well as the original procedures (Welker, 1915).

9. This procedure, introduced by Bial (1902), has been employed virtually unchanged for the qualitative and quantitative determination of pentoses. Militzer (1946) observed that the purity of the hydrochloric acid and the concentration of the ferric chloride are critical factors. He recommended as a confirmatory procedure that the absorption spectrum of the pigment in butyl alcohol be examined. Orcinol condenses with furfural (formed by decomposition of the pentose) to give the pigment. Procedures have been proposed for the quantitative determination of pentoses (Brown, 1946; Drury, 1948; McRary and Slattery, 1945) and of hexoses (in the absence of pentoses) (Brückner, 1943; Sørensen and Haugaard, 1933).

10. Periodic acid preferentially oxidizes compounds with adjacent hydroxy or hydroxy and amino groups (see Exp. 21, Step IX) as illustrated by the reactions (equations below) for a pentose and a methylpentose.

$$CH_2OH(CHOH)_3CHO + 4HIO_4 \rightarrow HCHO + 4HCOOH + 4HIO_3$$

$$CH_3(CHOH)_4CHO + 4HIO_4 \rightarrow CH_3CHO + 4HCOOH + 4HIO_3$$

Nicolet and Shinn (1941) determined acetaldehyde in the presence of formaldehyde in developing a procedure for the quantitative estimation of methylpentoses in the presence of other sugars.

11. Proceed with this section only after your flow sheet has been approved by the instructor.

12. The approximate volumes (in milliliters) of absolute methanol required to dissolve 1 g. of each of the listed carbohydrates (shaken for 2 min. at room temperature) are rhamnose, 10; fructose, 25; raffinose, 25; xylose, 130; maltose, 160; and arabinose, 320. The other sugars are appreciably less soluble. It should be noted that the solubility of each of these sugars is increased significantly in the presence of other sugars, that the methanol solution may contain appreciable quantities of sugars other than the three more soluble ones, and that these overlapping solubilities should cause no difficulties in any of the tests.

13. Test 30 mg. of the solid (P-2) for reducing disaccharides by the methylamine test (Step VI) if the latter was uncertain.

14. If no precipitate forms, preserve the solution (S-6) to confirm the absence of inulin (Step XI, Test 2). When inulin is heated in water, glycerol, or glycol and is precipitated from these solutions with ethanol, it may be converted to a cold-water-soluble form (Bates and associates, 1942).

15. If the separations given in Steps X-3 and X-4 have been omitted in your procedure, dissolve the unknown (P-1, P-2, or P-3) in 10 ml. of distilled water and designate this solution as S-5. Add 0.5 ml. of carbon disulfide as preservative.

16. A red pigment soluble in ethanol or other alcohols is formed when resorcinol and fructose (or a fructose-containing saccharide) are heated with hydrochloric acid. The specificity of this reaction was first observed by Seliwanoff (1887). Rosin (1903) found that the amyl alcohol extract of the neutralized acid mixture was colored light yellow, exhibited a green fluorescence, and had a characteristic spectrum. All ketohexoses and ketopentoses tested responded similarly. A red-colored solution is formed directly, using the ethanol-sulfuric acid reagent described by Pinoff (1905). Although other carbohydrates give no color, they diminish the sensitivity of the test. A colored product which has the same absorption spectrum is formed when glucose and glucose-containing oligosaccharides are heated for a relatively long time. According to Koenigsfeld (1912) this is explained by the formation of fructose from glucose by epimerization.

Sen and Sinha (1923) have postulated that resorcinol condenses with furfural by the following reactions:

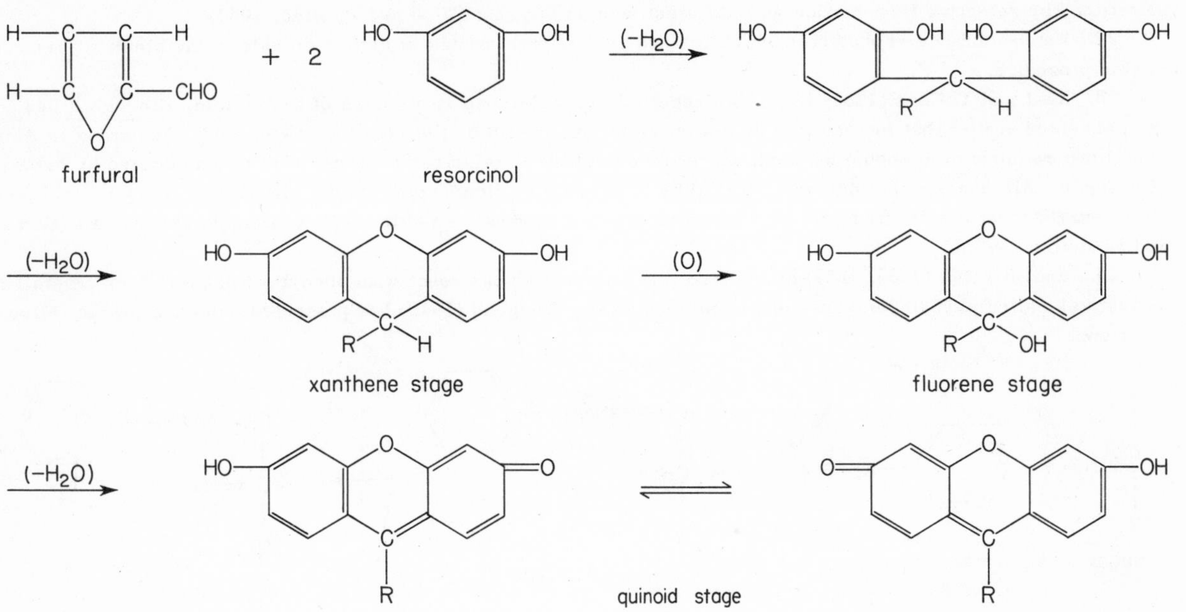

furfural   resorcinol $(-H_2O)$

$(-H_2O)$ xanthene stage (O) fluorene stage

$(-H_2O)$ quinoid stage

17. Heat this solution (and similar ones) in a boiling-water bath until the odor of carbon disulfide has disappeared.

18. Raybin (1933) discovered that a blue-colored solution is formed by the reaction of diazouracil with an alkaline solution of raffinose or sucrose.

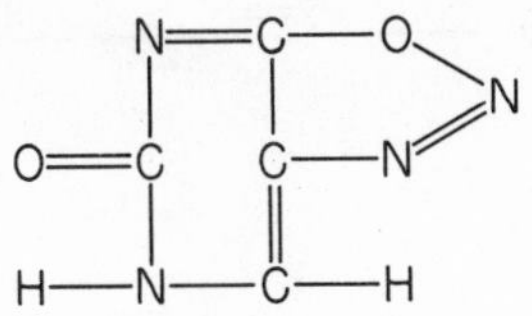

diazouracil

A compound which was salted out from neutral solution had indicator properties. The reaction is specific for the glucose-fructose linkage of sucrose and sucrose-containing oligosaccharides (Raybin, 1937).

19. The specificity of this reagent toward fructose was first observed by Dehn, Jackson, and Ballard (1932).

20. The benzidine test for the detection of pentoses was developed by Tauber (1937—1938). The sensitivity

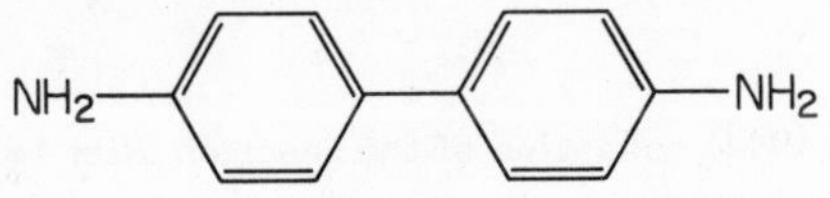

benzidine

of the test is 0.01 mg. of a pentose. It may be used for the detection of pentoses in urine, since other urinary constituents do not interfere. Riboflavin, nucleic acids, and other pentose-containing compounds which are hydrolyzed by acetic acid give the test.

21. Monosaccharides (glucose, mannose, and fructose) are fermented aerobically by brewer's yeast to ethanol and carbon dioxide by the action of enzymes known collectively as zymase.

$$C_6H_{12}O_6 + zymase \rightarrow 2C_2H_5OH + 2CO_2$$

Disaccharides are not fermented unless first hydrolyzed to monosaccharides by hydrolases. Since brewer's yeast does not contain lactase, lactose may be determined quantitatively after other sugars have been fermented (Baker and

Hulton, 1910). Products other than ethanol and carbon dioxide are formed during anaerobic dissimilation of a monosaccharide, but anaerobic fermentation may be inhibited by sodium azide (Winzler, 1944). Galactose has been determined by selective fermentation with different strains of yeast (Wise and Appling, 1944).

22. Water-soluble carbohydrates which tend to give a large amount of carbon dioxide in the blank are removed by this procedure.

23. Kent and Tollens (1884, 1885) first reported that galactose is a source of mucic acid, although it had been observed earlier that lactose may be converted to mucic acid by the action of nitric acid. According to Acree (1921) impure nitric acid should be used, since the oxidation of galactose to mucic acid is accelerated by oxides of nitrogen. All monosaccharides are oxidized by nitric acid to dicarboxylic acids, although only mucic acid precipitates. Saccharic acid (from glucose) is isolated as its sparingly soluble silver or monopotassium salt (Morrow and Sandstrom, 1935).

24. Emil Fischer (1884, 1887) discovered that reducing sugars react with phenylhydrazine to form crystalline derivatives called phenylhydrazones and phenylosazones. Weygand (1940) has presented evidence for the following reactions:

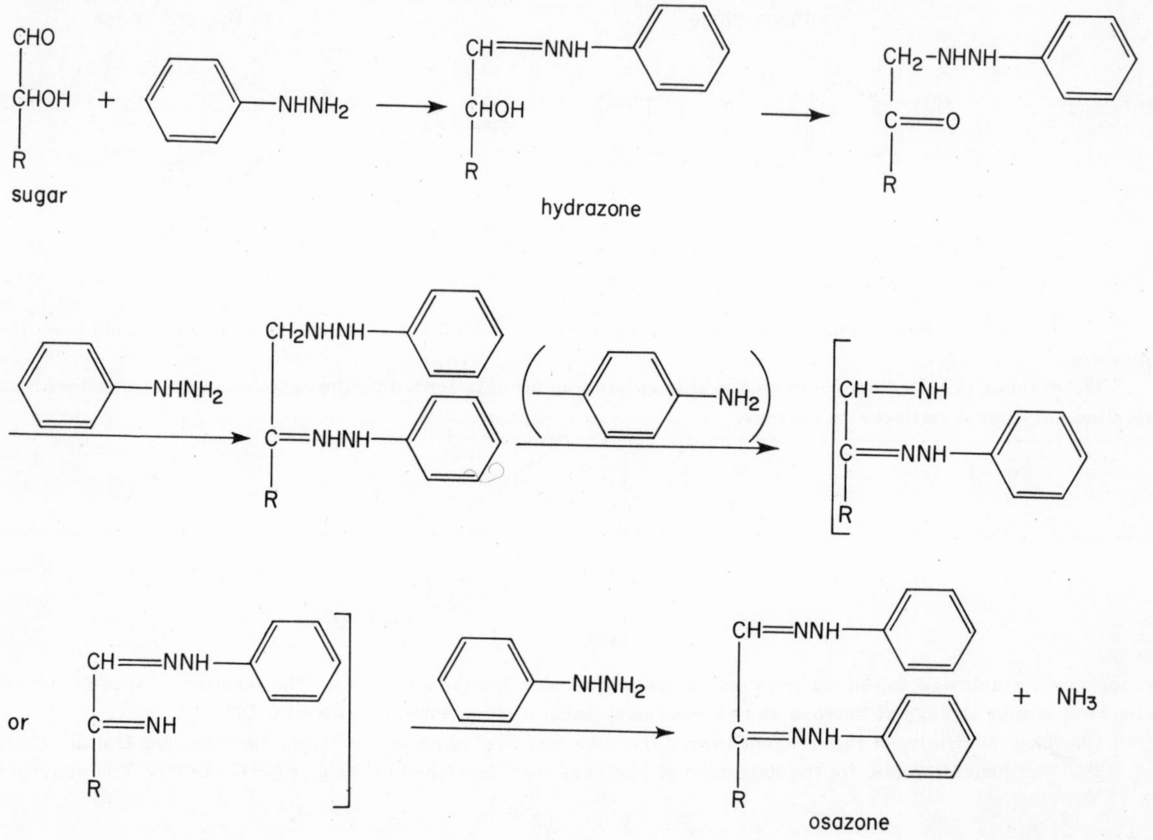

According to Fieser and Fieser (1944) cessation of the reaction after two molecules of phenylhydrazine have become attached is explained by the formation of tautomeric chelate rings (shown below) which, through resonance, are stabilized structures.

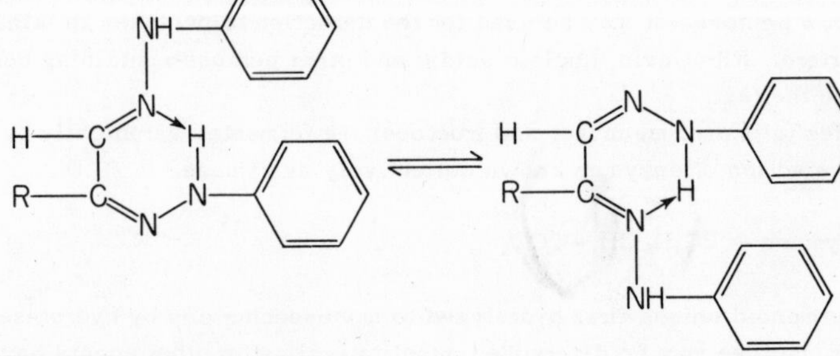

Fischer and Hirschberger (1888, 1889a) observed that mannose forms an insoluble phenylhydrazone in almost quantitative yield, and this principle was employed by Bourquelot and Hérissey (1899) for the quantitative determination of mannose in the presence of other sugars. Quantitative yields of osazones are obtained with 2,4-dinitrophenylhydrazine, but not with phenylhydrazine (Neuberg and Strauss, 1946). Numerous derivatives of phenylhydrazine have been utilized for the separation and identification of carbohydrates (van der Haar, 1920). Hann and Hudson (1944) prepared crystalline phenylosotriazoles by the reaction of osazones with copper sulfate.

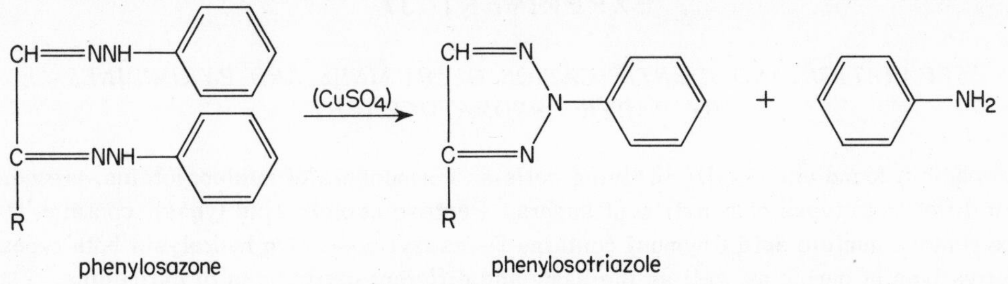

phenylosazone →(CuSO₄)→ phenylosotriazole

25. Dissolve the precipitate in the minimum volume of hot distilled water and allow the solution to cool spontaneously to room temperature. Examine a drop of the suspension under the low power of a compound microscope and compare the crystals with the photomicrographs supplied by the instructor.

26. Militzer (1941) reported that benzhydrazide ($C_6H_5CONHNH_2$) and arabinose react to form a slightly soluble hydrazone. This reaction has been employed for the quantitative determination of arabinose in plant gums (Hirst, Jones, and Woods, 1947). Glucose, galactose, mannose, and pentoses other than arabinose form readily soluble benzhydrazones. Rhamnose, when present in quantities larger than 300 mg., interferes with the preparation of arabinose benzhydrazone.

27. According to Breddy and Jones (1945) xylose is the only sugar which forms a crystalline derivative when treated under anhydrous conditions with benzaldehyde and methanol in the presence of acid. A possible structure of the derivative is shown below.

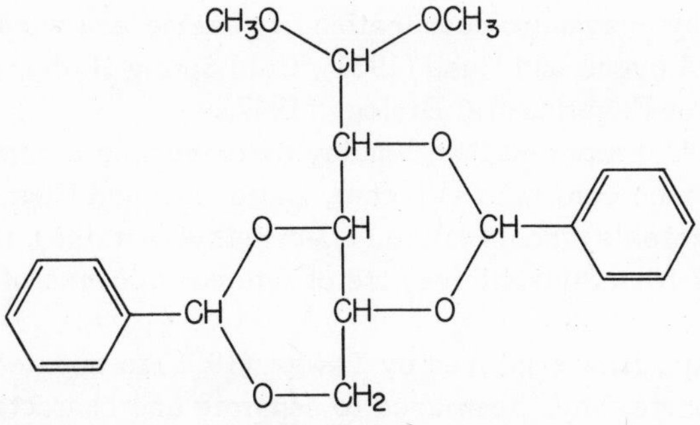

Cadmium bromide and cadmium xylonate form a characteristic double salt when the sugar is oxidized with bromine in the presence of cadmium carbonate (Bertrand, 1891). Procedures have been reported for the quantitative determination of xylose with the aid of these derivatives.

EXPERIMENT 37

SEPARATION AND IDENTIFICATION OF PURINES AND PYRIMIDINES
BY PAPER CHROMATOGRAPHY

Nucleic acids, found universally in living cells as components of nucleoproteins, are constituted similarly but differ as to types of constituent sugars. Pentose nucleic acid (yeast) contains D-ribose, while desoxypentose nucleic acid (thymus) contains D-desoxyribose. On hydrolysis both types yield the same derivatives of purine as well as the same and different derivatives of pyrimidine.

pyrimidine   purine

Both types of nucleic acids give adenine (6-aminopurine), guanine (2-amino-6-hydroxypurine), and cytosine (2-hydroxy-6-aminopyrimidine). In addition, pentose nucleic acid yields uracil (2,6-dihydroxypyrimidine) and desoxypentose nucleic acid thymine (2,6-dihydroxy-5-methylpyrimidine). Xanthine (2,6-dihydroxy-purine) and hypoxanthine (6-hydroxypurine) are not present in nucleic acids. They are widely distributed in nature and may be formed by enzymatic deamination of guanine and adenine. These topics have been reviewed by Davidson (1949, Levene and Bass (1931), Cold Spring Harbor Symposia on Quantitative Biology (1947), and Society for Experimental Biology (1947).

Johnson and Coghill (1925) reported that 5-methylcytosine was a component of tubercle bacilli, but this observation has not been confirmed (Vischer, Zamenhof, and Chargaff, 1949). The methylated purine derivatives (purine alkaloids) theophylline (1,3-dimethylxanthine), theobromine (3,7-dimethyl-xanthine), and caffeine (1,3,7-trimethylxanthine) are of interest because of their occurrence in tea, cocoa, and coffee.

Chromatographic methods, first employed by Tswett (1906) to separate the pigments of green leaves on a column of calcium carbonate, have been used to separate and characterize many types of biological substances. Substances have been separated by (a) adsorption on columns of starch, cellulose, activated carbon, silica gel, alumina, and other adsorbents, (b) ion exchange with columns of synthetic zeolites, synthetic resins, and other anionic- and cationic-exchange materials, and (c) partition on strips, cylinders and piles of filter paper. This topic has been reviewed by Cassidy (12 collaborators) (1948), Williams and Synge (1950), Strain (1942), Zechmeister (1950), and Zechmeister and Cholnoky (1941).

Methods have been described for the separation and identification of nucleosides (adenosine, guanosine, inosine, xanthosine, uridine, and cytidine), nucleotides (adenylic acid, guanylic acid, uridylic acid, and cytidylic acid), purines, and pyrimidines derived from pentose nucleic acids (yeast and pancreas) and from desoxypentose nucleic acids (yeast, thymus, spleen, and tubercle bacilli) by partition chromatography on starch (Reichard, 1948; Edman, Hammarsten, Löw, and Reichard, 1949; Daly and Mirsky, 1949), countercurrent distribution (Tinker and Brown, 1948), ion exchange (Carter and Cohn, 1949; Cohn, 1950), and paper chromatography (Carter, 1950; Hotchkiss, 1948; Markham and Smith, 1949; Vischer and Chargaff, 1948a). Individual compounds on chromatograms are identified by their ultraviolet absorption characteristics at wave lengths (region of 260 $m\mu$) corresponding to their absorption maxima and are determined from their extinction values. Chromatograms on paper strips are located by forming their uranyl salts (converted to brown-colored uranyl ferrocyanide) (Vischer, Magasanik, and Chargaff, 1949) or mercury complexes (converted to black mercuric sulfide) (Vischer and Chargaff, 1948 as well as by areas of fluorescence induced by a mercury-vapor lamp (Markham and Smith, 1949; Carter, 1950; Holiday and Johnson, 1949) and by contact prints of images obtained with filtered ultraviolet light on sensitized paper (Markham and Smith, 1949).

Purines and pyrimidines in a mixture of these substances are to be separated and identified by the chromatographic methods described in the experimental part.

EXPERIMENTAL[1]

Obtain approximately 0.1 g. of an unknown mixture containing ribonucleic acid and one or more of the following compounds: adenine, guanine, hypoxanthine, xanthine, caffeine, theobromine, theophylline, cytosine, 5-methylcytosine, thymine, and uracil.

Hydrolysis of Ribonucleic Acid.[2] Transfer 0.10 g. of the unknown to a 4-in. test tube, add 2 ml. (graduate) of 2 N sulfuric acid, and shake the suspension to dissolve most of the solid. Heat the tube, with occasional shaking, for 1 hr. in a boiling-water bath. Allow the tube to cool to room temperature and any sediment to settle. Use the supernatant solution for the experiments described below.

R_F Values of Purines and Pyrimidines.[3] Place 5 strips of filter paper of convenient dimensions (2 1/4 by 12 in.) on a clean sheet of waxed paper and draw on each a horizontal pencil line about 3/4 in. from one end. (The strips should be handled with forceps, since grease or dirt spots interfere with the development of the chromatograms.) Using small glass tubes drawn to capillary tips, apply each solution to be tested on a 1/2-in. section of the pencil line. A maximum of three spots should be applied to each strip in such a manner that the spots are separated and lie away from the edges of the paper. Before developing the chromatograms, allow the spots to dry in air.

Apply each of the following components[4] separately to paper strips: (a) cytosine and uracil, (b) guanine, thymine, and xanthine, (c) adenine and hypoxanthine, (d) caffeine, theobromine, and theophylline, and (e) adenine, guanine, and 5-methylcytosine.

Suspend the strips, in the vessel which is provided, in such a manner that the strips do not touch each other or the sides of the container and that the bottom edges dip about 1/8 in. below the surface of the solvent (1 part 2 N sulfuric acid and 3 parts n-propanol).[5] Allow the chromatograms to develop until the solvent front travels about 10 in. above the pencil line (16 to 20 hr.). Remove the strips, notch the edges at the position of the solvent fronts, hang the strips, and allow them to dry in air. Carry out the indicated tests (described below) on the following strips: (a) iron-bromine-ammonia test, (b) diazotized sulfanilic acid test, (c) silver-salt test, and (d) and (e) potassium-bismuth iodide test.

Color Tests for Purines and Pyrimidines. Since the reagents are toxic and corrosive, they should be stored at all times in separate, labeled glass atomizers in the fume hood, and they should be applied to the paper strips *only* in the fume hood. The strips should be sprayed uniformly, since excess reagent causes "running" of the solution. Since some colors fade rapidly, the position of each colored spot should be marked as soon as possible by notching the edges of the papers at positions corresponding to the centers of the spots.[6]

Iron-Bromine-Ammonia Test.[7] Spray a paper strip with $FeSO_4$-HCl solution, suspend the wet strip in bromine vapor (generated from liquid bromine in the bottom of the container) for 2 to 4 min., remove the strips, and allow the excess bromine to evaporate in the fume hood. Suspend the strip in ammonia vapor (generated from concentrated ammonium hydroxide in the bottom of a container) for about 3 min. Remove the strip and allow the ammonia to evaporate. Uracil forms a pink color rapidly on exposure to ammonia. Cytosine forms a fainter color which appears only after evaporating the ammonia.

Diazotized Sulfanilic Acid Test.[8] Spray a paper strip with diazobenzenesulfonic acid reagent (freshly prepared). A stable deep-red color is given by xanthine and guanine, while thymine yields a transient red color. The other purines and pyrimidines do not react.

Silver-salt Test.[9] Spray a paper strip with silver nitrate solution, immerse the wet strip twice in 0.5 N ammonium hydroxide, allowing the excess liquid to drain after each immersion, and expose the wet strip to hydrogen sulfide (generated by adding several drops of strong acid to a concentrated solution of sodium sulfide in the bottom of the container) until spots develop (10 to 20 min.). Adenine, guanine, hypoxanthine, and xanthine give a positive reaction.

Potassium-Bismuth Iodide Test.[10] Spray a paper strip with the potassium-bismuth iodide reagent, allow the strip to dry in air for 10 to 15 min., immerse the strip in distilled water for 5 sec., remove the strip, and mark the spots which develop. Adenine and caffeine (at relatively high concentration) give red or orange-red colored spots before treatment with water. Guanine develops this color immediately on immersion. Uracil, xanthine, and thymine do not react. The other nucleic acid components appear as red or orange spots on removing the strip from water. The colors produced by hypoxanthine, cytosine, and 5-methylcytosine fade rapidly. Excessive hydrolysis (blackening) may obscure some of the colors if the strip is permitted to remain too long in the water.

Identification of Purines and Pyrimidines in Unknown Mixture. Place four paper strips on waxed paper and mark the pencil line as described. Apply the unknown containing the hydrolyzed yeast nucleic acid to a 1/2-in. section of the pencil line at the center of each strip, using a capillary glass tube as described. Apply solution *A* (mixture of hypoxanthine, cytosine, 5-methylcytosine, thymine, and uracil, each at the concentration given in Note 4) and solution *B* (mixture of adenine, caffeine, guanine, theobromine, theophylline, and xanthine, each at the concentration given in Note 4) to each strip at either side of the unknown. Dry the strips in air and allow them to develop in the solvent mixture. Apply the four tests separately to the developed, dried strips, using only one test per strip. Mark the solvent fronts and the positions of the spots.

Submit a written report to the instructor giving the experimental R_F values, the results of the tests, and purines and pyrimidines identified in the unknown.

NOTES

1. Mitchell, H. K., and Drell, William (unpublished data). The authors are indebted to Dr. H. K. Mitchell, California Institute of Technology, for permission to use these procedures before publication.

2. Purines and pyrimidine nucleotides are readily liberated by mild acid treatment of nucleic acids. On the other hand pyrimidine nucleotides are resistant to hydrolysis. They are commonly hydrolyzed with partial destruction by treatment at 175° for several hours with 20 per cent hydrochloric acid (Hunter and Hyenka, 1937), 25 per cent sulfuric acid (Levene, 1903) or 98 to 100 per cent formic acid (Vischer and Chargaff, 1948b). Under these conditions the purines are destroyed, and cytosine may be, to a large extent, deaminated to uracil by hydrochloric acid and sulfuric acid, but not formic acid, treatment. Uridylic acid is partially resistant to formic acid hydrolysis, while cytidylic acid, which is hydrolyzed by formic acid under optimum conditions, gives recoveries of cytosine not higher than 80 per cent (Vischer and Chargaff, 1948b). Bacher and Allen (1950) have shown that pyrimidine nucleotides may be hydrolyzed to nucleosides in 95 per cent yield by treatment for 2 hr. at 100° with La(NO₃)₃ at pH 10.

3. In filter-paper chromatography the R_F value is defined as the ratio of the length of travel of a component (measured from the center of maximum concentration) to the length of travel of the solvent front (Consden, Gordon, and Martin, 1944). The R_F value of a given compound is constant for a particular solvent, and for mixed solvents (for example, *n*-butanol and water) it reflects the partition coefficient of the solute between the liquids. The separation of the component substances in a mixture probably is dependent in part upon the degree of adsorption by the filter paper.

4. The concentrations of the purine and pyrimidine solutions are 5 mg. per ml. except xanthine, which is 2.5 mg. per ml.

5. At higher proportions of *n*-propanol, unsubstituted purines separate more widely but methylated purines travel too close to the solvent front. Increasing the proportion of acid gives better separation of the methylated purines but poorer resolution of unsubstituted purines.

6. The positions of the purine and pyrimidine spots may be detected before color development by examining the air-dried strips under an ultraviolet (254-mμ, Mineralite) lamp (Carter, 1950). Under the influence of the absorbed light the compounds appear as dark zones. Guanine fluoresces and is somewhat difficult to detect. Since ultraviolet rays are harmful to the eyes, exposed strips should be examined only through a glass pane.

7. This test is based on the Wheeler and Johnson (1907) procedure for uracil and cytosine, which yield purple precipitates after treatment in aqueous barium hydroxide with excess bromine water or hypochlorous acid (Johnson, 1943). The pyrimidines are converted to the colored barium salt of dialuric acid through the intermediates shown on the following page.

dibromoxyhydrouracil　　　　　isodialuric acid　　　　　dialuric acid

3-Substituted uracil derivatives (such as uridine), thymine, and the purines do not respond to this test. Phenyl-hydrazine converts dibromoxyhydrouracil through isobarbituric acid (A) to the phenylhydrazone (B). Osazones (C) are formed from 3-substituted dibromoxyhydrouracil through the intermediate isodialuric acid (Levene, 1925).

(A)　　　　　　　　　　(B)　　　　　　　　　　(C)

　　The blue color produced by treating dibromoxyhydrouracil (or analogous uridine derivative) with urea, cya-nide, and lithium arsenophosphotungstate is the basis of the quantitative method employed to determine uracil, cytosine, uridine, and cytidine in nucleic acid hydrolysates (Pircio and Cerecedo, 1948; Soodak, Pircio, and Cerecedo, 1949). It is of interest that no color is produced from uracil or cytosine on paper strips treated with bromine and ammonia unless the strips are pretreated with iron.

　　8. Adenine, guanine, hypoxanthine, xanthine, and theophylline couple with diazobenzenesulfonic acid to give intensely colored compounds (Burian, 1904, 1907), which were shown by the following series of reactions (equations below) to be diazo compounds substituted in the 8 position (Fischer, 1909):

xanthine diazodichlorobenzene　　　　　8-aminoxanthine　　　　　uric acid

In contrast to guanine and xanthine, adenine and other purines do not couple in dilute solution or in the presence of excess base (Burian, 1904).

　　Pyrimidines react with diazobenzenesulfonic acid to give red-colored compounds. Thymine yields a more intense color than uracil or cytosine, and in general the 4-methyl and the 5-methyl analogues are more deeply colored than the unsubstituted pyrimidines (Johnson and Clapp, 1908–1909). Coupling is inhibited by substituents in the 3 position of pyrimidines and the 7 position of purines. A specific test for thymine, based on this reaction (Hunter, 1936), has been adapted to the quantitative estimation of thymine (Woodhouse, 1949).

　　9. Adenine, guanine, hypoxanthine, and xanthine form silver salts which are only slightly soluble in dilute ammonium hydroxide. Black silver sulfide, formed after the excess silver is removed, indicates the position of these purines. Under suitable conditions the purines and pyrimidines form silver, lead, mercury, and other metallic salts (Levene and Bass, 1931; Myers, 1909–1910). Purines are commonly determined as their silver salts, but this method has shortcomings (Hitchings and Fiske, 1941). Mercuric salts (Vischer and Chargaff, 1948a) and uranyl salts (Vischer, Magasanik, and Chargaff, 1949) have been used to identify purines and pyrimidines on paper strips.

　　10. Adenine forms a slightly soluble, red crystalline derivative of the following composition:

　　$C_5H_5N_5 \cdot HI \cdot 2BiI_3 \cdot H_2O$

(Bruhns, 1890). Guanine forms a similar derivative: $C_5H_5N_5O \cdot HI \cdot 2BiI_3 \cdot 2H_2O$ (Levene and Bass, 1931). It has been reported (Levene and Bass, 1931) that cytosine forms a red precipitate with this reagent. This reagent, pre-pared with strong nitric acid, has been used as a precipitant to identify alkaloids (Stephenson and Parker, 1921).

EXPERIMENT 38

DETERMINATION OF VITAMIN C IN GRAPEFRUIT JUICE

Vitamin C, the lactone of L-threo-3-ketohexuronic acid, is also known as cevitamic acid, ascorbic acid, and the antiscorbutic vitamin. The last two names denote the specific action of vitamin C in preventing scurvy in primates and the guinea pig. Other animals are not subject to this disease because of bacterial flora in their intestinal tracts which synthesize vitamin C. Scurvy has been known for centuries as an epidemic disease occurring especially among soldiers and sailors deprived for long periods of time of fresh fruit juices and vegetables. The disease is characterized by pathological changes in the teeth, bleeding gums, decreased resistance to infections, sore and swollen joints, anemia, hemorrhagic lesions of the skin and eyes, susceptibility to bone fracture, and delayed healing of wounds.

Szent-Györgyi (1928) isolated vitamin C from oranges, cabbage, paprika, and the adrenal gland. The constitution of vitamin C was determined through the work of Hirst (1933), Haworth (1933), and Haworth and Hirst (1933). Vitamin C was synthesized by Reichstein, Grüssner, and Oppenhauer (1933). The synthetic methods lead to vitamin C through the lactonization of 2-keto-L-gulonic acid (prepared from D-glucose through D-sorbitol and L-sorbose) and of 3-keto-L-gulonic acid (prepared from L-xylose).

2-ketogulonic acid   3-ketogulonic acid

Vitamin C has been determined in blood, urine, plant extracts, and other materials by biological, chemical, and physical methods. The biological methods depend upon the determination of the smallest amount of vitamin C which will prevent decrease in weight, the appearance of signs of scurvy (Sherman, LaMer, and Campbell, 1922), or histological changes in the teeth (Reid, 1947) of guinea pigs. Biochemical procedures are based on the preferential oxidation of vitamin C by ascorbic acid oxidase (Tauber and Kleiner, 1935). Because this reaction was nonspecific, Stewart and Sharp (1945) oxidized all reducing substances with an excess of the oxidase, selectively reduced the dehydroascorbic acid with *Escherichia coli*, and determined the ascorbic acid by titration with 2,6-dichlorophenol-indophenol. Vitamin C has been determined directly by titration with iodine (Adams, Acker, and Frediani, 1947), 2,6-dichlorophenol-indophenol (Tillmans, Hirsch, and Reinshager, 1928), methylene blue (Gal, 1936; Lund and Lieck, 1936), and other oxidizing agents. Physical methods include determination of the intensity of the absorption spectrum at 265 mμ (Robertson, 1934) and of the oxidation-reduction potential with the polarograph (Page and Waller, 1946).

Biological methods are time-consuming, expensive, and lacking in precision but have the advantage of specificity. Chemical procedures often are not highly reliable because of incomplete extraction of vitamin C, susceptibility of vitamin C to oxidation by air, and interference of other reducing substances.

The direct visual titration of vitamin C with 2,6-dichlorophenol-indophenol by the methods of Bessey (1938a, 1938b) and Bessey and King (1933) have been used widely, but numerous modifications have been suggested to permit more accurate determination by photometric and potentiometric procedures (Association of Vitamin Chemists, 1947; Bolomey and Kemmerer, 1947; King, 1936, 1941; Mills and Roe, 1947; Rosenberg, 1942; Satherfield, 1947).

It has been found (American Can Company, 1943) that citrus juices, peppers, strawberries, broccoli, beet greens, horse-radish, and kohlrabi are excellent sources of vitamin C. Good sources are tomatoes, cabbage, apples, grapes, and other fruits and vegetables, while poor sources include celery, asparagus, bananas, green peas and beans, rhubarb, and potatoes. The vitamin C contents (given in parentheses as milligrams per 100 g. of product) of representative foods are peppers (20 to 180), fresh lemon juice (53 to 56), fresh tomatoes (10 to 60), raw cabbage (18 to 180), fresh bananas (2 to 15), and celery (1 to 10). Significant studies have been made of vitamin C in canned foods, different types of foods under varying environmental conditions, and various body tissues and fluids in health and disease. The daily allowance of vitamin C recommended by the Committee on Foods and Nutrition of the National Research Council varies from 30 mg. for children under one year to 150 mg. for lactating mothers (National Research Council, 1943).

Vitamin C is to be determined in grapefruit juice by a modification of the method of Ramsey and Colichman (1942). Total reducing substances are determined by reaction with iodate, vitamin C in another aliquot is oxidized with 2,6-dichlorophenol-indophenol, and the remaining reducing substances in the dye-oxidized aliquot are determined by reaction with iodate. Equations for these reactions are shown below:

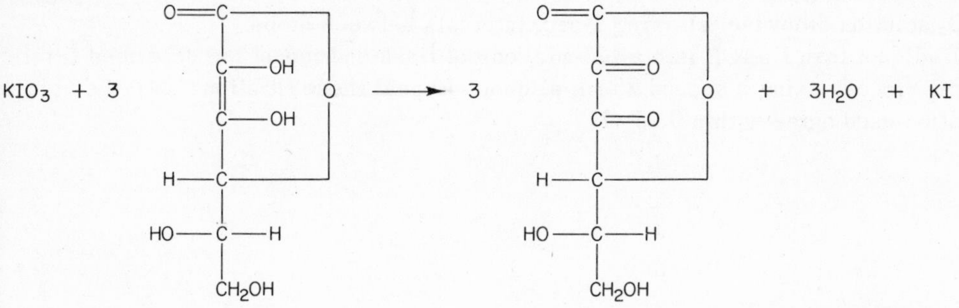

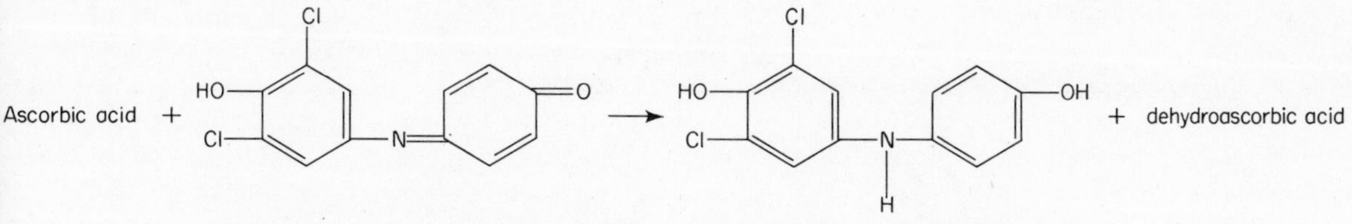

ascorbic acid   dehydroascorbic acid

$$KIO_3 + 5KI + 6HCl \longrightarrow 6KCl + 3H_2O + 3I_2 \quad \text{(detected at the end point by appearance of the starch–iodine blue complex.)}$$

2,6-dichlorophenol-indophenol (oxidized form), blue in alkali, red in acid   2,6-dichlorophenol-indophenol (reduced form) colorless   + dehydroascorbic acid

Fresh grapefruit juice contains an average of about 41 mg. of ascorbic acid per 100 g. compared with 33 mg. per 100 g. of the canned juice.

EXPERIMENTAL

Obtain about 210 ml. of grapefruit juice which has been protected from air by preservation with solid carbon dioxide. Pipette two 50-ml. aliquots into a 250-ml. volumetric flask, add 50 ml. of N hydrochloric acid and 1 ml. of a 5 per cent solution of 8-hydroxyquinoline sulfate as an inhibitor of atmospheric oxidation (Highet and West, 1942), mix the solutions, and dilute the mixture to the mark with distilled water. Mix the solutions and preserve the mixture in a stoppered flask labeled solution A.

Pipette one 50-ml. aliquot of the grapefruit juice into a second 250-ml. volumetric flask. Add 50 ml. of N hydrochloric acid, 1 ml. of a 5 per cent solution of 8-hydroxyquinoline sulfate, and an aliquot of a standard solution of pure ascorbic acid (the latter is to be added by the instructor). Mix the solutions, dilute the mixture to the mark with distilled water, mix the solutions, and preserve the mixture in a stoppered flask labeled solution B.

Pipette a 25-ml. sample from flask A into a 125-ml. conical flask. Add 1 ml. of iodine-free 0.1 N potassium iodide solution, 2 ml. of a 1 per cent starch indicator solution, and a piece of solid carbon dioxide about 1/2 in. in diameter. Titrate the solution with standard 0.001 M (0.006 N) KIO_3 solution (10-ml. burette). The end point is reached when the solution turns blue, owing to the formation of the starch-iodine complex.

Pipette a second 25-ml. sample from flask A into a 125-ml. conical flask. Maintain the temperature at 20 to 25°, protect the solution with solid carbon dioxide, and titrate the solution with a 0.1 per cent solution of 2,6-dichlorophenol-indophenol (sodium salt) delivered from a 50-ml. burette. The end point is reached when a definite pink color appears, indicating a slight excess of the red dye. Add 2 ml. of 0.1 N potassium iodide solution and 2 ml. of starch indicator solution. Continue the titration by adding standard 0.001 M KIO_3 solution dropwise, allowing 5-sec. intervals between drops.

Pipette a 25-ml. aliquot from flask B into a 125-ml. conical flask and repeat the described titration procedure. Repeat this process using a second 25-ml. aliquot. Repeat these titrations until the volumes of standard KIO_3 solution used agree within 0.05 ml.

EXPERIMENT 39

DETERMINATION OF NICOTINIC ACID BY MICROBIOLOGICAL ASSAY
WITH LACTOBACILLUS ARABINOSUS 17-5

Nicotinic acid was first prepared by Huber (1867) as an oxidation product of nicotine (equation below); it was first isolated from a natural material (rice) by Suzuki, Shinamura, and Odake (1912); and

nicotine   nicotinic acid

it was first determined to have vitamin activity by Elvehjem, Madden, Strong, and Woolley (1937). Nicotinic acid is widely distributed in natural materials, but liver, wheat bran, yeast, and peanut are among the best sources (Krehl, de la Huerga, Elvehjem, and Hart, 1946). Data are available on the nicotinic acid content of dehydrated foods (Heberlein and Clifcorn, 1944), canned foods (American Can Company, 1943), prepared foods (Sarett, Bennett, Riggs, and Cheldelin, 1946), meat (Greenwood, Kraybill, Feaster, and Jackson, 1944), feeds (Hale, Davis, and Baldwin, 1942), and germinating grains (Klatzkin, Norris, and Wokes, 1948).

The classical investigations of Goldberger and coworkers of the U. S. Public Health Service led to the discovery that nicotinic acid deficiency results in pellagra (dermatitis, redness of the tongue, and other symptoms) in humans, blacktongue in dogs, atrophy of the bone marrow in rats, and other manifestations in these and other animals. Sebrell (1934) has reviewed Goldberger's studies. Dietary nicotinic acid is required because it is concerned with glycolysis and respiration as a functional part of coenzymes I and II. The daily allowances of nicotinic acid recommended by the Food and Nutrition Board of the National Research Council (National Research Council, 1943) are 4 to 12 mg. for children up to twelve years and about 20 mg. for older children and adults.

Chemical and microbiological methods have been proposed for the quantitative determination of nicotinic acid, but there appears to be no satisfactory animal assay procedure (Dann, 1947). The chemical methods are based on the observation of König (1904), who found that pyridine reacts with cyanogen bromide and aniline, or other aromatic amine, to yield a yellow-colored compound.

Nicotinic acid has been determined microbiologically with *Proteus* (Lwoff, 1938) and with *Shigella paradysenteriae* (Dorfman, Horwith, Koser, and Saunders, 1939) but most commonly with *Lactobacillus casei* (Snell and Wright, 1941; Roberts and Snell, 1946). Nicotinic acid, nicotinamide, and nicotinuric acid (nicotinylglycine) have been determined microbiologically in urine with *Lactobacillus arabinosus* and *Leuconostoc mesenteroides* (Johnson, 1945; Johnson, Hamilton, and Mitchell, 1945b) and N^1-methylnicotinamide has been determined by a fluorometric method (Perlzweig, 1947). In *Neurospora crassa* mutants, hydroxyanthranilic acid is a precursor of nicotinic acid (Mitchell and Nyc, 1948).

Microbes were first observed by van Leeuwenhoek in 1685 (Harris, 1921), and they were shown to be the causative agents of fermentation, putrefaction, and disease by Pasteur about 1860. Investigations concerning the nutritional requirements of microorganisms by Uschinsky (1893), Henneberg (1903), Orla-Jensen (1919), Fred, Peterson, and Anderson (1921a, 1921b), Koser and Rettger (1919), Wood, Geiger, and Werkman (1939–1940), Mueller (1922, 1935a, 1935b), and later workers led to the discovery that some vitamins are essential growth substances for lactic acid bacteria. The first practicable microbiological assay procedure for the determination of a vitamin was that proposed for riboflavin by Snell and Strong (1939). Since that date analogous methods have been described for many vitamins and amino acids.

Microbiological methods are based on the premise that growth of the organism is directly proportional to the concentration of any essential nutrient. Growth produced in response to graduated amounts of the standard (pure nutrient) and the test sample is measured in terms of titratable acid (or density of cell suspensions), response curves are drawn, and the content of essential substance in the test sample is estimated by interpolating the standard curve.

Microbiological methods generally are reasonably satisfactory, although they vary widely in precision and accuracy depending upon the vitamin or amino acid to be determined, the material to be assayed, the types and amounts of interfering stimulatory or inhibitory substances in the test sample, the microorganism employed, the number of levels and the number of replicate tubes at each level of standard and unknown, the composition of the basal medium, the skill of the microbiologist, and other factors. Assay results are considered to be dependable if the mean deviation from the mean of the titrations at different levels of sample is low (2 or 3 per cent), if added pure substance is recovered nearly quantitatively (usually 100 ± 5 per cent), and if the values found agree closely with those obtained by chemical or other methods known to be reliable.

The chemistry, physiological activity, microbiological assay, and clinical uses of nicotinic acid have been reviewed by Rosenberg (1942), Association of Vitamin Chemists (1947), Merck and Company (1939), Snell (1947), Dann 1947), Perlzweig (1947), and György (1950).

Nicotinic acid is to be determined in a vitamin tablet by a microbiological procedure adapted from literature methods (Barton-Wright, 1944, 1945; Krehl, Strong, and Elvehjem, 1943; Lamb, 1943; Melnick and Oser, 1943; Snell and Wright, 1941; Snell in György, 1950).

EXPERIMENTAL

Obtain a commercial vitamin tablet[1] containing nicotinic acid (niacin) or nicotinamide (niacinamide). Weigh the tablet to 1 mg. and grind it with 0.5 ml. of distilled water in a clean mortar. Add 5 ml. of distilled water, stir the suspension, and transfer the supernatant solution quantitatively to a volumetric flask of such size that, when filled to the mark, it will contain approximately 0.050 μg (1 μg equals 0.001 mg.) of nicotinic acid (from the tablet) per milliliter. Add 5 ml. of distilled water to the residue in the mortar, stir the mixture, and transfer the suspension quantitatively to the volumetric flask. Add distilled water to the mark and mix the liquids (and any suspended material) thoroughly.

Pipette 50.0 ml. of the diluted solution into a 100-ml. volumetric flask; submit the flask to the instructor, who will add a known quantity of pure nicotinic acid. Add distilled water to the mark and mix the liquids thoroughly.

Pipette into (duplicate) clean, dry 4-in. test tubes distilled water, standard, sample, recovery sample, and basal medium (in the order given) according to the schedule shown in the accompanying table. A graduated pipette or a pipetting machine may be used. Place the 40 tubes in a rack, mark the position of each tube on a diagram of the rack, cover the rack with a double-layered cap of clean Boote toweling, constructed so as to fit snugly, and autoclave the rack of tubes for 15 min. at 15 p.s.i. pressure (about 121°C.). Allow the tubes to cool to room temperature and store them in the refrigerator.

Prepare an inoculum of *Lactobacillus arabinosus* 17-5 (American Type Culture Collection No. 8014), which has been carried on a yeast-glucose-agar stab preserved in the refrigerator, by the following procedure: While holding in the right hand a Nichrome wire attached to a nonconducting handle, pass the wire through a blue gas flame until all parts of the wire have been heated to redness. In this and all subsequent operations avoid touching the wire to any object. Allow the wire to cool in air for about 15 sec. Hold the tube containing the *L. arabinosus* stab culture and a 50-ml. centrifuge tube containing 20 ml. of sterile inoculum medium in the left hand, grasp the two cotton plugs between the three smallest fingers of the right hand with the palm held upward, remove the cotton plugs and rotate the tubes for about 10 sec. while holding the mouths in a blue gas flame. Insert the sterile wire into the agar stab containing the culture, place the wire tip in the liquid inoculum medium, and stir the liquid for a few seconds. Repeat this inoculating process once without resterilizing the needle. Flame the mouths of the tubes and replace the cotton plugs. Turn down the edges of the cotton plug over the edge of the centrifuge tube and place a rubber band over the cotton edges. Incubate the inoculum for 24 hr. at 35° and preserve the inoculum (not longer than 24 hr.) in the refrigerator.

Centrifuge the inoculum culture, remove the plug, flame the mouth of the tube, decant the supernatant liquid, add (aseptically) 10 ml. of sterile saline (0.9 per cent sodium chloride solution), using a sterile pipette[2] or automatic pipette with sterile syringe assembly, stir the mixture with a sterile wire, flame the mouth of the tube, replace the plug, centrifuge the suspension, decant the supernatant liquid, add 40 ml. of sterile saline, and stir the mixture. Pipette 0.1 ml. (2 drops) of the inoculum suspension into each of the forty 4-in. test tubes (while pipetting, uncover only about half of the tubes at a time) and incubate the rack of (covered) tubes for 72 hr. at 35°. Steam the rack of tubes for 10 min. (about 100°C.) in the autoclave to stop acid production (by destroying most of the organisms) and to remove carbon dioxide.

Transfer the contents of each tube quantitatively to a 50-ml. conical flask, using two 5-ml. portions of distilled water as rinse fluid. Add 2 drops of bromthymol blue indicator solution to each tube and titrate the acid in each tube with standard, approximately 0.030 N sodium hydroxide delivered from a 50-ml. burette. A blue-green color appears at the end point (pH 6.8). Titrate the acid in the remaining tubes to the same end-point color (preserve the solution first titrated, and each fifth one thereafter, for comparison).

Plot the experimental data on millimeter coordinate paper, label the ordinate Volume of _____ N sodium hydroxide and the abscissa Micrograms of nicotinic acid per tube, draw a smooth curve, and interpolate this standard curve.

TYPES AND VOLUMES IN MILLILITERS OF SOLUTIONS TO BE PIPETTED INTO 4-INCH TEST TUBES

Solution	Tube number									
	1	2	3	4	5	6	7	8	9	10
Distilled water	2.50	2.25	2.00	1.75	1.50	1.25	1.00	0.75	0.50	0
Standard[a]	0	0.25	0.50	0.75	1.00	1.25	1.50	1.75	2.00	2.50
Basal medium	0.50	0.50	0.50	0.50	0.50	0.50	0.50	0.50	0.50	0.50

Solution	Tube number									
	11	12	13	14	15	16	17	18	19	20
Distilled water	2.00	1.50	1.00	0.50	0	2.00	1.50	1.00	0.50	0
Sample[b]	0.50	1.00	1.50	2.00	2.50	0	0	0	0	0
Recovery sample[b] . . .	0	0	0	0	0	0.50	1.00	1.50	2.00	2.50
Basal medium	0.50	0.50	0.50	0.50	0.50	0.50	0.50	0.50	0.50	0.50

[a] 0.060 μg of nicotinic acid per milliliter.
[b] About 0.050 μg of nicotinic acid per milliliter.

COMPOSITION OF BASAL MEDIUM[a]

Constituent	Quantity	Concentration, per cent[b]
Casein, 10 per cent hydrolysate	22.5 ml.	0.75
Glucose, anhydrous	6.0 g.	2.0
Sodium acetate, anhydrous	3.6 g.	1.2
Amino acid solution.	5.0 ml.	
L-Cysteine hydrochloride	. . .	2×10^{-2}
L-Tryptophan.	. . .	5×10^{-3}
Ammonium chloride	. . .	1×10^{-1}
Vitamin solution	5.0 ml.	
Thiamine chloride.	. . .	1×10^{-4}
Calcium *d*-pantothenate	. . .	1×10^{-4}
Pyridoxine hydrochloride	. . .	2×10^{-4}
Riboflavin.	. . .	2×10^{-4}
p-Aminobenzoic acid	. . .	1×10^{-5}
Biotin	. . .	5×10^{-7}
AGU solution	2.5 ml.	
Adenine sulfate	. . .	1×10^{-3}
Guanine hydrochloride	. . .	1×10^{-3}
Uracil.	. . .	1×10^{-3}
Salts A solution	1.5 ml.	
K_2HPO_4	. . .	5×10^{-2}
KH_2PO_4	. . .	5×10^{-2}
Salts B solution	1.5 ml.	
$MgSO_4 \cdot 7H_2O$.	. . .	2×10^{-2}
$FeSO_4 \cdot 7H_2O$.	. . .	1×10^{-3}
$MnSO_4 \cdot 4H_2O$	. . .	1×10^{-3}

[a] The specified quantities of the indicated substances and solutions (preparation described in the Appendix) are dissolved in 45 ml. of distilled water, N sodium hydroxide solution is added dropwise to pH 6.8 (olive-green color of bromthymol blue indicator solution tested on a spot plate), and the mixture is diluted to 50.0 ml. with distilled water.

It is convenient to prepare a dry ball-mill mixture of the components (except glucose and casein hydrolysate), as described by Camien and Dunn (1948), and to prepare the basal medium as follows: Suspend 0.49 g. of the dry ball-mill mixture in 20 ml. of distilled water, add 6.0 g. of glucose and 22.5 ml. of the casein hydrolysate, stir and heat the mixture until the solids dissolve, neutralize the solution to pH 6.8, and dilute the neutral solution to 50.0 ml. This solution should be preserved under toluene.

[b] The values refer to the concentrations in the final 3-ml. volumes per tube prepared as described in the preceding table.

NOTES

1. If a tablet containing yeast or other food material is to be assayed, suspend it in 10 parts of 3 N sulfuric acid and autoclave the suspension for 30 min. at 15 p.s.i. pressure.

2. Remove one of the sterile pipettes carefully from the can of pipettes provided by the instructor. The pipette will contain a piece of cotton inserted about 1/2 in. into its mouth. Sterilization is effected by wrapping each pipette in a towel and autoclaving for 15 min. or by placing the pipettes in a metal can and heating the can for 1 1/2 hr. in an oven at 160 to 180°.

EXPERIMENT 40

DETERMINATION OF CHOLINE IN EGG YOLK BY MICROBIOLOGICAL ASSAY WITH CHOLINELESS NEUROSPORA CRASSA

Choline (trimethylhydroxyethylammonium hydroxide), first isolated by Strecker (1849) from the lecithin of bile, appears to be a universal component of plant and animal cells. Animal organs, egg yolk, and nerve tissue are better sources than any plant material, the values ranging from about 0.1 mg. per g. of (dry) corn meal to 33 mg. per g. of (dry) egg yolk (Engel, 1942; Luecke and Pearson, 1944a, 1944b; McIntire, Schweigert, and Elvehjem, 1944; Rhian, Evans, and St. John, 1943; Street, Kenyon, and Watson, 1946). Neurine (trimethylvinylammonium hydroxide) and muscarine are toxic amines formed anaerobically from choline by microorganisms, and acetylcholine is released when parasympathetic nerves controlling involuntary muscle and secretory cells are stimulated. Formulas for these compounds are shown below:

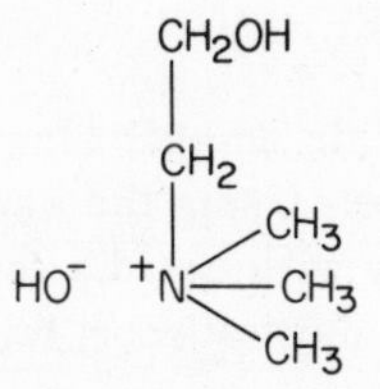

choline

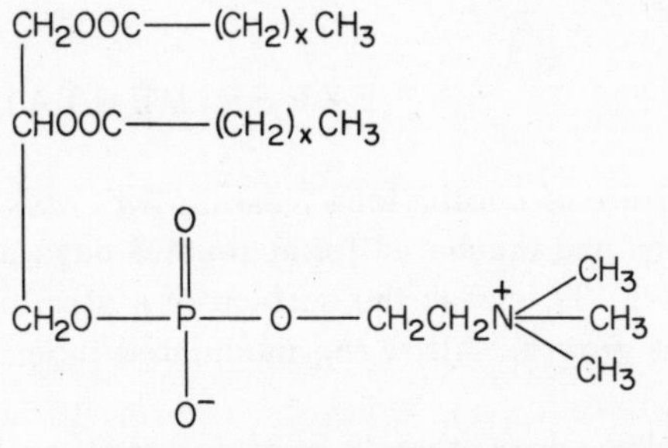

lecithin

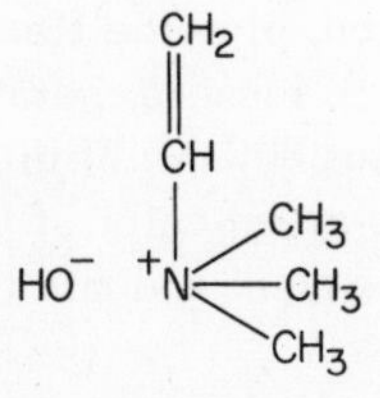

neurine

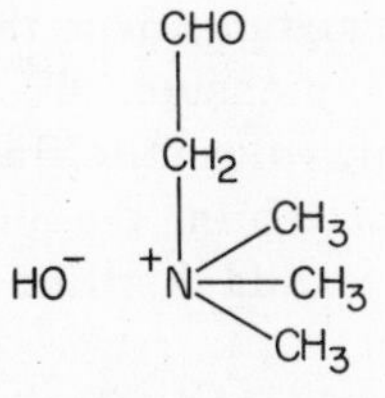

muscarine

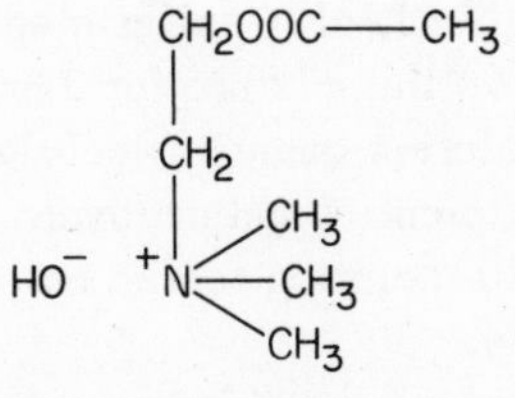

acetylcholine

On diets deficient in choline, fat is deposited in the liver and hemorrhages occur in the kidneys (Best, Hershey, and Huntsman, 1932; Griffith and Wade, 1940). Disorders arising from choline deficiency include disturbance of the blood lipid levels (Paul, Daum, and Kemp, 1947), decreased erythropoiesis (Nutr. Rev., 1948a), and formation of neoplasms in the liver and other organs (Copeland and Salmon, 1946). It has been found that choline is an antiperosis (perosis, slipped tendon) factor for chicks (Almquist, 1946). About 2 mg. of choline are excreted daily in the urine of adults (Borglin, 1947) and 3 to 15 μg per 100 ml. of sweat (Johnson, Hamilton, and Mitchell, 1945a). The lethal dose of choline (for the rat) is 29 to 75 μg of choline chloride per 100 g. of body weight, depending upon the mode of administration (Hodge, 1944).

Choline is synthesized in the body, but the rate is too slow to provide for all of the metabolic needs (Stetten, 1942). The in vivo precursors of choline are ethanolamine ($NH_2CH_2CH_2OH$) and methyl groups, the latter derived from methionine, sarcosine (CH_3NHCH_2COOH), and betaine [$(CH_3)_3$—^+N—CH_2COO^-]. The need for choline and other methyl donors is accentuated on diets high in nicotinic acid, owing to the formation and excretion of methylated compounds such as N^1-methylnicotinamide, nicotinuric acid, and trigonelline (methylbetaine of nicotinic acid) (Perlzweig and Huff, 1945). Methionine, the active methylating agent in the synthesis of creatine from glycocyamine, may be formed from choline and homocystine (Almquist, 1946). Choline may function other than as a methyl donor, since nonmethyl-ated analogues are effective lipotropic agents (McArthur, 1946). The role of choline in transmethylation (du Vigneaud, 1941, 1942–1943) and as a lipotropic factor (Nutr. Rev., 1948b) has been reviewed.

Choline has been estimated biologically by determining the level of test material required to pro-tect against fatty infiltration of the liver (Griffith, 1941) or kidney hemorrhage (Engel, 1942) and by determining the acetylcholine (formed from choline), assayed with the aid of isolated rabbit intestine (Fletcher, Best, and Solandt, 1935). The liberation of trimethylamine by oxidative deamination is the basis of a quantitative method employed by Klein and Linser (1932b, 1933). The precipitation of the periodate (Roman, 1930), the reineckate (Paal, 1929), and the phosphotungstate (Street, Kenyon, and Watson, 1946) has been utilized for the determination of choline. The most satisfactory method probably is microbiological assay with cholineless *Neurospora crassa*, as described by Horowitz and Beadle (1943). This procedure has been modified by Luecke and Pearson (1944a, 1944b), Siegel (1945), and Hodson (1945). Methods for the determination of choline have been reviewed by Handler (1947b).

The choline content of egg yolk is to be determined by microbiological assay with cholineless (strain No. 34486) *Neurospora crassa*, essentially by the method of Horowitz and Beadle (1943), as modified by Hodson (1945).

EXPERIMENTAL

Prepare a stock culture of cholineless *Neurospora crassa* as follows: Obtain an agar slant in-oculated with the organism and incubated for at least 3 days at room temperature. Using the aseptic technique described in Exp. 39, streak the surface of a sterile agar slant lightly with conidia (spores) from the tinted part of the growth. Allow the inoculated tube to stand for 5 to 7 days at room tempera-ture.

Obtain an egg (chicken, duck, turkey, or other type), boil the egg for 10 min., separate the yolk, and weigh (to ±1 mg.) about 200 mg. of the yolk on weighing paper. Transfer the weighed quantity of yolk quantitatively to a 50-ml. conical flask, add 3 ml. of N sulfuric acid, break up the particles with a stirring rod, add 17 ml. of N sulfuric acid, stir the mixture, rinse the stirring rod, plug the flask with cotton, and autoclave the mixture for 3 hr. at 15 p.s.i. pressure. Cool the flask to room temperature, transfer the acid solution quantitatively to a 1,000-ml. volumetric flask, add about 800 ml. of distilled water, and add sufficient N sodium hydroxide (20 ml.) to bring the pH to 7 (olive-green color of brom-thymol blue indicator solution tested on a spot plate). Add distilled water to the mark and mix the solutions thoroughly.

Pipette 50.0 ml. of the solution into a 100-ml. volumetric flask, add distilled water to the mark, and mix the solutions thoroughly. Pipette 25.0 ml. of the egg solution into a 100-ml. volumetric flask and submit the flask to the instructor, who will add a known quantity of choline. Add distilled water to the mark and mix the solutions thoroughly.

Pipette distilled water, standard solution, and basal medium (see the accompanying table) into one series of clean, dry, numbered (with a pencil on the frosted spot) 50-ml. conical flasks (or 2-oz. widemouthed bottles), according to the schedule shown in the accompanying table. Similarly, pipette distilled water, sample solution, and basal medium into a second series of flasks, and distilled water, recovery-sample solution, and basal medium into a third series of flasks. Use a 10-ml. graduated pipette for these transfers. Pipette 10 ml. of distilled water to two additional 50-ml. conical flasks.

Plug each flask with cotton. Autoclave the flasks, a 1-ml. graduated pipette, and a metal spatula at 15 p.s.i. pressure for 15 min. Allow these articles to cool to room temperature. Using aseptic tech-nique, transfer with the aid of the spatula several portions of conidia from the growth on the *Neurospora* slant to a flask containing 50 ml. of sterile distilled water, and prepare a uniform suspension by rotating the flask. Pipette 1 drop of the suspension to each of the 16 flasks and allow the inoculated solutions to stand at room temperature for 5 to 7 days.

Swirl the mixture in each flask to collect the growth as a single mass, transfer the contents of each flask to a Hirsch funnel, apply suction until nearly all the liquid has been removed, wash the solid mat of mycelium once with 5 ml. of distilled water, roll the mat into a compact mass, and transfer it to a 4-in. test tube which is numbered and labeled. Treat the other samples similarly. Dry the unstoppered tubes overnight at 90°. Weigh each mycelium mat to 0.2 mg. (a Roller-Smith precision torsion balance is convenient for this purpose).

Plot the experimental values obtained from the standard solutions on millimeter coordinate paper, label the ordinate Milligrams of mycelium and the abscissa Micrograms of choline, and draw a smooth curve. Estimate the choline in the test and recovery samples by interpolating the standard curve.

TYPES AND VOLUMES IN MILLILITERS OF SOLUTIONS TO BE PIPETTED INTO CONICAL FLASKS

Solution	Flask number															
	1	2	3	4	5	6	7	8	9	10	11	12	13	14	15	16
Distilled water.........	4.5	4.0	3.0	2.0	1.0	0	4.0	3.0	2.0	1.0	0	4.0	3.0	2.0	1.0	0
Standard solution[a].......	0.5	1.0	2.0	3.0	4.0	5.0										
Sample[b].............	..	..	..	..	..	..	1.0	2.0	3.0	4.0	5.0					
Recovery sample[b].......	..	..	..	..	..	..	..	..	..	..	..	1.0	2.0	3.0	4.0	5.0
Basal medium..........	5.0	5.0	5.0	5.0	5.0	5.0	5.0	5.0	5.0	5.0	5.0	5.0	5.0	5.0	5.0	5.0

[a] 1.20 μg of choline (as choline chloride) per mililiter.
[b] Approximately 1.0 μg of choline per milliliter.

COMPOSITION OF BASAL MEDIUM[a]

Constituent	Quantity	Concentration, per cent[b]
Sucrose...	4.0 g.	2.0
Biotin solution.............................	1.0 ml.	5×10^{-7}
Salts solution................................	50.0 ml.	
$NH_4OOC(CHOH)_2COONH_4$...................	...	0.5
NH_4NO_3.	...	0.1
K_2HPO_4...	...	0.1
$MgSO_4 \cdot 7H_2O$..	...	0.05
NaCl..	...	0.01
$CaCl_2 \cdot 6H_2O$.......................................	...	0.01
Microconstituents solution.....................	10.0 ml.	
Zinc..	...	2×10^{-4}
Iron...	...	2×10^{-5}
Copper...	...	1×10^{-5}
Manganese..	...	2×10^{-6}
Molybdenum.......................................	...	2×10^{-6}
Boron..	...	1×10^{-6}

[a] The specified quantities of the indicated substances and solutions are dissolved in distilled water, and the solution is diluted to 100 mL in a volumetric flask. Check the pH with a pH meter and, if necessary, adjust the pH to 5.5. Preserve the solution under toluene. If any suspended material is present, shake the mixture thoroughly before removing an aliquot.

[b] The values refer to the concentrations in the final 10-ml. volume per flask as described in the preceding table.

EXPERIMENT 41

DETERMINATION OF VITAMIN D BY THE CHICK BONE-ASH METHOD

The chemistry and physiology of vitamin D have been reviewed by Rosenberg (1942) and Bills (1935). The discovery by Mellanby (1919) that animal fats promote normal calcification of bones was followed by the postulate of McCollum, Simmonds, and Becker (1922) that a vitamin was responsible for this effect.

It was shown later by Windaus, Rosenheim, Hess, Steenbock, and others that cholesterol irradiated with ultraviolet light had antirachitic activity and that ergosterol, present as an impurity, was the substance activated. The irradiated products include calciferol (vitamin D_2) and the inactive or relatively toxic substances lumisterol, tachysterol, toxisterol, and suprasterols I and II. Crystalline vitamins D_2 and D_3 have been isolated from tuna-liver oil (Brockman, 1936; Brockman and Busse, 1938), and vitamin D_3 has been synthesized from cholesterol (Windaus, Lettré, and Schenck, 1935; Schenck, 1937). 7-Keto-cholesterol, formed by the oxidation of cholesterol, was reduced to 7-hydroxycholesterol, and the latter (as its dibenzoate) was decomposed by heat to 7-dehydrocholesterol. Vitamin D_3 was isolated from the irradiated products of 7-dehydrocholesterol. Formulas are given below for vitamin D_2, vitamin D_3, and related compounds (see Exp. 27 for cholesterol and the numbers of the carbon atoms).

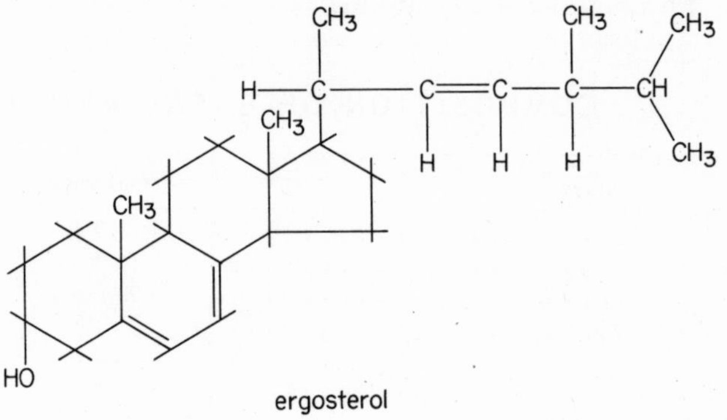

ergosterol

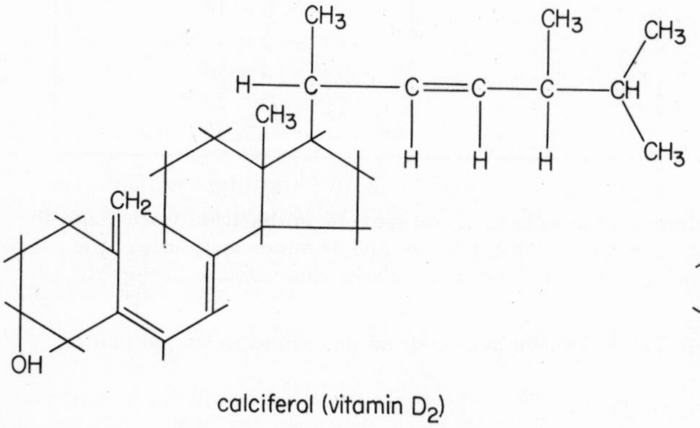

calciferol (vitamin D_2)

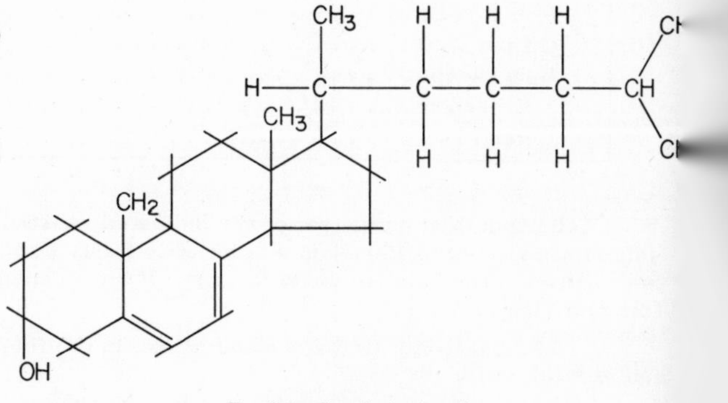

7–dehydrocholesterol
(provitamin D_3)

vitamin D$_3$

Milk, eggs, and other common foods are relatively poor sources of vitamin D, but the liver oils from the cod and other fish (especially tuna and other members of the Percomorphi are excellent sources (Bills, 1935). It has been reported that the liver oil of the California bluefin tuna contains 46,000 International Units of vitamin D per gram and Japanese bluefin tuna 61,000 International Units per gram. Fish synthesize vitamin D, but higher animals depend upon exogenous sources, although some antirachitic substance is formed in the skin by the action of ultraviolet light. Vitamin D is stored by animals as long as 12 weeks, and it is transferred from the mother to the fetus (Embleton and Collings, 1947). The Committee on Foods and Nutrition of the National Research Council (1943) has recommended a daily allowance of 400 to 800 International Units of vitamin D for all individuals. The toxic effects of massive doses of vitamin D$_2$ and D$_3$ on dogs, rats, humans, and other animals have been reviewed by Morgan (1943), Paul (1946), and Ziskin, Gibson, Skarka, and Bellows (1943). Chicks deficient in vitamin D develop black pigmentation of the feathers (Decker and McGinnis, 1947).

The rat line test for the bioassay of vitamin D was devised by Shipley, Park, McCollum, Simmonds, and Parson (1920–1921) and McCollum, Simmonds, Shipley, and Park (1922), who stated that "this test depends on the power of a given substance to cause the reappearance of a provisional zone of calcification in epiphyseal cartilages of animals with very severe rickets whose cartilages had been rendered calcium free by faulty diets." A chick bone-ash method proposed by Hart, Kline, and Keenan (1931) was the outgrowth of earlier observations made by Bethke, Steenbock, and Nelson (1923–1924). The rat line test has been discussed by Bills (1947) and the chick bone-ash procedure by Waddell and Kennedy (1947b). The line test cannot be used with chicks since a line of calcification does not form during the healing process. The rachitogenic diet proposed by Hart, Kline, and Keenan (1931) has been modified by later workers, and numerous comparative studies have been made of methods for the determination of vitamin D. Willgeroth, Halpin, Halloran, and Fritz (1944) have described a method for the determination of vitamin D with turkeys.

The International Unit of Vitamin D was defined originally as the vitamin D activity of 1 mg. of the international standard solution (olive oil) of ergosterol irradiated under defined conditions. Later it was stated that the International Unit was the vitamin D activity of 1 mg. of the international standard solution of irradiated ergosterol which had been found equal in potency to 0.025 μg of crystalline vitamin D$_2$ (calciferol). One unit had a potency such that, given to a rachitic rat for 8 successive days, a wide line of calcium deposit was produced in the metaphysis of the proximal ends of the tibiae and of the distal ends of the radii.

The United States Pharmacopeia unit is equal in antirachitic potency for the rat to 1 International Unit, but cod-liver oil is employed as the reference standard. The U.S.P. reference cod-liver oil has been adopted as the standard for the bioassay of vitamin D oils by the chick bone-ash method, where the chick unit was equal to 1 unit of vitamin D in the U.S.P. reference cod-liver oil. The first reference oil contained 95 units per gram and the second 115 units per gram. Crystalline vitamin D$_3$ was assigned a potency of 40 million units per gram, but Waddell and Kennedy (1947a) have reported that it contains 50 million units per gram.

Vitamin D$_2$ and vitamin D$_3$ have approximately equal potency for the rat, but vitamin D$_2$ has almost no chick activity. Hence the response of chicks to vitamin oils varies, depending upon the proportions of the various forms of vitamin D present. The livers of the white sea bass, the dogfish, and other species of fish contain forms of vitamin D which give more than 100 per cent activity when tested by the chick method (Jukes and Sanford, 1939).

Vitamin D is to be determined in an unknown fish-liver oil by the chick bone-ash procedure described in the experimental part.

EXPERIMENTAL[1]

Obtain a sample of vitamin D oil (standard or test) containing 0 to 20 A.O.A.C. units per gram.

Prepare 3 kg. of the A.O.A.C. rachitic basal ration[2] as follows: Transfer the weighed quantity of each food material to a large dish, knead the foods until they are thoroughly mixed, and sieve the mixture through the screen provided for that purpose. Place the vitamin D oil in a 1-oz. sample bottle fitted with a cork and a medicine dropper, weigh the bottle with its assembly to 10 mg., and transfer 20.0 g. of the oil to a 100-ml. beaker. Add 60 ml. of petroleum ether (b.p. 30 to 60°) and stir the mixture until the oil dissolves. Transfer the ether solution to the food in the dish, using 15 ml. of ether as rinse fluid, mix the ether solution with the feed, and sieve the material twice. Remix any large particles of corn with the main part of the feed. Spread the mixture in a thin layer on paper and allow it to stand (2 hr.) until the ether evaporates. Store the mixture in a tightly capped tin container or amber bottle.

Obtain assignment to a thermostatically controlled electric brooder which is located in a room free from draft. The room should be dark except for a 15- to 25-watt light bulb suspended near the food trough in each brooder compartment. Chicks will not eat properly if the illustration is inadequate. Observe and record the temperature at intervals. If necessary, adjust the thermoregulator to maintain the temperature at 95 ±1°.

Obtain a group (8 to 10) of day-old chicks which have been starved or have been fed a basal ration containing little, or no, vitamin D since birth. Weigh the group of chicks and place them in a brooder compartment. Fill the special water container and the special feeder. Refill these containers as required but not less often than once a day. If necessary, clean the feeders before adding water or feed. Remove and clean the dropping pans twice weekly. At the expiration of 7 days adjust the thermoregulator so that the temperature of the brooder is 90 ±1°. After 3 days adjust the thermoregulator to give a temperature of 85 ±1°.

At the end of 21 days remove and weigh the group of chicks. Decapitate each chick (if desired, after anesthetizing them in a closed container with ether). Remove and keep separate the tibiae from the right and left legs. In preparing the tibiae for extraction, immerse the legs to a point above the hip joint in boiling water for about 1 min. Remove the legs and defeather them. Lay each chick on its back, bend the leg forward until the skin over the hip joint is taut, cut with a sharp knife through the skin and flesh at the hip joint, and completely sever the leg at the hip joint. Take care not to cut the bony part of the tibiae.

Bend each leg backward at the knee joint until the skin is taut, cut the skin and halfway through the flesh at the knee joint, and remove the skin from the tibia by pulling on the claws while holding the tibia firmly. Place the tibiae in boiling water for 5 min. and dissect *all* the flesh from the bones, being careful not to remove *any* of the cartilage attached at the end of the tibiae.

Wrap each tibia (from left and right legs) separately in a circle of filter paper. Crush the ends of each bone by a sharp blow from a hammer. Tie all of the wrapped and crushed tibiae in a bundle labeled appropriately with india ink. Place the bundle in a Soxhlet apparatus (preferably one large enough to hold several students' samples) fitted with an electric heating mantle and extract the bones for 20 hr. with 95 per cent ethanol or isopropyl alcohol. Preserve the solvent and observe any material which deposits on standing. Reextract the bones in the Soxhlet for 20 hr. with diethyl ether, remove the bundles, and allow them to stand in air until the ether evaporates.

Label a No. 2 porcelain crucible with a marking pencil, heat the crucible to redness, and continue to heat at this temperature for 30 min., using a blue gas flame. Place the hot crucible in a desiccator (before closing the lid completely allow the hot expanding air to escape for 30 sec. through a slight opening) over anhydrous calcium chloride, allow the crucible to cool to room temperature, and, as rapidly as possible, weigh the crucible to ±1 mg.

Untie the bundle of bones, unwrap each bone, place all the bones in the weighed crucible, and crush the bones in crucible, using a pestle. Avoid loss of material during these manipulations. Heat the bones in the crucible for 70 hr. at 100° in an electric oven. Allow the crucible to cool to room temperature (at least 3 hr.) in a desiccator over anhydrous calcium chloride. Open the desiccator slowly in a manner such that the inrushing air will not sweep the powdered sample from the crucible. Weigh the crucible to ±1 mg., recording the weight found exactly 5 min. after the crucible has been removed from the desiccator.

Heat the crucible for 2 hr. at 800° (red heat) in a muffle furnace, allow the crucible to cool to room temperature in a desiccator over anhydrous calcium chloride, and weigh the crucible to ±1 mg., recording the weight found exactly 3 min. after the crucible has been removed from the desiccator.

Plot the per cent bone ash found for the various levels of vitamin D (supplied by instructor) on co-ordinate paper, label the ordinates, and draw a smooth standard curve. Interpolate the standard curve to determine the number of units of vitamin D in the unknown oil.

Optional Procedure. Sever the upper joint (first exposed joint from the foot) of the middle toe of the left leg (toes from right legs are to be treated similarly) by stretching the toe and cutting between the ends of the bones. Be careful not to cut the cartilage. Wipe the middle toes of all the left legs with a clean cloth and place them in a crucible prepared as described previously.

Heat the crucible for 70 hr. at 100°, cool it in a desiccator for 3 hr., and weigh it as described. Heat the crucible in a muffle furnace at 800° for 1 to 2 hr., cool the crucible in a desiccator as described, and weigh it to ±1 mg. as described.

NOTES

1. The authors are indebted to Dr. Sven Lassen, Van Camp Laboratories, Terminal Island, California, for helpful suggestions.

2. Ground yellow corn, 58; wheat-flour middlings or wheat gray shorts, 25; crude domestic precipitated casein, 12; precipitated calcium phosphate, 2; iodized salt (0.02 per cent potassium iodide), 1; nonirradiated yeast (7 per cent minimum nitrogen), 1; and $MnSO_4 \cdot 4H_2O$, 0.02 (Association of Official Agricultural Chemists, 1945).

A ration of the following composition has been used satisfactorily: ground yellow corn, 43; ground whole wheat, 13; ground whole oats, 13; dried skim milk, 11; precipitated casein, 8; dehydrated alfalfa-leaf meal, 8; steamed bone meal, 2.7; and U.S.P. sodium chloride, 1.1. During the experimental period (21 days) each chick will consume (including spillage) from 350 to 500 g. of this ration.

EXPERIMENT 42

DETERMINATION OF THE ACTIVITY OF SALIVARY AMYLASE AND THE CONCENTRATION OF UNKNOWN STARCH SOLUTION

The chemistry, action, and function of amylases have been reviewed by Hopkins (1946), Caldwell and Adams (1946), Hanes (1937), and Tauber (1949). Amylases are enzymes which catalyze the hydrolysis of starch and glycogen to dextrins, maltose, and glucose. They occur in nearly all animals, seeds and germinating sprouts, bacteria, molds and fungi, blood (plasma and leucocytes), and organs (especially the pancreas) of higher animals. In a few species [man, pig, rat, and mouse but not dog, cat, sheep, and goat (Cohn and Brookes, 1936)] they are found in high concentration in the saliva.

The significance of wheat amylases in milling and baking technology has been discussed by Geddes (1946). Wheat amylase was discovered by Kirchoff (Sumner and Somers, 1947) in 1811 and malt amylase by Payen and Persoz (1833). α-Amylase (dextrinizing enzyme), the predominant form in bacteria, fungi, and animal fluids, rapidly cleaves starch to products (achrodextrin, maltose, and glucose) which give no color with iodine. α-Amylase, liberated from the bound form during germination, effects internal disintegration of starch by fission of the 1,4-glycosidic linkages. β-Amylase (saccharifying enzyme), free in ungerminated cereal grains, is inactive toward raw starch but splits mildly degraded starch to liberate terminal maltose units from the starch molecule. The amylase of sweet potatoes is largely in the beta form (Balls, Walden, and Thompson, 1948).

The methods employed for the isolation of amylases depend upon the destruction of α-amylase with acid and β-amylase by heat (Kneen and Beckord, 1946). Purified amylases have been prepared from pancreas (van Thoai and Bernere-Silhol, 1946), soybean (Newton, Hixon, and Naylor, 1943), wheat flour (Ballou and Luck, 1941), sweet potatoes (Balls, Thompson, and Walden, 1946), saliva (Stark, 1942), bacteria (Kneen and Beckord, 1946), and fungi (*Aspergillus oryzae*) (Volz and Caldwell, 1947) by fractionation of materials extracted with organic solvents. It has been proposed that crystalline α-amylase is a "pure" protein with a molecular weight of 20,000 (Meyer, Fischer, and Bernfeld, 1947) or 45,000 (Caldwell, Booher, and Sherman, 1931). According to Williams, Schlenk, and Eppright (1944) a sample of purified amylase contained per gram 4.1 mg. of inositol and lesser amounts of nicotinic acid, pantothenic acid, biotin, and folic acid. It has been reported that free amino groups, free —SH, and tyrosine are essential for amylase activity (Caldwell, Weill, and Weil, 1945) and that amylase action is inhibited by vitamin C (Seshagirirao and Giri, 1942) and proteins isolated from wheat (Militzer, Ikeda, and Kneen, 1946a, 1946b).

Methods for the quantitative determination of amylases are based on the time of hydrolysis to substances which yield a blue or reddish color with iodine in potassium iodide (Redfern, 1947), the quantity of maltose formed in a definite time (Willstätter, Waldschmidt-Leitz, and Hesse, 1923), the decrease in viscosity of a starch substrate, and the total reducing substances formed from starch (Andersch, 1946; Somogyi, 1938). Blood amylases in diseases of the pancreas have been discussed by Myers (1943).

Saccharogenic time has been defined as the time in minutes required at 40° to hydrolyze a buffered (pH 6.8) solution containing 0.5 per cent (by volume) saliva, 0.25 per cent soluble starch, and 0.09 per cent sodium chloride. According to Bauer and Martin (1948) saccharogenic activity is highest after breakfast and lowest at night, decreases markedly in saliva which has stood for 1 hr. at room temperature, and decreases slowly thereafter up to 1 week. Saliva preserved with toluene decreases little in potency under these conditions. Saccharogenic time varies from 1 to 6 min. for normal individuals, but in individuals with skin disorders it may be as long as 1 hr.

The activity of salivary amylase (ptyalin) and the concentration of an unknown starch solution are to be determined by an adaptation of the Wohlgemuth (1908) method. The time required to digest whole starch solutions of known and unknown concentrations, from the colloidal opalescent state (blue color with iodine in potassium iodide) through the erythrodextrin stage (red color) to the achrodextrin end point (no color), is to be measured. These data are to be used in making the required calculations.

EXPERIMENTAL

Obtain (from the instructor) two pieces of paraffin and two unknown starch solutions (prepared from intact, not soluble, potato starch). Shake these solutions well before removing aliquots.

Chew a piece of paraffin and expectorate into a dry filter paper. Collect about 2 ml. of the filtered saliva. Pipette 1.00 ml. of the filtered saliva into a 100-ml. graduate, add water to the 20-ml. mark, and mix the liquids thoroughly. Pipette into separate 6-in. test tubes (in such a manner that none of the liquids comes into contact with the walls of the tubes) 5.0 ml. of each unknown starch solution and 5.0 ml. of a standard 0.5 per cent starch solution. Add to each tube (10-ml. graduate) 4.0 ml. of a sodium chloride-phosphate buffer solution (pH 6.8). Pipette 1.00 ml. of the diluted saliva into the tube containing the 0.5 per cent standard starch solution. Mix the liquids quickly and immediately place the tube in a 40° water bath. Record the time (the aid of another student is permitted). At 1-min. intervals transfer (medicine dropper) 1 drop of the mixture to a spot-plate depression containing 2 drops of 0.01 M iodine in 0.01 M potassium iodide solution (this solution should be used within 1 min. after dispensing since it fails to give a satisfactory color on longer standing). Near the end point (disappearance of red color) perform this test at 15-sec. intervals. Record the time required to reach the end point. Repeat this procedure while testing the unknown starch solutions simultaneously.

Calculate the dilution of saliva required to digest the 0.5 per cent starch solution, assuming an inverse proportionality between concentration of saliva and end-point time. Calculate the approximate end-point times for the unknown starch solutions.

Collect 2 ml. (or larger volume up to 20 ml., if the amylase activity was found to be low) of the filtered saliva, pipette 1.00 ml. into a 100-ml. graduate, dilute the saliva to the desired (calculated) volume with distilled water, and mix the liquids thoroughly. Pipette into separate 6-in. test tubes 5.0 ml. of the unknown starch solutions and standard starch solutions of the following concentrations: 0.20, 0.50, 1.0, 1.5, 2.0, and 2.5 per cent. Add 4.0 ml. (graduate) of the sodium chloride-phosphate buffer solution to each tube. Pipette 1.00 ml. of the diluted saliva into the tube containing the 0.2 per cent starch solution. Repeat the procedure described previously and record the end-point time.

Test each of the other starch solutions similarly and simultaneously. The color tests should be made at the stated intervals, although it is unnecessary to begin testing a given known starch solution until the digestion of that of the next lower concentration is complete. Plot the data relating time and starch concentration on coordinate paper, label the ordinates, and draw a smooth curve. Estimate the concentration of each unknown starch solution by interpolating the standard curve.

Determine the activity (units) of the amylase preparation by calculating the milliliters of 1 per cent starch solution which would be digested to the achromic point in 30 min. at 40° by 1.0 ml. of undiluted saliva.

EXPERIMENT 43

DETERMINATION OF ALKALINE PHOSPHATASE ACTIVITY IN BLOOD SERUM

The determination, functions, and clinical significance of phosphatases have been discussed by Barker (1949), Roche (1946), Sunderman (1942), Bodansky and Jaffe (1934), Baur (1949), and the Paul Lewis Laboratories (1948). Normal ranges of alkaline phosphatase per 100 ml. of serum are 1.5 to 4.0 Bodansky units for adults and 5.0 to 13.0 units for children. Alkaline phosphatase activity is reduced in fasting and on fat-free diets. It is increased on high-fat diets, and values up to 190 units have been observed in rickets, bone malignancy, obstructive jaundice, and other diseases. The phosphatase activity of rat blood serum is approximately 80 Bodansky units per 100 ml. in the presence of magnesium ions (added to activate the enzyme), and it is about 25 per cent lower in the absence of magnesium ions. The urinary excretion of alkaline phosphatase by men and women is scanty and irregular (Burgen, 1947).

The normal function of alkaline phosphatase may be to stimulate protein synthesis in the development of bone-marrow cells, teeth, hair, mammary gland, and epithelial cells of the small intestine. Since phosphatase activity is intense in embryonic tissue, it may be concerned with the formation of nucleic acids and protein in the cytoplasm and the nucleus of cells. Nucleic acids may act as phosphate donors to "funnel" energy into the protein-synthesis mechanism during peptide-bond formation.

The increase in alkaline phosphatase in blood serum in bone disease may result because of (a) overproduction of the enzyme from the injured bone tissue or (b) the increased capacity of bone for cellular activity in the absence of bone synthesis.

Acid phosphatase (optimum pH, 5.5) was first observed in the urine of subjects with carcinoma of the prostate, and it is known to increase in blood serum with the onset of metastases. Females of all ages excrete about 50 units of acid phosphatase per day and males variable amounts up to 350 units per day after puberty (Burgen, 1947; Kirk, 1948). The acid phosphatases of the prostate gland and of the red cell appear to be different enzymes (Abul-Fadl and King, 1949). Gottschalk (1945) has proposed a micromethod for the determination of acid phosphatase.

The alkaline phosphatase of rat blood serum is to be determined by the method of Bodansky (1933), as modified by Flock and Bollman (1948). Inorganic phosphate (corrected for preformed inorganic phosphate), liberated from β-glycerophosphate under standardized conditions, is to be estimated by the photometric method of Fiske and Subbarow (1925), essentially as modified by King (1932). According to Bodansky each phosphate unit is equivalent to the "liberation of 1 mg. of phosphorus as phosphate ion during the first hour of incubation at 37° and at pH 8.6, with a substrate containing sodium β-glycerophosphate, hydrolysis not exceeding 10 per cent of the substrate."

EXPERIMENTAL[1]

Place a rat and a wad of cotton saturated with ether under a bell jar. When the rat has been anesthetized, place it on its back on a board and tie its legs to nails at the corners of the board. Pick up the skin on the left ventral side adjacent to the heart, make a longitudinal incision with sharp scissors through the skin and body wall, cut and remove a section of the body wall of a size sufficient to expose the heart, and carefully remove the heart from the thoracic cavity, with as little damage as possible to the connecting blood vessels. Hold the animal in such a position that its exposed heart is directly over the mouth of a 15-ml. centrifuge tube, make an incision in the heart with scissors, and collect as much blood as possible by pressing on the animal. Allow the blood to stand for 15 min. Wrap the carcass in a paper towel and discard it in the waste container. Centrifuge the blood-clot suspension, pour the clear supernatant serum into a test tube, and stopper the tube. Label the tube, preserve the serum in the refrigerator, and retain serum for use in Exp. 46.

Submit a labeled 6-in. test tube to the instructor, who will add 0.40 ml. of an unknown phosphate solution. Transfer approximately 17 ml. of the sodium β-glycerophosphate reagent (preserved in the refrigerator) and allow it to warm to 37° in a water bath. Add to the test tube 0.40 ml. of distilled water, 5.0 ml. (10-ml. graduate) of the warmed glycerophosphate reagent, and 0.100 ml. of the rat blood serum (1-ml. graduated pipette). Immediately stopper the tube with a clean, dry rubber stopper, invert the tube several times, and place the stoppered tube in a water bath at 37°. Record the time. Carry out the described procedure, adding 0.40 ml. of distilled water, 5.0 ml. of the glycerophosphate reagent, and 0.100 ml. of the serum to a second tube, and 0.50 ml. of distilled water and 5.0 ml. of the glycerophosphate reagent to a third tube. During the incubation period, add to a fourth tube 0.50 ml. of the serum and 5.0 ml. of distilled water for use in determining "preformed" phosphate.

After 60 min. incubation at 37° remove each tube in turn from the bath and add immediately to each tube 4.5 ml. of 10 per cent trichloroacetic acid to stop enzymatic action and to precipitate the blood serum proteins. Stopper each tube, shake each tube vigorously, and filter each mixture on dry filter paper of low ash content. Pipette 5.0 ml. of each filtrate into separate test tubes calibrated to contain 10.0-ml. volumes (or into 10-ml. glass-stoppered graduated cylinders). The filtrates are stable if preserved in the refrigerator.

Pipette into separate calibrated test tubes (or 10-ml. graduated cylinders) 1.00 ml., 2.00 ml., and 3.00 ml., respectively, of a standard phosphate solution containing approximately 0.02 mg. per ml. of phosphorus. Add to each tube (by means of a 10-ml. graduated pipette using the house vacuum or water aspirator but *not* the mouth) 2.25 ml. of 10 per cent trichloroacetic acid and sufficient distilled water to bring the volume to 5.0 ml. Add in turn to each of the seven tubes 1.0 ml. of 5 per cent ammonium molybdate in 7 N sulfuric acid, 0.50 ml. of 1,2,4-aminonaphtholsulfonic acid reagent, and sufficient distilled water to bring the volume to 10.0 ml. Stopper each tube, invert each tube several times, and allow the tubes to stand for 10 min.

Using a visual colorimeter, determine the relative color intensity of each unknown solution compared with that of the standard (set at 20 mm.) of nearest color intensity. If any color is observed in the control tube, compare its intensity with that of the most dilute standard (set at 10 mm.). If the intensity is measurable, calculate the concentration of phosphorus liberated from the glycerophosphate reagent and apply this correction to the unknown solutions.

Optional Procedure. Prepare the solutions described previously and, in addition, a solution containing 3.0 ml. of distilled water, 2.25 ml. of 10 per cent trichloroacetic acid, 1.0 ml. of the ammonium molybdate reagent, 0.50 ml. of the aminonaphtholsulfonic acid reagent, and sufficient distilled water to bring the volume to 10.0 ml. Adjust the photoelectric colorimeter [Lumetron, Model 400A, equipped with a red (650-mμ) filter] to give an optical density reading of 0 with this solution. Measure the color intensities of the unknown, standard, and blank solutions. Plot the data from the standard, draw a smooth curve with Optical Density as the ordinate and Phosphorus Concentration as the abscissa, and estimate the values of the unknown and blank solutions by interpolating the standard curve. Correct the phosphorus values of the unknowns for the phosphorus liberated in the blank solution.

NOTE

1. If the total phosphorus approaches 60 mg. per cent, the determination must be repeated at lower concentration or shorter incubation time, since the enzyme is inhibited under these conditions.

EXPERIMENT 44

ASYMMETRIC ENZYMATIC SYNTHESIS OF ACETYL-L-PHENYLALANINE p-TOLUIDIDE
AND ISOLATION OF L- AND D-PHENYLALANINES

L- and D-phenylalanines have been prepared by (a) asymmetric enzymatic synthesis, with papain, of acetyl-L-phenylalanine phenylhydrazide (private communication from Dr. Carl Niemann, California Institute of Technology, Pasadena, California) and of acetyl-L-phenylalanylglycine anilide (Behrens, Doherty, and Bergmann, 1940), (b) asymmetric enzymatic hydrolysis, with chymotrypsin, of acetyl-L-phenylalanine methyl ester (private communication, Dr. Carl Niemann), (c) resolution of DL-phenylalanine through the brucine salts of the formyl derivatives (Fischer and Schoeller, 1907; du Vigneaud and Meyer, 1932; du Vigneaud and Irish, 1938) and the cinchonine salts of the benzoyl derivatives (Fischer and Mouneyrat, 1900), and (d) the destruction of L-phenylalanine in DL-phenylalanine by the action of yeast (Ehrlich, 1908) and L-amino acid oxidase (Stumpf and Green, 1944).

Papain (Balls, Thompson, and Jones, 1940; Lewis and Woodward, 1948; Sumner and Somers, 1947) is the dried albuminous exudate of the fruit of *Carica papaya* L., a member of the Caricaceae family of tropical palms native to Latin America and the West Indies. The latex is obtained by scarifying the green fruit from trees which grow from 20 to 40 ft. high. About 5 lb. of fresh latex is required to give 1 lb. of dried latex. Each tree produces from 3 to 8 oz. of dry latex per year, each acre of trees yields from 80 to 175 lb. per year, and the production is maximum when the trees are 12 to 14 months old. Dried papain was first made in 1878 by Henri Widmark of Berlin but was first produced commercially in Ceylon. At the present time papain is marketed from most of the tropical countries, but it comes principally from Ceylon and Tanganyika (British protectorate on the East African Coast).

In 1935 more than 300,000 lb. of papain was imported into the United States for the preparation of protein hydrolysates, the tenderization of meat, and other uses. Commercial papain varies in color from light yellow to chocolate brown, but there is no relation between color and activity. The proteolytic activity of papain is inhibited or destroyed by oxidation and is increased by hydrogen sulfide, hydrogen cyanide, glutathione, cysteine, and other reducing agents (Scott and Sandstrom, 1942). The relative proteolytic activity of papain preparations is measured by determining the extent to which a protein such as fibrin (Heyl, Caryl, and Staley, 1914), casein (Balls, Swenson, and Stuart, 1935) beef powder (Maher and Wirth, 1946) or hemoglobin (Anson, 1937) is digested under standard conditions. Crystalline papain has been prepared as thin needles of molecular weight $27,000 \pm 2,000$ (Balls and Lineweaver, 1939; Lineweaver and Schwimmer, 1941).

Acetyl-DL-phenylalanine, prepared by acetylation of DL-phenylalanine, is treated at pH 4.5 with papain, cysteine, and toluidine. The acetyl-L-phenylalanine p-toluidide, which separates from the solution as soon as it is formed, is hydrolyzed, and L-phenylalanine is isolated from the hydrolysate. The unreacted acetyl-D-phenylalanine is hydrolyzed, and D-phenylalanine is isolated. The described experimental directions are essentially those kindly provided by Dr. Carl Niemann.

EXPERIMENTAL

Acetyl-DL-phenylalanine. Add 10 g. (0.06 mole) of DL-phenylalanine (prepared in Exp. 8), 21 ml. (0.13 mole) of 6.0 N sodium hydroxide, and 40 ml. of distilled water to a 250-ml. conical flask. Stir the mixture until the phenylalanine dissolves. Immerse the flask in an ice-water bath, cool the mixture to 5°, add 17 ml. (0.18 mole) of acetic anhydride (99 to 100 per cent) from a dropping funnel at the rate of about 1 ml. (20 drops) per minute while rotating the flask at frequent intervals. Allow the mixture to stand for 1 hr. in an ice-water bath. Add sufficient concentrated hydrochloric acid (3 to 4 ml.) dropwise with stirring to reduce the pH from 4 to 2, as determined with universal indicator paper. Scratch the sides of the vessel and allow the mixture (turbid if crystallization has begun) to stand for 1 hr. or longer in the ice-water bath. Filter the suspension on a Buchner funnel, wash the crystals on the funnel twice with 20-ml. portions of ice-cold distilled water, and dry the product overnight at 50° or in air in a covered evaporating dish. Weigh the product, retain 10 g., and submit the excess to the instructor in a tared, labeled sample bottle.

Acetyl-L-phenylalanine p-Toluidide. Add 2 g. of commercial papain powder and 20 ml. of distilled water to a 125-ml. conical flask. Stopper the flask, immerse the flask in an ice-water bath, and shake it vigorously at intervals for 30 min. Centrifuge the suspension 15 min. Add to a 250-ml. conical flask 10 g. (0.05 mole) of acetyl-DL-phenylalanine, 180 ml. of pH 4.5 buffer (acetic acid and sodium acetate) solution, and 0.6 g. of L-cysteine hydrochloride. Stir and heat (not above 50°) the mixture until the solids dissolve. Add 5 g. (0.05 mole) of p-toluidine (m.p. 42 to 43°) and the nearly clear papain solution. Stopper the flask, shake it until the solid dissolves, and place the flask immediately (to avoid precipitation of the acetyl-DL-phenylalanine) in an oven at 40°. Crystallization of the acetyl-L-phenylalanine p-toluidide usually begins within 1 hr. Allow the flask to stand at this temperature for at least 5 days, immerse the flask for 20 min. in an ice-water bath while rotating it at intervals, filter the suspension on a Buchner funnel, and wash the crystals twice on the funnel, with 25-ml. portions of distilled water.[1]

Suspend the crystals in 80 ml. of absolute ethanol, heat the mixture in a boiling-water bath until the crystals dissolve, and filter the hot solution through a heated Buchner funnel. Transfer the hot solution to a beaker, cool the beaker for 30 min. in an ice-water bath (or allow it to stand overnight in the refrigerator), filter the suspension on a Buchner funnel, and dry the precipitate for an hour at 50° or overnight in air. Weigh the product, retain 5 g., and submit the excess to the instructor in a tared, labeled sample bottle.

L-Phenylalanine.[2] Add 5 g. of the acetyl-L-phenylalanine p-toluidide and 65 ml. of 6 N hydrochloric acid to a 200-ml. round-bottomed flask, attach a reflux condenser, and heat the mixture until the solvent refluxes vigorously. Continue vigorous refluxing for 8 hr. Set up the reduced-pressure distillation apparatus shown in Fig. 7 (see Distillation in the Appendix) and distill the clear solution *in vacuo*. Dissolve the residual material in 15 ml. of distilled water. Add 30 ml. of concentrated ammonium hydroxide and note that a copious precipitate of p-toluidine forms almost immediately. Cool the mixture for 30 min. in an ice-water bath, filter the suspension, wash the crystals on the funnel with 5 ml. of distilled water, and extract the combined filtrate and washing twice with 20-ml. portions of chloroform, to remove the dissolved p-toluidine. Remove the excess ammonia by evaporating the aqueous phase to about 30 ml., cool the residual liquid for 30 min. in an ice-water bath, filter the suspension, wash the crystals of L-phenylalanine successively with 5-ml. portions of ice-cold distilled water and 95 per cent ethanol, and dry the product at 50° or in air. Submit the product to the instructor in a tared, labeled sample bottle.

D-Phenylalanine.[2] Evaporate *in vacuo* the filtrate preserved for this purpose to half its volume, add concentrated hydrochloric acid to pH 2 (tested with universal indicator paper), scratch the sides of the vessel, and cool the mixture for 1 hr. in an ice-water bath. Filter the suspension and crystallize the product (acetyl-D-phenylalanine[3]) from water. Hydrolyze the product by refluxing it with 6 N hydrochloric acid. Isolate the D-phenylalanine. Submit the product to the instructor in a tared, labeled sample bottle.

NOTES

1. Allow the filtrate to stand for several days until nearly all the L-phenylalanine derivative has precipitated, filter the suspension, and retain the precipitate for the isolation of L-phenylalanine and the filtrate for the isolation of D-phenylalanine.

2. According to Fisher and Schoeller (1907) the specific rotation in water of L-phenylalanine is $[\alpha]_D^{20} = -35.1$ deg., and that of D-phenylalanine is $[\alpha]_D^{20} = +35.0$ deg.

3. According to du Vigneaud and Meyer (1932) the specific rotation of acetyl-D-phenylalanine in absolute ethanol is $[\alpha]_D^{26} = -51$ deg. Knoop and Blanco (1925) found $[\alpha]_D = -51.8$ deg.

EXPERIMENT 45

DETERMINATION OF CHOLESTEROL IN BLOOD SERUM

The chemistry and physiology of cholesterol have been discussed by Bills (1935), Bloor (1943), and Peters and Van Slyke (1946). Cholesterol was first isolated from gallstones by workers in the seventeenth century. It has been shown subsequently to be a constituent of bile, blood, intestinal concretions, cysts, eggs, tubercle bacilli, milk, and numerous other types of biological materials. There is a close relationship between cholesterol and other sterols including the bile acids, vitamins D_2 and D_3, male and female sex hormones, carcinogenic hydrocarbons, and hormones of the suprarenal cortex.

Nearly all the cholesterol of bile and red blood cells, and from 20 to 40 per cent of that in blood plasma, is in the free form. The concentration of total cholesterol in human blood plasma ranges from 150 to 275 mg. per 100 ml. under normal conditions to as much as 800 mg. per 100 ml. in uncontrolled *diabetes mellitus*, lipoid nephrosis, obstructive jaundice, hypothyroidism, and hemorrhagic and aplastic anemias. Plasma cholesterol levels as low as 50 mg. per 100 ml. are associated with hyperthyroidism, pernicious anemia, hemolytic jaundice, acute liver diseases, infections, and malnutrition. Cholesterol is excreted into the intestine, where it is converted by bacterial action into its saturated isomers coprosterol and dihydrocholesterol. It has been suggested that cholesterol may be a precursor of vitamin D and that it may play a role in the absorption and transportation of fat, regulation of cell permeability and membrane equilibria, neutralization of bacterial toxins, and growth of normal and malignant cells. Steiner (1948) has discussed the significance of cholesterol in coronary arteriosclerosis.

Free cholesterol is determined quantitatively by gravimetric analysis of its slightly soluble digitonide and by colorimetric analysis of the colored complex formed with the Liebermann-Burchard reagent (acetic anhydride and sulfuric acid). Total cholesterol is determined similarly after saponification of cholesterol esters. Procedures for the quantitative determination of cholesterol and data on the cholesterol content of blood and other tissues have been reported by Bloor (1943), Clarke and Marney (1945), Foldes and Murphy (1946a, 1946b), Hepburn and Kotlikoff (1943), Hodges, Sperry, and Anderson (1943), Hoffmeyer (1944), Lamb, Mueller, and Beach (1946), Leiboff (1942), Levin (1945), Marquardt (1947), Popjak (1943, 1946), Saifer and Kammerer (1946), Sobel and Mayer (1945), Teeri (1944), and other workers.

Total cholesterol (free cholesterol and cholesterol esters) is to be determined in rat blood serum by photometric analysis of the colored complex formed with the Liebermann-Burchard reagent, essentially by the procedure of Kingsley and Schaffert (1949). According to these authors the color intensity of hydrolyzed serum is about 84 per cent that of unhydrolyzed serum, owing to the greater color intensity of cholesterol esters compared with free cholesterol. Monnier, Farchadi, and Maulbetsch (1941) found that the cholesterol content of rat blood serum averages 80 mg. per cent.

EXPERIMENTAL

Obtain the rat blood serum preserved in Exp. 43. Soften six No. 7 corks with a rotary press and shake them for 15 min. with 75 ml. of chloroform in a stoppered flask. Submit a clean, dry, labeled 6-in. pyrex test tube to the instructor, who will add 10.0 ml. of a chloroform solution containing a known quantity of pure cholesterol. Add (1-ml. graduated pipette) to this recovery solution 0.20 ml. of the serum and 0.20 ml. of distilled water. Add to a second tube 10.0 ml. of anhydrous C.P. chloroform and 0.40 ml. of the serum. Add to a third tube 10.0 ml. of the chloroform and 0.40 ml. of distilled water. If a check on the completeness of the extraction procedure is desired, set up an additional tube containing 7.0 ml. of chloroform, 0.40 ml. of distilled water, and 3.0 ml. of the standard cholesterol solution.

Obtain assignment to a Kahn shaker and a centrifuge before proceeding with the next steps, which must be carried out without long (more than 1 or 2 min.) delay. Add to each tube in turn 1.5 g. of powdered anhydrous magnesium sulfate. Stopper each tube and shake it (by hand) for about 10 sec. to prevent the salt from caking. Agitate the tubes in the shaker for 5 min., add 0.5 g. of fuller's earth to each tube, shake the (stoppered) tubes for 10 sec. by hand, and centrifuge the tubes at 3,000 r.p.m. for 10 min.

Obtain assignment to a photoelectric colorimeter. Cautiously transfer (graduate) 16.0 ml. of cold C.P. acetic anhydride (preserved in the refrigerator) to a 125-ml. conical flask and add 4.0 ml. of cold C.P. concentrated sulfuric acid (stored in the refrigerator). Stopper the flask, immerse it in an ice-water bath, and *(Cautiously)* rotate the flask to mix the solutions. Pipette into separate clean, dry, 6-in. test tubes 5.0-ml. portions of the serum, the blank solution, and the serum plus recovery solution. Add to each tube (by means of a 10-ml. graduated pipette, using the house vacuum or the water aspirator but *not* the mouth) 2.0 ml. of the cold, freshly prepared acetic anhydride—sulfuric acid reagent. Stir each mixture with a clean, dry stirring rod. Stopper the tubes and allow them to stand for 10 min. in a water bath at 20 ± 0.5°.

Transfer the solutions to matched test tubes and determine (within 15 min.) the optical densities, using a photoelectric colorimeter [Lumetron, Model 400A, equipped with a red (650-mμ) filter] adjusted so that the optical density reading of the blank is zero. While the colors are developing, pipette 0, 1.00, 2.00, 3.00, and 5.00 ml. of the standard (0.12 mg. per ml.) cholesterol solution into separate test tubes. Dilute each solution to 5.0 ml. with chloroform, add 2 ml. of the freshly prepared acetic anhydride—sulfuric acid reagent, stir each mixture, stopper the tubes, and immerse the tubes for 10 min. in a water bath at 20 ± 0.5°. Determine the optical densities with a photoelectric colorimeter adjusted as described.

Plot the data obtained with the standard solutions using Optical Density as the ordinate and Cholesterol Concentration as the abscissa, draw a smooth curve, and estimate the values of the unknown solutions by interpolating the standard curve.

EXPERIMENT 46

DETERMINATION OF NITROGEN COMPOUNDS IN URINE

This topic has been reviewed by Hawk, Oser, and Summerson (1947), Peters and Van Slyke (1946), Harrison (1947), Todd and Sanford (1948), Cantarow and Trumper (1945), Kleiner (1945), Marshall (1926), and Bodansky and Bodansky (1940).

Normal and abnormal constituents in urine include (a) *inorganic cations*: ammonium, sodium, potassium, calcium, and magnesium; (b) *inorganic anions*: carbonate, chloride, sulfate, phosphate, and nitrate; (c) *organic acids*: oxalic, ethereal sulfuric, hippuric, benzoic, lactic, acetoacetic, β-hydroxybutyric, phenaceturic, homogentisic, phenylpyruvic, phenyllactic, *p*-hydroxyphenylpyruvic, and urocanic acids; (d) *nitrogen compounds*: amino acids, urea, creatinine, creatine, allantoin, uric acid, purines, pyrimidines, peptides, and proteins; (e) *carbohydrates*: glucose, fructose, galactose, and pentoses; and (f) *miscellaneous*: taurine, thiocyanates, glutathione, ergothioneine, acetone, fat, blood, bile, pus, pigments, hormones, enzymes, and vitamins.

Urine is formed by filtration of the diffusible constituents of plasma through the glomerulus. Water, chloride, bicarbonate, potassium, phosphate, uric acid, urea, sulfates, and glucose are partially reabsorbed as the filtrate passes along the tubules. Chloride is preferentially reabsorbed in the distal tubule and glucose in the proximal tubule. Although the total volume of the glomerular filtrate may be as much as 150 liters per 24 hr., only from 1 to 2 liters of urine are excreted. The volume of urine is decreased by high temperature, physical exercise, acute nephritis, diarrhea, diseases of the heart and lungs, and other disorders. It is increased in diabetes mellitus, diabetes insipidus, and degeneration of the kidney and by drugs such as calomel, digitalis, acetates, and salicylates.

Normally urine is colored amber yellow, although it may be nearly colorless, milky, dark yellow, brownish red, brownish black, greenish yellow, or orange in pathological conditions. Urine which is clear when voided may become turbid on standing, owing to the formation of agglomerates (nucleoprotein and epithelial cells) or the precipitation of phosphates. The odor normally is faintly aromatic, but it may become ammoniacal because of bacterial decomposition. The pH varies from 5 to 8 depending upon the relative amounts of monohydrogen and dihydrogen phosphates excreted by the kidney as required to maintain a nearly constant (about 7.4) pH of the blood. The pH, as well as the total acid, of urine varies with the time of day, and usually acidity is increased in pathological states. Alkaline urine results from the ingestion of sodium bicarbonate or alkali-forming salts of organic acids (such as tartaric and citric acids) found in citrus juices and other foods. Acid urines are excreted following the ingestion of acid-forming foods such as bread, cereals, and meat. The specific gravity of urine usually varies from 1.015 to 1.025, although it may fall to about 1.00 after excessive water ingestion and may rise to 1.04 in chronic nephritis or after excessive sweating.

The average values found for the volume, specific gravity, total nitrogen, urea nitrogen, ammonia nitrogen, uric acid nitrogen, creatinine nitrogen, and undetermined nitrogen of 400 urine specimens were obtained by Beard (1935) and are shown in the accompanying table. According to Schmidt and Allen (1938) total-nitrogen values may fall as low as 3.6 g. for low-protein diets and rise as high as 23.0 g. on high-protein diets. It has been observed that creatinine and uric acid excretion is practically constant on diets varying widely in amounts of nitrogenous components.

Proteins, reducing substances, and acetone are to be determined qualitatively and total nitrogen, ammonia nitrogen, urea nitrogen, creatinine nitrogen, and uric acid nitrogen are to be determined quantitatively in 24-hr. urine samples collected on low- and high-protein diets. Knowledge of the composition of urine aids in understanding the metabolic processes of the body and is indispensable for clinical purposes. For the latter purpose it is also necessary to have complete information on the subject's diet and clinical history.

AVERAGE AMOUNTS OF DIFFERENT FORMS OF NITROGEN EXCRETED ON HIGH-, LOW-, AND-, NORMAL-PROTEIN DIETS

Characteristic	High protein	Low protein	Normal
Volume, ml.	1,472	1,408	1,364
Specific gravity.	1.023	1.019	1.022
Total nitrogen, g.	15.3	8.0	11.2
Urea nitrogen, g.	13.2	6.2	9.5
Ammonia nitrogen, g.	0.68	0.43	0.54
Uric acid nitrogen, g.	0.21	0.18	0.19
Creatinine nitrogen, g.	0.66	0.62	0.63
Undetermined nitrogen, g.	0.55	0.57	0.34

EXPERIMENTAL

Select from Tables of Food Composition (see Experiments in the Appendix) a high- or low-protein diet approved by the instructor. Restrict the food intake to this diet for 2 days prior to and during the collection of a 24-hr. urine sample. In collecting the urine, empty the bladder at 6 or 7 A.M. and discard this urine. Collect all urine voided during the succeeding 24 hr. in a clean 2.5-liter screw-capped amber bottle containing 10 ml. of toluene as preservative. Measure the total volume (graduate), dilute the urine to the 2-liter mark with distilled water, and thoroughly mix the liquids. Transfer about 200 ml. of the diluted urine to a glass-stoppered bottle, add 5 ml. of toluene, label the bottle, and store it in the refrigerator. Discard the remainder of the original urine. Pipette two 25.0-ml. portions of the diluted urine (free from toluene) into separate 50-ml. volumetric flasks. Label these flasks, one for qualitative and one for quantitative recovery, and submit them to the instructor at the beginning of the laboratory period. The instructor will add known quantities of the pure substances to be determined. Transfer these solutions to glass-stoppered bottles, label, add 5 ml. of toluene to each bottle, and store in the refrigerator.

QUALITATIVE TESTS

Proteins.[1] 1. *Coagulation Test.* Transfer about 5 ml. of the urine to a test tube and heat the upper third of the solution to boiling. Add 5 drops of N acetic acid and mix the solutions thoroughly. A precipitate which forms on heating but which dissolves when the urine is acidified with acetic acid is calcium or magnesium phosphate or a mixture of these substances. A flocculent precipitate which does not dissolve in the acetic acid solution is protein, usually albumin.

2. *Heller's Nitric Acid Ring Test.* Place 5 ml. of concentrated nitric acid in a test tube. Incline the tube and pour 5 ml. of the urine carefully down the side of the tube. Place the tube in a vertical position and allow it to stand for about 1 min. A ring of white precipitate appearing at the interface of layers usually indicates a protein.

Reducing Substances.[2] If the test for protein was positive, add 5 drops of 6 N acetic acid to 5 ml. of urine in a test tube and heat the mixture to boiling. Filter the suspended coagulum and add 5 drops of 6 N sodium hydroxide to the filtrate. Heat 5 ml. of Benedict's qualitative reagent (cupric sulfate, sodium sulfate, and sodium carbonate) to boiling in a test tube, add 0.5 ml. of the protein-free urine filtrate, and heat the mixture for 5 min. in a boiling-water bath. Remove the tube from the bath and observe any color or precipitate which may form immediately and after 5 min.

Acetone.[3] *Behre's (1928) Salicylaldehyde Test.* Add 3 drops of a 10 per cent solution of salicylaldehyde in 95 percent ethanol to 5.0 ml. of the urine. Add a 1/2-in. piece of solid sodium hydroxide. A deep-red color (30 min.) indicates the presence of dihydroxybenzalacetone (formula at right).

Total Nitrogen.[5] Pipette 5.0-ml. aliquots of the urine and the urine recovery samples into separate 100-ml. volumetric flasks, add distilled water to the marks, and mix the liquids thoroughly. Pipette 1.00 ml. of each urine sample into separate 8-in. pyrex test tubes. Pipette (using the house vacuum or water aspirator but *not* the mouth) 1.0 ml. of 18 N sulfuric acid (5-ml. graduated pipette) into each tube. Heat the tubes with microburners (Tirrill burner with barrel top removed) until dense white fumes of sulfur trioxide fill the tubes. Cool each tube for 1 min., add 2 drops of 30 per cent hydrogen peroxide from a dropping bottle, and heat until white fumes appear. If the solution is discolored (brown or yellow), add 1 drop of 30 per cent hydrogen peroxide and reheat the solution until white fumes appear. If necessary, repeat this procedure until the solution is colorless. Heat each solution to boiling and continue gentle boiling for 5 min. Cool each solution to room temperature.

Transfer each solution quantitatively to separate 100-ml. volumetric flasks, add sufficient distilled water to bring the total volumes to 75 ml., and pipette (using the house vacuum or water aspirator but *not* the mouth) 15.0 ml. (25-ml. graduated pipette) of Nessler reagent[6] (potassium mercuric iodide and sodium hydroxide) into each flask.

Pipette into separate 100-ml. volumetric flasks 5.0 ml. and 10.0 ml. of a standard ammonium sulfate solution containing 0.080 mg. of nitrogen per milliliter. Pipette into each flask 1.0 ml. of 18 N sulfuric acid (see precaution described previously), add sufficient distilled water to bring the volume of solution to 75 ml., and while rotating the flask, pipette into each flask (see precaution described previously) 15.0 ml. of Nessler reagent. Add distilled water to the mark and mix the solutions in each flask thoroughly. Using a visual colorimeter, compare the color intensity of each unknown solution with that of the standard solution which matches it more closely.

Ammonia.[7] Pipette 10.0-ml. aliquots of the urine and the urine recovery samples into separate 100-ml. volumetric flasks, add distilled water to the mark, and mix the liquids thoroughly. Transfer 2.0-g. portions of dry, activated Permutit[8] (treated with 0.3 N acetic acid, washed with water, and dried in air) to separate clean, dry 100-ml. volumetric flasks. Pipette 10.0 ml. of each diluted urine into one of the flasks in such a manner that it falls directly on the Permutit without coming in contact with the walls of the flask. Rotate the suspension gently but continuously for 5 min. Allow the suspension to settle for 1 min. Tie a piece of filter paper over the tip of a 2.00-ml. pipette and pipette 2.00 ml. of the supernatant liquid into a 250-ml. volumetric flask which has been rinsed with two 10-ml. portions of 0.1 M potassium iodide solution and finally with distilled water, to remove any traces of mercury compounds inhibitory to the action of urease. Preserve these solutions for the determination of urea.

Add 25 ml. of distilled water to each of the volumetric flasks containing the Permutit, rotate the flask gently for about 10 sec., allow the suspension to settle for 1 min., and decant as much supernatant liquid as possible without disturbing the Permutit. Repeat the described procedure using a second 25-ml. portion of distilled water. Add 10 ml. of 0.5 N sodium hydroxide (graduated pipette), rotate the flask for 20 sec., and add distilled water to bring the volume to about 75 ml.

Pipette into separate 100-ml. volumetric flasks 5.0 ml. and 10.0 ml. of a standard ammonium sulfate solution containing 0.080 mg. of nitrogen per milliliter. Add 10 ml. of 0.5 N sodium hydroxide to each flask (graduated pipette) and sufficient distilled water to bring the total volume to 75 ml. While rotating each flask (unknown and standard) in turn, add (graduated pipette, using described technique) 10.0 ml. of Nessler reagent. Immediately dilute the solution in each flask to the mark with distilled water, mix the solutions in each flask thoroughly, and allow the flasks to stand for 10 min. or longer. Compare the color intensities in a visual colorimeter, using the standard solution which matches the unknown more closely.

Urea.[9] Place one commercial urease tablet (containing phosphate buffer salts) on a sheet of smooth paper, crush the tablet, and transfer the powder to one of the 250-ml. volumetric flasks (prepared as described under Ammonia) containing 2.00 ml. of the supernatant liquid preserved for the determination of urea. Add a (powdered) urease tablet to the second 250-ml. flask (15 to 20 mg. of urease powder and 1 ml. of pH 6.8 phosphate buffer may be used instead), and heat both flasks for 5 min. at 45 to 50° in a water bath. Remove the flasks, add 200 ml. of distilled water, and mix the solutions thoroughly.

Pipette into separate 250-ml. volumetric flasks 5.0 ml. and 10.0 ml. of a standard ammonium sulfate solution containing 0.25 mg. of nitrogen per milliliter. Add 200 ml. of distilled water to each flask and mix the solutions in each flask thoroughly. Add (graduated pipette with described precautions) 15.0 ml. of Nessler reagent to each flask (while rotating the flask), immediately dilute the solution in each flask to the mark with distilled water, and mix the solutions in each flask thoroughly. Compare the color intensities, using a visual colorimeter and the standard solution which matches the unknown more closely.

Creatinine.[10] Pipette 1.00-ml. aliquots of the urine and the urine recovery samples into separate 100-ml. volumetric flasks. Pipette into separate 100-ml. volumetric flasks 1.00 ml. and 2.00 ml. of a standard creatinine solution containing 0.50 mg. of creatinine per milliliter. Pipette into each flask 20.0 ml. of a saturated solution of purified picric acid and 1.0 ml. of 3.0 N sodium hydroxide. Rotate each flask until the solutions are mixed and allow the flasks to stand for 10 min. Add distilled water to the mark, mix the solutions in each flask thoroughly, and compare the color intensities, using the standard solution which matches the unknown more closely.

Uric Acid.[11] Pipette 2.00-ml. aliquots of the urine and the urine recovery samples into separate 100-ml. volumetric flasks, add distilled water to the mark, and mix the solutions in each flask thoroughly. Pipette into separate 50-ml. volumetric flasks 5.00 ml. of each diluted (1:50) urine sample and 5.00 ml., 10.0 ml., and 15.0 ml. of a standard (freshly prepared) uric acid solution containing 0.0040 mg. of uric acid per milliliter. (*Caution:* The sodium cyanide solution and the uric acid reagent described below are *very* poisonous. These solutions should *never* be pipetted by mouth. Discard them directly into the drain, rinse the container thoroughly, and flush the drain with running water.) Transfer (graduate) into each of the flasks 10 ml. of a 12 per cent (freshly prepared) solution of sodium cyanide, 10 ml. of a 50 per cent solution of urea, and 8 ml. of uric acid reagent (phosphotungstic acid). Allow the flasks to stand for 20 min., add distilled water to the mark, mix the solutions in each flask thoroughly, and compare the color intensities of the solutions, using the standard which matches each unknown most closely.

NOTES

1. Other protein-precipitation tests include those of Roberts (nitric acid and magnesium sulfate), Exton and Osgood-Haskins (sulfosalicylic acid and sodium sulfate) and Purdy (acetic acid and sodium chloride). Relative quantities of albumin observed clinically are estimated as *trace* (visible ring or cloudiness), *small* (distinct granular cloud which settles to about one-tenth the height of the urine column and is equivalent to about 0.1 per cent albumin), *moderate* (dense cloud with marked flocculation indicating 0.2 to 0.3 per cent albumin), and *large* (heavy, curdy precipitate tending to solidify and indicative of more than 0.5 per cent albumin).

2. Other tests include (a) reduction of copper (Fehling and Haines), bismuth (Nylander), mercury, iron, and silver ions in alkaline solution, (b) formation of a crystalline osazone with phenylhydrazine (Kowarsky-Blumel), (c) optical rotation, and (d) fermentation with yeast. Reducing substances are recorded clinically as *absent* (no precipitate and original blue color unchanged), *reducing substances equivalent to 0.1 to 0.5 per cent glucose* (solution green or greenish opalescent), and *reducing substances equivalent to 1 to 2 per cent glucose* (orange-brown precipitate and blue supernatant fluid or heavy, bright-red precipitate with faintly blue supernatant liquid).

3. Acetone appears in the urine in diabetes, fevers, gastrointestinal disturbances, nervous disorders, eclampsia, pernicious vomiting of pregnancy, and after chloroform anesthesia. Other tests are those of Liebin (iodoform) and Rothera and Lange (nitroprusside). Acetone is formed from acetoacetic acid and β-hydroxybutyric acid, primary products of fatty-acid oxidation. Acetoacetic acid is detected by Gerhardt's (ferric chloride) and Lindemann's (iodine) tests and β-hydroxybutyric acid by the Black and Bart (oxidation to acetone by hydrogen peroxide) and Osterberg and Helmotz (1934) (sodium nitroprusside and ammonium hydroxide) tests.

4. The quantitative procedures described below are applied as required in clinical laboratories:

Acetone. Acetone is determined by iodometric titration (Behre and Benedict, 1926), gravimetric (Denigès, 1898a, 1898b) or iodometric (Van Slyke, 1917, 1929a) analysis of its slightly soluble basic mercuric sulfate complex, and colorimetric determination of its salicylaldehyde complex (Behre and Benedict, 1926; Behre, 1940; Sumner, 1921). About 20 mg. of total acetone bodies is excreted daily by the normal adult. In severe diabetes the daily excretion of acetoacetic acid and acetone may be as much as 6 g. and of β-hydroxybutyric acid 100 g.

Allantoin. Allantoin is determined by colorimetric analysis of the complex formed with Folin's ammoniacal copper and phosphomolybdate reagent (Larson, 1932; Young and Conway, 1942; Young, MacPherson, Wentworth, and Hawkins, 1944). Allantoin is the principal purine excreted by all mammals except man, the anthropoid ape, and the Dalmatian coach dog.

Amino Acids. Most of the amino acids have been determined in urine by microbiological assay (Dunn, Camien, Shankman, and Block, 1947; Eckhart, Cooper, Faloon, and Davidson, 1948; Frankl and Dunn, 1947; Woodson, Hier, Solomon, and Bergheim, 1948; Dunn, Akawie, Yeh, and Martin; 1950; Wheeler and György, 1948; Yeh, Frankl, Dunn, Parker, Hughes, and György, 1947; Frankl, Martin, and Dunn, 1947). Studies have been made of the renal clearance of essential amino acids and urinary excretion of methionine and other amino acids in liver disease and in cystinuria. The normal 24-hr. excretion varies from 1 mg. of apparent free aspartic acid to 190 mg. of apparent free histidine and from about 10 mg. of total (free plus combined) methionine to 350 mg. of total glutamic acid.

Total amino acids in urine have been determined by manometric measurement of the carbon dioxide formed from reaction with ninhydrin (Hamilton and Van Slyke, 1943; Van Slyke, Dillon, MacFadyen, and Hamilton, 1941; Van Slyke and Folch, 1940; Van Slyke, MacFadyen, and Hamilton, 1943), formol titration (Henriques and Sörensen, 1910; Northrop, 1926), colorimetric determination of the naphthoquinonesulfonic acid complex (Folin, 1922a, 1922b), and iodometric determination of copper in the filtrate separated from the precipitate formed with copper phosphate (Albanese and Irby, 1944). The daily excretion of alpha-amino nitrogen is 100 to 150 mg. or about 1 per cent of the total nitrogen. The excretion is increased in typhoid fever, acidosis, atrophy of the liver, and other wasting diseases.

Hippuric Acid. Hippuric acid is determined by extracting urine with ether, destroying urea in the extract with bromine and hypobromite, and estimating nitrogen in the residual material by Kjeldahl analysis (Griffith, 1926; Quick, 1926). Quick (1940) has employed hippuric acid excretion as a test of liver function and a measure of hepatic damage. The average daily excretion of hippuric acid normally is about 0.7 g. The excretion is increased after ingesting plums, prunes, cranberries, and other foods containing hippuric acid or its precursors.

Lactic Acid. Lactic acid is determined by oxidizing it to acetaldehyde, forming acetaldehyde bisulfite, and titrating the bound bisulfite iodometrically (Friedemann and Graeser, 1933). The normal daily excretion (about 10 mg.) of lactic acid is increased after exercise and in pneumonia, eclampsia, atrophy, and other pathological conditions where tissue oxidation is diminished.

Organic Acids. Urine, freed from carbonates and phosphates, is titrated to pH 2.7 (Van Slyke and Palmer, 1920). The normal 24-hr. excretion, equivalent to 400 to 750 ml. of 0.1 N acid, is increased markedly in diabetes.

Protein. Protein is determined by biuret (Hiller, Greif, and Beckman, 1948) or Kjeldahl (Folin and Denis, 1914) analysis of the precipitate formed with trichloroacetic acid or heat, by measuring the volume of the protein precipitated with Esbach's reagent (picric acid and citric acid) or with the reagent of Shevky and Stafford (1923) (alcoholic solution of phosphotungstic acid and hydrochloric acid), and by estimating the concentration of the suspension formed with sulfosalicylic acid (Kingsbury, Clark, Williams, and Post, 1926). Although albumin is not detectable, normal urine probably contains traces of this protein. Clinically, albumin values must be correlated with other diagnostic tests.

Purines. Uric acid and other purines are precipitated as their copper salts, uric acid is separated as its hydrochloride, and nitrogen in uric acid and remaining purines is determined by the Kjeldahl method (Hitchings and Fiske, 1941). The daily excretion of purines, normally 16 to 60 mg., is increased in leukemia.

Reducing Substances. Reducing substances are determined by oxidation with cupric ion and determination of excess cupric ion through formation of white cuprous thiocyanate (Benedict, 1911), iodometric analysis (Shaffer and Hartmann, 1921; Shaffer and Somogyi, 1933), and colorimetric analysis of the colored complex formed with dinitrosalicylic acid (Sumner, 1921, 1925) or phosphomolybdic acid (Folin and Berglund, 1922; Folin and Svedberg, 1926; Benedict, 1931). Other methods include oxidation with ferricyanide and iodometric determination of the excess of this reagent (Hagedorn and Jensen, 1923a, 1923b; Hanes, 1929), time required to decolorize a standard ferricyanide solution (Hawkins, 1929; Hawkins and Van Slyke, 1929; Hoffman, 1937), and colorimetric analysis of the picric acid complex (Benedict, 1918; Benedict and Osterberg, 1918; Lewis and Benedict, 1915).

Relatively high concentrations of reducing substances (mainly glucose) are found in pathological conditions (diabetes), especially following the administration of a standard dose (50 g.) of pure glucose. Concentrations may rise as high as 10 per cent in severe diabetes.

Titratable Acidity. The urine is titrated to pH 8.5 or 9.0 by Folin's (1903) method or to pH 7.4 by the procedure of Henderson and Palmer (1914). Although the titratable acidity varies widely, since it is dependent upon the diet, the average 24-hr. excretion is equivalent to about 350 ml. of 0.1 N acid.

Miscellaneous. Procedures are available for the quantitative determination of indican, phenols, urobilinogen, oxalic acid, sulfur, ethereal sulfates, inorganic sulfate, phosphate, chloride, fixed bases (sodium, potassium, calcium, and magnesium), iron, iodine, heavy metals (lead, mercury, arsenic, and zinc), inulin, citric acid, vitamin C, the B-complex vitamins, and numerous other constituents of normal and pathological urines.

5. The procedure to be used in this experiment is essentially that of Koch and McMeekin (1924). Nitrogen may be determined by other methods, including those described in Exps. 9 and 20. Urea contributes about 80 per cent of the daily nitrogen excretion, which averages 12 to 18 g. Relatively little nitrogen is excreted in the feces. Nitrogen equilibrium (nitrogen balance) is defined as the state of a normal adult in which the nitrogen of the ingested food and that excreted are approximately equal.

6. The reaction of Nessler reagent with ammonia may be represented as $NH_4OH + 2HgI_4^{--} + 3OH^- \rightarrow NHg_2I +$ $7I^- + 4H_2O$. The colored product, present in the colloidal state, is precipitated at higher concentrations of ammonia (0.1 N or greater). Chloride ion interferes with color formation.

7. The procedure to be employed is essentially that of Folin and Bell (1917). Ammonia may be determined by aerating it into boric acid and titrating the mixture with standard acid using bromcresol green indicator (Van Slyke and Cullen, 1914). The average daily output of ammonia is about 0.7 g., which is equivalent to 2.5 to 4.5 per cent of the total nitrogen. Ammonia excretion is increased in acidosis of starvation or diabetes and by the in-ingestion of acids or acid-forming foods. It is decreased in alkalosis and by the ingestion of alkali-forming foods. Amino acids and glutamine are probable precursors of ammonia.

8. Permutit is a synthetic aluminum silicate (zeolite) of the approximate composition $(2SiO_2 \cdot Al_2O_3 \cdot Na_2O \cdot 6H_2O)$. Ammonium ion is selectively adsorbed by ion exchange reaction on the Permutit displacing an equivalent amount of sodium (or hydrogen) ion. At pH 7 ammonium ion is adsorbed by Permutit in the presence of sodium ion and in alkaline solution ammonium ion is displaced by sodium ion. Permutit may be reactivated by treatment with acetic acid.

9. The procedure to be employed is essentially that of Folin and Youngberg (1919). Ammonia may be determined by aerating it into boric acid and back-titrating with standard sulfuric acid (Van Slyke and Cullen, 1914) or by allowing the ammonia to diffuse into standard acid in an adjoining compartment of the Conway micro-diffusion apparatus and determining the ammonia by titrating the solution or by colorimetry (Conway, 1933; Conway and Byrne, 1933). The average daily excretion of urea is 25 to 35 g., which is 80 to 90 per cent of the total nitrogen. Urea excretion is increased in fevers and is decreased in kidney and liver diseases.

10. The procedure to be employed is essentially that of Folin (1905, 1914). Creatinine may be determined by photometric analysis of its red-colored picrate (Greenwald, 1925, 1928; Greenwald and Gross, 1924; Bonsnes and Taussky, 1945; Peters, 1942) or 3,5-dinitrobenzoate (Benedict and Behre, 1936; Langley and Evans, 1936). The average excretion of creatinine is 1.0 to 1.8 g. daily, although considerably higher values have been reported (Hobson, 1939). Except for dietary fluctuations of creatinine intake, the daily creatinine excretion is nearly constant for a given individual. Most of the body creatinine is found in muscle tissues. Creatinine appears to be a waste product not utilized by the body. Creatinine excretion is increased in fevers and decreased in muscular disorders.

11. The procedure to be employed is essentially that of Folin (1933, 1934). Uric acid may be determined by photometric analysis of the colored complex formed with arsenophosphotungstic acid and sodium cyanide (Benedict and Franke, 1922; Buchanan, Block, and Christman, 1945; Christman and Ravwitch, 1932), phosphotungstic acid and alkali (Benedict, 1915; Benedict and Hitchcock, 1915; Folin and Denis, 1913a, 1913b; Folin and Wu, 1919), or 2,6-dichloroquinone chloroimide (Fearon, 1944). Other methods include precipitation of ammonium urate and titration of the latter with standard permanganate solution (Folin and Shaffer; quoted by Mathews, 1925).

APPENDIX

APPARATUS

General (available at all times in the laboratory)
        Aspirators, water, each with trap
        Balances, quantitative, sensitivity, 0.1 mg.
        Balances, triple-beam, capacity, 610 g., extra kilogram weight
        Centrifuge, clinical
        Centrifuge, International
        Cork borers
        Cork-borer sharpener
        Cork press
        Corks
        Dryer, air, gas-heated
        Files, triangular, 5-in.
        Grease, stopcock
        Hood, fume
        Icebox and ice
        Labels
        Oven, electric with thermoregulator, 35 to 180°C.
        Paper, roll, 6-in. diameter
        Refrigerator, electric, +5°C.
        Stoppers, rubber
        Tubing, soft-glass
        Water, distilled
        Water, tap

Individual (in each student's locker)
        Beakers, 50-ml., 100-ml., 600-ml., 1,000-ml., 1,500-ml., 2,000-ml.
        Bottles, sample, 2-oz., widemouthed (6)
        Bottles, weighing (3)
        Brush, test-tube
        Burette, 50-ml.
        Burner, Tirrill, 30 in. of rubber tubing and wing top
        Clamp holders (4)
        Clamps, extension, equipped with rubber fittings (2)
        Clamps, screw (2)
        Clamps, universal or Fisher Castaloy with three-pronged grip (2)
        Condenser, Liebig, 3-ft. with two 30-in. pieces of rubber tubing
        Dish, evaporating, 100-mm. diameter
        Filter paper, 7-cm. diameter
        Flasks, conical, 50-ml., 125-ml., 250-ml., 500-ml.
        Flask, filter, 500-ml.
        Flask, Florence, 1,000-ml.
        Flask, round-bottomed, 2,000-ml.
        Flask support, cork or wood
        Flasks, volumetric, glass-stoppered, 50-ml., 100-ml., 250-ml.
        Funnel, Buchner, 71-mm. inside diameter
        Funnel, glass (60 deg.), 50-mm. top diameter
        Graduate, 10-ml. cylinder

Lock, combination
Matches, box
Medicine dropper
Pan, enamel, 2-qt.
Pipettes, volumetric, 1-ml., 5-ml., 10-ml., 25-ml.
Plate, spot
Policeman, rubber (2)
Rings, iron extension, 3- and 5-in. diameters
Rods, stirring (2)
Rubber tubing, pressure, 3 ft.
Spatula, metal
Sponge
Test tubes, soft-glass, 6-in. (6)
Test-tube holder
Test-tube rack
Thermometer, 110°C.
Towel
Tripod, iron, 6-in. outside diameter
Tweezers, metal
Watch glass, 125-mm. diameter
Wire gauze, galvanized-iron, 16-mesh, 6-in. square (2)

Special (issued by the storekeeper or instructor). More than one piece is required in some experiments.

Apparatus	Experiment number
Aeration assembly	21,36
Amino nitrogen, Van Slyke macro volumetric	10
Asbestos board with hole for 3-in. test tube	21,28
Atomizer, all glass with rubber bulb (DeVilbiss No. 31)	37
Autoclave, steam-heated	39,40
Balance, horn-pan	21,26
Balance, platform, with weights, 2-kg. capacity	41
Balance, Roller-Smith torsion	40
Balloon, rubber	9
Barometer	10
Bath, hydrogenated-cottonseed-oil	4,14
Bath, sand	12,15,30,32
Bell jar	43
Board, with nails	43
Bottle, amber, screw-capped, narrow-mouthed, 2.5-liter	46
Bottle, amber, screw-capped, widemouthed, 2.5-liter	41
Brooder, electric with thermostat	41
Bucket, enamel, 5-gal.	41
Burette, 10-ml.	24,29,38
Cabinet, lightproof, equipped with 4 trays, sand, air vents, and drain, 32 by 47 by 58 in.	19
Centrifuge bottle, 200-ml.	22
Centrifuge tube, 15-ml.	43
Centrifuge tube, 50-ml.	14,21,36,39,44
Cheesecloth	16,19,28,31,32
Chromatographic container. Glass jar, 4 3/4 by 9 7/8 by 14 in., with wood cover (5 by 10 in.) containing 8 slits, 4 evenly spaced per side. Slits and cover are sealed with scotch tape after paper strips are inserted in slits	37

Apparatus	*Experiment number*
Clock, time	34
Colorimeter, photoelectric, Lumetron, Model 400A, Klett-Summerson, or other	35,43,45
Colorimeter, visual, Duboscq	13,14,18,23,35, 43,46
Condenser, Hopkins	21,25,35
Condenser, Liebig, 10-in.	14,29
Crucible, porcelain, No. 2	41
Cylinder, graduated, glass-stoppered, 10-ml.	43
Desiccator with cover and crucible plate, 100-mm. inside diameter	41
Distillation apparatus (see Techniques, Appendix)	2,4,8,12,16,19, 30,31,32,44
Distillation apparatus (see Techniques, Appendix)	27
Drying tube, 3-in.	8
Filter flask (see Flask, filter)	
Filter paper, 15-cm. diameter	31,32,41
Filter-paper strips, 2 1/4 by 12 in.	37
Flask, conical, 1-liter	30
Flask, conical, 2-liter	30,32
Flask, distilling, 500-ml.	20
Flask, filter, 125-ml.	21
Flask, filter, 500-ml.	9
Flask, Florence, 1.5-liter	21
Flask, glass-stoppered, 250-ml.	26
Flask, Kjeldahl, 800-ml.	9
Flask, pyrex round-bottomed, 200-ml.	3,44
Flask, pyrex round-bottomed, 500-ml.	2
Flask, pyrex round-bottomed, 1-liter	8,12,19
Flask, pyrex three-necked, 1-liter	8
Flask, volumetric, 25-ml.	10,13,35
Flask, volumetric, 100-ml.	11,18,40,46
Flask, volumetric, 500-ml.	13,14,35
Flask, volumetric, 1,000-ml.	29,40
Funnel, Buchner, 151-mm. inside diameter at plate	32
Funnel, glass (60 deg.), 150-mm. top diameter	31,32
Funnel, glass (60 deg.), 300-mm. top diameter	16
Funnel, Hirsch, 15-mm. diameter of perforated plate	19,21,36,40
Furnace, electric muffle, 1000°C.	41
Graduate, 250-ml. cylinder	20
Graduate, 2-liter cylinder	46
Grinder, food	27,28,30
Hammer	4
Incubator, 25 to 70°C.	36,39,40
Inoculating needle with holder (resistance wire, 3 in., B. & S. gauge No. 26)	39,40
Kjeldahl digestion apparatus (macro)	9
Kjeldahl distillation apparatus (macro)	9
Knife	41
Lamp, ultraviolet (Mineralite), 254 mμ peak emission	37
Mantle, electric (for heating Soxhlet extraction apparatus)	41
Melting-point apparatus with Dow-Corning silicon fluid No. 702	21,27,36
Microscope, compound	36
Mortar with pestle, 100-mm. outside diameter	36,39

Apparatus	*Experiment number*
Pencil, wax	28
pH meter, Beckman (Model M equipped with 4990-42 glass electrode), or other make	20,22,40
Pipette, graduated, 1-ml.	40,43,45
Pipette, graduated, 10-ml.	39,40,43
Pipette, graduated, 25-ml.	46
Pipette, heavy-walled capillary, 2-mm. inside diameter	37
Pipette, volumetric, 2-ml.	18,35,46
Pipette, volumetric, 50-ml.	9,35,40
Pipetting machine, Brewer automatic (Baltimore Biological Company), or other make	39
Plate, pie, heat-resistant-glass, 12-in. diameter	27
Polarimeter, sensitivity 0.05 deg.	17,30,31,32, 33,34
Rods, stirring	45
Saccharometer, Einhorn	36
Scissors	43
Shaker, Kahn	45
Sieve, 20-mesh	32
Sieve, 10-mesh	41
Slide, glass	36
Soxhlet extractor	41
Stirrer, Hershberg	8
Stirrer, motor	7
Test tubes, pyrex, 8-in.	23
Test tube, soft-glass, 3-in.	28,36
Test tubes, soft-glass, 4-in.	36,37,39,40
Test tubes, soft-glass, 8-in.	36
Test-tube rack to hold 4-in. test tubes	39
Thermometer, 360°C.	4,14,15,21,27, 36
Tubing, glass, capillary	37
Waring Blendor	19,33
Weights, calibrated quantitative, 1 mg. to 50 g.	1,9,11,13,14,17, 18,20,23,24, 25,26,34,39, 40,41

EXPERIMENTS

The student's experimental data should be recorded immediately, legibly, and completely in a tightly bound notebook to be submitted at intervals for grading. The final data are to be submitted on the data sheets or cards, except in certain experiments where special reports are required.

It is assumed that the student is familiar with the principles of organic and quantitative chemistry and that he has had adequate training in laboratory techniques. In most of the quantitative experiments the highest degree of precision and accuracy is not attainable, owing to uncontrollable variables inherent in the determination of biological substances. On the other hand, precision and accuracy within about 1 per cent are usually possible and often realized by the best qualified students. It has been found desirable, therefore, to furnish quantitative balances of ± 0.1 mg. sensitivity, calibrated weights, and high-grade (Exax) but uncalibrated volumetric apparatus. In most of the experiments the quantities of substances have been selected so that weighings need be made only to ± 1 mg.

Instructions to Students
Construct a wash bottle during first laboratory period.

Work carefully with a minimum of noise and confusion.

Keep flames away from inflammable chemicals.

Follow directions closely to avoid explosions or other accidents.

Conserve chemicals.

Keep your desk clean.

Handle special (expensive) apparatus carefully.

Store all unused equipment (cleaned and set to drain) in the locker.

Label and cover all containers placed in the refrigerator, incubator, oven, and other special places.

Do not store solutions in volumetric flasks.

Do not autoclave volumetric apparatus (except graduated pipettes).

Record experimental data completely and neatly in a tightly bound notebook.

Study the directions for each experiment before the assigned laboratory period.

Study the explanatory material given in the manual.

Submit reports of preparations on 3- by 5-in. cards according to instructions given by the instructor. Special reports are to be made on Exp. 21, 36, and 37. The report on each of the other experiments is to be made using only the data-sheet form provided (or a verbatim copy).

Preparations are to be submitted in sample bottles each labeled with the student's name and the date, the tare (weight, empty) of the bottle, and the name and yield of the product.

Suggestions to Instructor.
Double or larger quantities of chemicals and solutions specified under Reagents are used by students in most of the experiments. It has been found advantageous in determining the purity of students' preparations to issue three preparations to each student. By this means the analytical skill of the student, as well as the purity of the preparations, may be evaluated with reasonable reliability. In grading the students' results, the authors' practice has been to assign 10 per cent to yield, 40 per cent to purity, and 50 per cent to analytical skill.

Students' laboratory observations and calculations, recorded in bound notebooks, are graded on the basis of completeness, neatness, and accuracy. Students' reports are limited in most experiments to the data and calculations recorded on the data sheets provided. The results of students' preparations are submitted on cards of uniform (3- by 5-in.) size. Special reports are submitted on the procedures followed and the results obtained in Exps. 21 (identification of amino acids), 36 (identification of carbohydrates), and 37 (separation and identification of purines and pyrimidines).

Specific suggestions are given below on each of the experiments:

1. Organic acids suitable for use are (molecular weights given in parentheses) citric acid [(COOH)$_3$(CH$_2$)$_2$COH (192)], oxalic acid [(COOH)$_2$·2H$_2$O (126)], potassium acid oxalate [KHC$_2$O$_4$·½H$_2$O (137)], potassium acid o-phthalate [C$_6$H$_4$COOKCOOH (205)], potassium acid sulfate [KHSO$_4$ (136)], potassium tetroxalate [KH$_3$(C$_2$O$_4$)$_2$·2H$_2$O (254)], sodium acid oxalate [NaHC$_2$O$_4$·H$_2$O (130)], succinic acid [(COOH)$_2$(CH$_2$)$_2$ (118)], and tartaric acid [(COOH)$_2$(CHOH)$_2$ (150)].

It has been desirable to issue C.P. organic acids which have been analyzed by the instructor. The students' results are rated satisfactory if they fall within ±0.5 per cent of the instructor's value. Usually results of this quality are obtained by about 10 per cent of the class. Values within ±1.5 per cent have been reported by about 75 per cent of the students.

2. The students' yields of recrystallized glycine have averaged 70 (50 to 80) per cent of the theoretical amount based on chloroacetic acid.

3. The students' yields of recrystallized glycine methyl ester hydrochloride have averaged 60 (35 to 80) per cent of the theoretical amount based on glycine. The purity (Volhard analysis) of students' individual preparations have ranged from 97.0 to 104.0 per cent and the average purity of preparations by different classes from 99.0 to 101.2 per cent.

4. The students' yields of recrystallized glycine anhydride have averaged 25 (10 to 45) per cent of the theoretical amount based on glycine.

5. The students' yields of recrystallized glycylglycine hydrochloride monohydrate have averaged 50 (15 to 80) per cent of the theoretical amount based on glycine anhydride. The purity (Kjeldahl and Volhard analyses) of individual students' preparations has ranged from 81 to 102 per cent and the average purity of preparations by different classes from 95.0 to 99.2 per cent (Kjeldahl) and 99.2 to 100.1 per cent (Volhard).

6. The students' yields of glyclyglycine have averaged 70 (30 to 95) per cent of the theoretical amount based on glycylglycine hydrochloride monhydrate. The purity (Kjeldahl analysis) of individual students' preparations has ranged from 91 to 102 per cent and the average purity of preparations by different classes from 93 to 101 per cent.

7. The students' yields of hippuric acid have averaged 85 (88 to 100) per cent of the theoretical amount based on glycine.

8. The students' yields of 4-benzylidine-2-phenyl-5-oxazolone have averaged 85 (80 to 90) per cent of the theoretical amount based on hippuric acid. The yields of DL-phenylalanine have averaged 50 (38 to 60) per cent based on 4-benzylidine-2-phenyl-5-oxazolone. The purity of students' DL-phenylalanine preparations has ranged from 94 to 101 per cent (Kjeldahl analysis).

9. Amino Acid Manufactures' A.P. grade of amino acids has been found satisfactory. The percentage deviations (average and range given in the parentheses) from the theoretical nitrogen reported by students are alanine (1.2, 0.4 to 2.2), α-amino-n-butyric acid (2.0, 1.5 to 3.0), aspartic acid (1.9, 0.2 to 2.8), glutamic acid (2.9, 0.5 to 5.6), glycine (2.0, 0.1 to 3.5), leucine (1.6, 0.6 to 2.1), norleucine (1.0, 0.1 to 2.8), norvaline (1.4, 1.0 to 1.8), phenylalanine (1.5, 0.7 to 2.4), serine (2.6, 1.2 to 3.0), and tyrosine (1.1, 0.1 to 2.5). Students' preparations of glycine, glycine methyl ester hydrochloride, glycylglycine hydrochloride monohydrate, glycylglycine, phenylalanine, tyrosine, and cystine have been analyzed by the Kjeldahl method.

10. Amino Acid Manufactures' A.P. grade of amino acids has been found satisfactory. The percentage deviations (average and range given in the parentheses) from the theoretical amino nitrogen reported by students are alanine (1.6, 0.1 to 6.4), α-amino-n-butyric acid (1.6, 0.3 to 3.0), aspartic acid (4.0, 0.2 to 9.5), glutamic acid (2.2, 0.2 to 8.5), isoleucine (1.7, 0.1 to 12), leucine (1.1, 0.0 to 13), methionine (2.7, 0.0 to 9), norleucine (1.4, 0.2 to 12), norvaline (3.0, 1.5 to 4.2), phenylalanine (1.1, 0.4 to 15), tryptophan (2.7, 0.9 to 6.9), tyrosine (2.4, 0.9 to 9), and valine (2.5, 0.1 to 11).

11. Glycylglycine hydrochloride monohydrate, glycine methyl ester hydrochloride, tyramine hydrochloride, and sodium chloride have been issued as unknowns.

12. The students' yields of recrystallized L-tyrosine have averaged 5.5 (2.7 to 9.5) per cent of silk and 1.6 (0.5 to 3.0) per cent of commercial casein. The average purity of preparations by different classes ranged from 97.5 to 102 per cent, according to students' Kjeldahl analyses, and from 88 to 100.2 per cent, by students' photometric analyses.

13. The students' preparations of L-tyrosine have been analyzed.

14. The percentages of L-tyrosine found in commercial casein (uncorrected for moisture or ash) have averaged 6.1 (5.3 to 6.8) per cent and the recoveries of added pure tyrosine have averaged 110 (98 to 119) per cent.

15. The students' yields of recrystallized tyramine hydrochloride have averaged 20 (5 to 45) per cent of the theoretical amount based on L-tyrosine.

16. The students' yields of recrystallized L-cystine have averaged 4.7 (2.0 to 7.0) per cent of purified human (male) hair. The purity of preparations by different classes has averaged 98 (85 to 102) per cent by Kjeldahl analysis, 100.5 (99 to 104) per cent by photometric analysis, and 95 (82 to 100.5) per cent by polarimetric analysis.

17. Students' preparations of L-cystine have been analyzed. The percentage deviations from the accepted specific rotation of pure L-cystine issued as unknowns have averaged 2.1 (0.0 to 5.1) per cent.

18. Students' preparations of L-cystine have been analyzed.

19. The students' yields of recrystallized asparagine monohydrate have averaged 7.6 (2.6 to 11.7) per cent of *Lupinus albus* seeds and 1.2 (0.2 to 2.4) per cent of *Lupinus angustifolius* seeds. The purity (amide-nitrogen analysis) of individual students' preparations has ranged from 72 to 129 per cent and the average purity of preparations by different classes from 102 to 106 per cent.

20. Students' preparations of asparagine monohydrate have been analyzed. The purity of pure asparagine monohydrate issued as unknowns has averaged 98 (63 to 148) per cent. Recoveries of pure asparagine monohydrate added (50 to 85 mg., added as 5.0 to 8.5 ml. of a solution containing 10 mg. per ml.) to students' solutions containing about the same amount of asparagine have averaged 115 (69 to 150) per cent.

21. Amino acids (L and DL forms) which have been issued as unknowns (two to five amino acids) include alanine, arginine monohydrochloride, aspartic acid, cystine, glutamic acid, glycine, histidine monohydrochloride monohydrate, hydroxyproline, isoleucine, lysine monohydrochloride, methionine, phenylalanine, proline, serine, threonine, tryptophan, tyrosine, and valine (or leucine). The last two amino acids are indistinguishable by available methods.

Of the amino acids issued, 78 per cent were identified, 22 per cent were present but not reported, and 23 per cent were reported although not present. All the amino acids in 26 per cent of the 200 mixtures issued were identified. The accuracy of the reports increased as the number of amino acids in the unknowns decreased from five to two. The number of amino acids identified increased if the number of amino acids present was made known to the student. Each unknown consisted of a homogeneous mixture containing 0.4 g. of each component amino acid (0.2 g. each of tyrosine and cystine).

22. The students' yields of purified casein have averaged 2.8 (0.4 to 4.0) g. per 100 ml. of skim milk. The phosphorus content of purified casein (photometric analysis) has averaged 0.70 (0.53 to 0.83) per cent.

23. Phosphorus has been determined in students' purified casein preparations. The recoveries of phosphorus added (0.08 to 0.13 mg. of phosphorus added as 3 to 5 ml. of a solution containing 0.025 mg. of phosphorus or 0.11 mg. of KH_2PO_4 per milliliter) to students' solutions estimated to contain about the same amount of phosphorus have averaged 99.6 (79 to 111) per cent. It has been found that (prior to the supplementary oxidation with $HClO_4$) as many as five treatments with the H_2SO_4-HNO_3 digestion mixture were required to effect complete digestion of some samples of casein. Under these conditions the phosphorus content of casein averaged 0.72 (0.50 to 0.92) per cent and the recoveries averaged 100 (75 to 139) per cent.

24. Four stock oils (linseed, peanut, castor, and mustard) have been issued to successive classes. Little oxidation occurred when these oils were stored in the dark in tightly stoppered bottles. The acid numbers have averaged 1.88 (1.78 to 1.98), 2.30 (2.07 to 2.45), 3.65 (3.39 to 4.18), and 2.52 (2.07 to 2.77), respectively, for these oils.

25. The saponification numbers of the oils listed above under Exp. 24 have averaged 221 (211 to 230) for linseed, 206 (190 to 212) for peanut, 183 (176 to 192) for castor, and 199 (185 to 221) for musta

26. The iodine numbers of the oils listed above under Exp. 24 have averaged 179 (167 to 187) for linseed, 93.0 (86.5 to 95.6) for peanut, 91.6 (84.4 to 97.9) for castor, and 114 (104 to 116) for mustard. The decline in iodine numbers after 10 years' storage was no change for linseed, 95.0 to 91.3 for pea-

nut, 97.6 to 87.1 for castor, and 115.5 to 112.5 for mustard. Satisfactory unknowns have been prepared from combinations of any two of these oils.

27. The students' yields of recrystallized cholesterol have averaged 4.9 (1.0 to 8.7 per cent of dry spinal cords and 2.8 (0.8 to 4.6) per cent of moist spinal cords. The melting points of students' preparations have averaged 144° (139 to 148.5°), corrected.

28. The students' yields of purified starch have averaged 12 (6 to 18) per cent of moist potatoes.

29. Unknowns containing starch and protein (purified gelatin) have been issued. Recoveries of glucose added to purified starch have ranged from 98.1 to 103 per cent when experimentally determined starch factors varying from 0.96 to 1.06 were employed.

30. The students' yields of recrystallized D-xylose have averaged 5 (0 to 11) per cent of air-dried corncobs.

31. The students' yields of recrystallized L-arabinose have averaged 11 (0.5 to 20) per cent of commercial mesquite gum. Yields of the crude carbohydrate have averaged 21 (3 to 36) per cent.

32. The students' yields of crude D-mannose have averaged 12 (0.3 to 23) per cent of the ivory-nut meal.

33. The students' yields of recrystallized D-lactose have averaged 9.7 (0.8 to 28) per cent of whey powder. The purity (polarimetric analysis) of these products has averaged 94.5 (88 to 98) per cent.

34. Students' preparations of D-lactose have been analyzed.

35. The percentages of reducing substances (calculated as glucose) found in colorless corn sirup have averaged 31 (23 to 40) per cent before hydrolysis and 73 (48 to 85) per cent after hydrolysis, as determined photometrically with a visual colorimeter. The percentages averaged 31.5 (24 to 40) per cent before hydrolysis and 74 (59 to 116) after hydrolysis, as determined photometrically with a photo-electric colorimeter. Recoveries of glucose added to corn sirup have averaged 105 (71 to 137) per cent by visual photometric analysis of unhydrolyzed corn sirup and 96 (56 to 147) per cent by analysis of hydrolyzed corn sirup. Recoveries have averaged 96 (82 to 127) per cent by photoelectric photometric analysis of unhydrolyzed corn sirup and 95 (57 to 116) per cent by analysis of hydrolyzed corn sirup. The quantities of pure glucose added to students' solutions estimated to contain about the same amount of glucose were 8 to 16 mg. (8 to 16 ml. of a solution containing 1.0 mg. of glucose per milliliter) for unhydrolyzed sirup and 1.5 to 3.8 mg. (10 to 25 ml. of a solution containing 0.15 mg. of glucose per milliliter) for hydrolyzed sirup. On this basis the quantities of glucose added per 2-ml. aliquot (see data sheet) were 0.064 to 0.128 mg. and 0.060 to 0.15 mg., respectively.

36. Carbohydrates which have been issued in unknown mixtures (two to four carbohydrates) include starch, glycogen, dextrin, inulin, raffinose, lactose, maltose, fructose, galactose, glucose, mannose, rhamnose, arabinose, and xylose. Of the carbohydrates issued, 74 per cent were identified, 26 per cent were present but not reported, and 35 per cent were reported although not present. All the carbohydrates in 32 per cent of the 220 unknown mixtures issued were identified. The accuracy of the reports increased as the number of carbohydrates per mixture decreased from four to two and in cases where a preliminary test was made of an unknown consisting of only one carbohydrate. The number of carbohydrates identified increased if the number of carbohydrates present was made known to the student. Each sample consisted of a homogeneous mixture prepared from 1 g. of each component (0.5 g. of starch, dextrin, or glycogen). Glucose was omitted in mixtures containing other reducing saccharides except rhamnose and fructose.

Whole (not soluble) starch should be used. Most commercial preparations of dextrin have been found unsatisfactory because of contaminating reducing substances (probably maltose). Dextrins may be purified by precipitating them from a 0.5 per cent aqueous solution with sufficient ethanol to give a 70 per cent solution. Most commercial glycogens are unsatisfactory, since they give little or no color with iodine. Glycogen prepared from clam muscle or rabbit liver has been found satisfactory. Inulin prepared from dahlia bulbs has been found more satisfactory than the commcerical preparations tested.

37. Unknown mixtures are prepared by mixing 10 mg. of each purine or pyrimidine with sufficient ribonucleic acid to give a total weight of 100 mg. Unknowns (one to three components) have been issued containing adenine sulfate dihydrate, caffeine, guanine hydrochloride dihydrate, hypoxanthine, theobromine, theophylline, xanthine, cytosine, 5-methylcytosine, thymine, and uracil. Of the substances issued (40 unknowns) 93 per cent were identified, 7 per cent were present but not reported, and 10 per cent were reported, although not present. All the components in 30 unknown mixtures were identified.

38. Students have reported canned grapefruit juice to contain from 36 (27 to 43) to 45 (35 to 48) mg. of ascorbic acid per 100 ml. Recoveries of ascorbic acid added to grapefruit juice have averaged 97 (80 to 115) per cent. The quantities of ascorbic acid added to students' solutions estimated to contain about the same amount of ascorbic acid were 15 to 30 mg. (15 to 30 ml. of a solution containing 1 mg. of ascorbic acid per milliliter). On this basis the quantities of added ascorbic acid per 25-ml. aliquot (see data sheet) were 1.5 to 3.0 mg.

The ascorbic acid (U.S.P.) utilized in recovery experiments has been found to be 97 to 98 per cent pure when titrated with standard KIO_3 solution. Ascorbic acid solutions should be protected from atmospheric oxidation immediately after preparation by adding 8-hydroxyquinoline sulfate (10 mg. per 100 ml.) and by storing the solution in a nearly filled, tightly stoppered container. Under these conditions the reducing power of the ascorbic acid decreases nearly linearly at the rate of 0.1 per cent per hr. up to 48 hr. and probably longer. Correction factors, if established accurately, may be used satisfactorily, although the correction is negligible provided the solution is used within an hour or two after preparation.

39. Students have reported that commercial tablets (stated to contain 100 mg. of nicotinic acid per tablet) contained 104 (82 to 130) mg. of nicotinic acid per tablet. The volumes of standard (0.03 N) base required to titrate the acid formed per tube have ranged from 0.8 to 4.0 ml. (standard solutions) at 0 μg of nicotinic acid and from 8.0 to 11.0 at 0.15 μg of nicotinic acid. Recoveries of nicotinic acid added to students' solutions estimated to contain about the same amount of nicotinic acid have averaged 93 (44 to 131) per cent. The quantities of nicotinic acid added to students' solutions were 1.0 to 2.0 μg (10 to 20 ml. of a solution containing 0.1 μg of nicotinic acid per milliliter). Natural products to be analyzed for nicotinic acid should be autoclaved to ensure complete liberation of the active vitamin. A dry ball-mill mixture may be used in place of the amino acids, vitamins, AGU solution, and salts solution. In preparing this mixture, transfer the indicated quantities of components to a dry, sealed ball-mill jar, rotate the mill overnight, and store the mixture in a tightly stoppered amber bottle. The quantities of substances to be used are L-cysteine hydrochloride, 5 g.; DL-tryptophan, 2 g.; thiamine chloride, 20 mg.; calcium d-pantothenate, 20 mg.; pyridoxine hydrochloride, 40 mg.; riboflavin, 40 mg.; p-aminobenzoic acid, 2 mg.; biotin, 0.1 mg.; adenine sulfate dihydrate, 200 mg.; guanine hydrochloride dihydrate, 200 mg.; uracil, 200 mg.; K_2HPO_4, 10 g.; KH_2PO_4, 10 g.; $MgSO_4$ (anhydrous), 2.2 g.; $FeSO_4 \cdot 7H_2O$, 0.2 g.; and $MnSO_4 \cdot 4H_2O$ 0.15 g. To prepare 50 ml. of the basal medium, mix 0.44 g. of the ball-mill mixture, 0.3 g. of $(NH_4)_2SO_4$, and the indicated (see Exp. 39) quantities of casein hydrolysate, glucose, and sodium acetate.

40. Students have reported that boiled egg yolk contained 1.25 (1.10 to 1.56) mg. per cent of choline. The milligrams of mycelium obtained at different levels of choline (standard) ranged from 2.5 to 2.8 mg. at 0.6 μg of choline and from 23 to 28 mg. at 6.0 μg of choline per tube. Recoveries of choline added to students' solutions estimated to contain about the same amount of choline have averaged 108 (87 to 128) per cent. The quantities of choline added to students' solutions were 0.15 to 1.5 μg (10 to 25 ml. of solutions containing 0.015 or 0.060 μg of choline per milliliter. These amounts are equivalent to 0.17 and 0.068 μg of choline chloride).

41. The students are divided conveniently into groups of two, each group caring for 8 to 15 chicks. The right tibiae should be utilized by one student and the left tibiae by the other student of each group. It is desirable that the chicks be obtained from eggs of hens maintained on a diet relatively low in vitamin D. The feed (Exp. 41, Note 1) for each group of chicks is to be prepared separately by each group of students, and it should be stored in 5-gal. widemouthed metal containers which are kept tightly closed when not in use. The food components may be obtained readily from grain milling companies, feed supply stores, and chemical supply houses. U.S.P. standard vitamin D oil for use in chick (not rat) assays is obtainable from the U. S. Reference Standards, 4738 Kingsessing Ave., Philadelphia 43, Pennsylvania.

Relatively smooth response curves are obtained over the range of 0 to 15 units (A.O.A.C.) per 100 g. of feed, although the most useful range is 5 to 15 units. Students have reported per cent ash ranging from 34 (0 units of vitamin D) to 46 (15 units of vitamin D) per cent for tibiae and 8.5 (8 units of vitamin D) to 10.7 (16 units of vitamin D) per cent for toes.

Day-old starved chicks average about 40 g. in weight. The average weight on the twenty-second day is about 180 g. for chicks with adequate vitamin D and about 140 g. for chicks on vitamin D–deficient diets. Both groups consume about the same quantity of food.

At the start of the ashing procedure place the covered crucible at the front of the muffle furnace (800°C.). After 15 min. remove the cover, move the crucible to the rear of the furnace, and continue heating for 60 min. with the furnace door slightly open.

Chick assay values of commercial vitamin D oils usually are at least 50 per cent below the stated potencies because chicks do not respond to vitamin D_2, which, in addition to D_3, is present in the sample.

42. Students have reported 515 (155 to 1,110) units for the activity of salivary amylase. Absolute errors found for the unknown starch solutions have averaged 5 (0 to 21) per cent.

43. The quantities of phosphorus added to recovery solutions estimated to contain about the same amount of phosphorus (as phosphate) were 0.02 to 0.04 mg. of phosphorus (0.088 to 0.176 mg. of KH_2PO_4) dissolved in 0.3 ml. of solution.

44. The students' yields of acetylphenylalanine have averaged 84 (70 to 95) per cent, acetylphenyl-alanine p-toluidide 90 per cent, and L-phenylalanine ($[\alpha]_D^{25} = +35$ to $+36$ deg.) 30 per cent of the theoretical amounts.

45. Cholesterol recoveries (largely previous determinations by Bloor's method) have averaged 53 (27 to 85) per cent. Values for rat serum cholesterol have averaged 60 to 110 mg. per 100 ml.

46. Of the qualitative unknowns issued, 92 per cent were identified, 7 per cent were present but not reported, and 14 per cent were reported although not present. In preparing the recovery solutions for the qualitative tests, bovine plasma albumin (Armour's) or egg albumin scales (5 ml. of a 2.5 per cent solution), glucose (0.5 to 2.0 ml. at the low level and 5.0 to 10.0 ml. at the high level of a 10 per cent solution), and acetone (0.5 ml.) were added to urine aliquots.

Nitrogen values reported for 24-hr. urine samples from low- and high-protein diets are distributed generally according to the data shown in the table accompanying Exp. 46. Recoveries of substances added to students' urines have averaged 98 (93 to 105) per cent for total nitrogen, 99 (77 to 120) per cent for urea nitrogen, 84 (63 to 108) per cent for ammonia nitrogen, 115 (70 to 154) per cent for creatinine nitrogen, and 102 (56 to 133) per cent for uric acid nitrogen. The quantities of substances added, estimated to be about the same as those in the urine aliquot, were 200 to 600 mg. of ammonium sulfate [2 to 6 ml. of a solution containing 10.6 mg. of $(NH_4)_2SO_4$ per milliliter], 10 to 30 mg. of creatinine (2 to 6 ml. of a solution containing 5 mg. of creatinine per milliliter), and 4 to 12 mg. of uric acid (4 to 12 ml. of a solution containing 1 mg. of uric acid per milliliter).

Consult Tables of Food Composition, Bureau of Human Nutrition and Home Economics, U. S. Department of Agriculture, Miscellaneous Publication No. 572, December, 1949, for the percentages of proteins in a large variety of foods.

FIRST AID

Burns, Acid or Base. Flood face, eyes, or other parts with running water from the tap. Neutralize acid burns with saturated sodium bicarbonate solution, base burns with saturated boric acid solution, and oxidizing agents with sodium thiosulfate solution.

Burns, Fire. Apply analgesic, antiseptic ointment and bandage with sterile gauze.

Fire, Chemicals. Smother with sand, carbon dioxide gas from pressure cylinder, or with both materials. Use water from fire hose or other source, except for burning oil.

Fire, Clothes. Extinguish with water (shower, if available), wrap in fire blanket, or use both methods.

Call Instructor Immediately.

Supplies and Equipment Available in Laboratory

Adhesive tape
Antiseptic solution
Blanket, fire
Boric acid, saturated (5 per cent) solution
Cotton, sterile
Eyecups
Fire extinguishers, carbon dioxide under pressure
Fire hose
Gas masks
Gauze, sterile
Ointment, analgesic antiseptic
Sand
Shower
Sodium bicarbonate, saturated (10 per cent) solution
Sodium thiosulfate solution (250 g. of $Na_2S_2O_3 \cdot 5H_2O$ and 100 g. of anhydrous Na_2CO_3 dissolved in 1 liter of distilled water)

Unless specified otherwise, all reagents are prepared from high-quality (analyzed, C.P., or reagent-grade) chemicals.

Acids and Bases. Common concentrated, C.P. acids and bases have the following specifications:

Acid or base[a]	Specific gravity	Per cent	Normality (approximate)	Molecular weight
Acetic acid, glacial	1.051	99.5	17	60.1
Ammonium hydroxide.	0.899	28.9[b]	15	17.0[b]
Hydrochloric acid	1.180	36.0	12	36.5
Nitric acid	1.422	70.3	16	63.0
Phosphoric acid (ortho-)	1.689	85.0	44	98.0
Sodium hydroxide (saturated)	1.525	50.0	19	40.0
Sulfuric acid.	1.836	96.0	36	98.1

[a]The specific gravity and per cent of acid or base for commercial products often vary from the values for highly purified samples given in the table.

[b]NH_3.

Shelf. Concentrated and 6 N solutions of the acids and bases listed in the table are available. Directions for the preparation of saturated sodium hydroxide solutions are given below under Special. A saturated solution of (technical) *sodium dichromate* with which to prepare cleaning solution (see Cleaning Glassware, under Techniques) is provided. To prepare this solution, dissolve 3,050 g. of $Na_2Cr_2O_7 \cdot 2H_2O$ in 1 liter of distilled water with stirring and moderate heating.

Special. Special reagents are available on the side shelf as required for the designated experiments. The chemicals are obtainable from concerns listed below and other companies given in the Chemical Guide Book (Chemical Markets, 25 Spruce St., New York City), Green Book, Buyers Directory (Schnell Publishing Company, 59 John St., New York City), and Buyers Guidebook Number (Chemical Industries, 522 Fifth Ave., New York City).

Amend Drug and Chemical Company, 117 E. 24th St., New York City (ivory-nut meal)

American Type Culture Collection, 2029 M St., Washington, D. C. (test-tube and lyophilized cultures of bacteria, fungi, yeasts, algae, protozoa, and bacteriophages)

Arthur H. Thomas Company, West Washington Square, Philadelphia, Pennsylvania

Baker and Adamson (General Chemical Company), 40 Rector St., New York City (inorganic and organic chemicals)

Carbide and Carbon Chemicals Company, 30 E. 42d St., New York City (inorganic and organic chemicals)

Cheney Brothers, Manchester, Connecticut (silk waste)

Coleman and Bell Company, Norwood, Ohio (urease tablets)

Commercial Solvents Corporation, 17 E. 42d St., New York City (organic solvents)

Difco Laboratories, Detroit, Michigan (microbiological culture media)

Dougherty Chemical Company, 87-34 134th St., Richmond Hill 18, New York (cytosine and other nucleic acid derivatives)

Dow Chemical Company, Midland, Michigan (inorganic and organic chemicals)

E. I. du Pont de Nemours, Wilmington, Delaware (inorganic and organic chemicals)

Eastman Kodak Company, Rochester, New York (organic chemicals)

Eimer and Amend, 635 Greenwich St., New York City (bacteriological culture media, indicators, indicator paper, and papain)

Fleischmann Yeast Company, New York City

General Biochemicals, 677 Laboratory Park, Chagrin Falls, Ohio (amino acids, proteins, and vitamins)

G. Frederick Smith Chemical Company, 867 McKinley Ave., Columbus, Ohio (acids and salts of cerium, iodine, and chlorine)

H.G. Hastings Company, Atlanta, Georgia (*Lupinus albus* seeds)

H.M. Chemical Company, 144 N. Hayworth Ave., Los Angeles, California (amino acids, microbiological assay media, and vitamins)

Hoffman-LaRoche, Nutley, New Jersey (amino acids and vitamins)

Huron Milling Company, 9 Park Place, New York City (glutamic acid and other amino acids)

International Minerals and Chemical Company, 20 N. Wacker Drive, Chicago, Illinois (glutamic acid and other amino acids)

J.T. Baker Chemical Company, Phillipsburg, New Jersey (analyzed chemicals)

Kraft Foods Company, 500 Peshtigo Court, Chicago, Illinois (sweet whey powder "Krafen")

Mallinckrodt Chemical Works, St. Louis, Missouri (inorganic chemicals)

Martin Drug Company, Tucson, Arizona (mesquite gum)

Meat packers (spinal cords, fresh beef)

Merck and Company, Rahway, New Jersey (amino acids, inorganic and organic chemicals, and vitamins)

Nutritional Biochemicals Corporation, Cleveland, Ohio (amino acids, enzymes, nucleic acids and derivatives, and vitamins)

Paragon Division, Matheson Company, East Rutherford, New Jersey (organic chemicals)

Pfanstiehl Chemical Company, Waukegan, Illinois (amino acids and carbohydrates)

Schwarz Laboratories, 202 E. 44th St., New York City (diazouracil, nucleic acids, and derivatives)

Ultra-Violet Products, 5205 Santa Monica Blvd., Los Angeles, California (ultraviolet lamp Mineralite)

Van Camp Laboratories, Terminal Island, California (amino acids, vitamins, and vitamin D concentrates)

Wallerstein Company, 180 Madison Ave., New York City (papain)

Winthrop Chemical Company, 170 Varick St., New York City (amino acids)

Unless otherwise specified, all solutions listed below as per cent are prepared by dissolving the required amount of substance in distilled water and diluting the solution to 100 ml. Each special reagent bottle (or other container) should be labeled with the name of the reagent, the experiment number, the date on which the reagent was prepared, the date on which the reagent (if unstable) is to be discarded, and the exact concentration (normality or molarity, if a standard solution). Reagents marked with asterisk are to be dispensed from dropping bottles.

Reagent	Experiment number	Required per student
Acetic anhydride (purity 99–100 per cent)	8,44,45	16–72 ml.
Acetone (b.p. 55.5–55.8°)	27,36,46	0.5–1,750 ml.
Acid, boric, 4 per cent solution	20	30 ml.
Acid, chromotropic (1,8-dihydroxynaphthalene-3,6-disulfonic acid), technical	21	20 mg.
Acid, hydriodic, constant-boiling (57 per cent)	8	180 ml.
Acid, hydrochloric, 0.1 N	22	56 ml.
Acid, hydrochloric, 0.1 N (standard)	20,21	5–100 ml.
Acid, hydrochloric, N	16,21,29, 35,38	20–100 ml.
Acid, hydrochloric, 1.0 N (standard)	17	200 ml.
Acid, hydrochloric, 3 N	10,12	40–50 ml.
Acid, hydrochloric, 8 N	12,16	300–1,000 ml.
Acid, oxalic, M. Dissolve 12.6 g. of $H_2C_2O_4 \cdot 2H_2O$ in distilled water and dilute the solution to 1 liter.	21	1 ml.
*Acid, perchloric, 60 per cent solution	23	1 ml.
Acid, periodic, 0.5 M. Dissolve 114.0 g. of $HIO_4 \cdot 2H_2O$ in distilled water and dilute to 1 liter.	21,36	1–4 ml.
Acid, phosphoric, 85 per cent	36	1 ml.

Reagent	Experiment number	Required per student
Acid, phosphotungstic ($P_2O_5 \cdot 12WO_3 \cdot 42H_2O$), 20 per cent solution. Commercial phosphotungstic acid is purified by dissolving it in water and extracting with diethyl ether. The ether solution which settles below the water phase is washed twice with water and is evaporated to dryness on a steam bath.	21	1–50 ml.
Acid, phosphotungstic (Folin's improved reagent). Mix 20 g. of molybdate-free sodium tungstate ($Na_2WO_4 \cdot 2H_2O$), 8.5 ml. of 85 per cent H_3PO_4, and 30 ml. of distilled water. Stir the mixture and heat it under a reflux condenser until the liquid refluxes gently. Continue heating for 1 hr. Add bromine water dropwise until the solution is decolorized, heat the solution to boiling, continue heating until the bromine is removed, and dilute the residual liquid to 100 ml.	18,46	8–40 ml.
Acid, picric, saturated (1.2 per cent) solution. Commercial picric acid contains as much as 10 per cent water. *Purified picric acid*, required only in Exp. 46, is prepared essentially by the methods of Folin and Doisy [*J. Biol. Chem.*, 28, 349 (1917)] and Benedict [*J. Biol. Chem.*, 82, 1, (1929)]. Dissolve 125 g. of anhydrous Na_2CO_3 and 250 g. of commercial picric acid (2,4,6-trinitrophenol) in 3 liters of boiling distilled water. Filter the hot solution and allow the filtrate to stand for 24 hr. Filter the suspension and wash the crystals on the funnel with 1 liter of ice-cold 10 per cent NaCl solution. Suspend the washed crystals in 100 ml. of distilled water and add slowly with stirring 150 ml. of ice-cold 3 N HCl. Filter the picric acid and wash the crystals on the funnel with five 100-ml. portions of ice-cold distilled water. Dry the product between filter papers and store it in a brown bottle.	21,46	15–80 ml.
Acid, sulfuric, 0.1 N	9	150–250 ml.
Acid, sulfuric, 0.5 N	9,10,13, 18,21	1–1,500 ml.
Acid, sulfuric, 0.5 N (standard)	25	50 ml.
Acid, sulfuric, N	30–32,40	20–1,000 ml.
Acid, sulfuric, 2 N	37	2 ml.
Acid, sulfuric, 5 N	14,29	10–30 ml.
Acid, sulfuric, 18 N	31,46	2–30 ml.
Acid, sulfuric, 24 N	32	60 ml.
Acid, trichloroacetic, 10 per cent solution	43	20 ml.
Adenine, 0.5 per cent solution in 2 N H_2SO_4. Dissolve 50 mg. of $C_6H_5N_5 \cdot 2H_2SO_4 \cdot H_2O$ in 10 ml. of 2 N H_2SO_4.	37	0.1 ml.
Agar slant (for *Neurospora crassa* mutant No. 34486). Dissolve 15 g. of agar in 1 liter of boiling distilled water. Add the quantities of stock-medium components indicated below. Stir the mixture until the solids dissolve, transfer 10-ml. aliquots of the hot solution to 6-in. test tubes, stopper the tubes, and autoclave them for 15 min. at 15 p.s.i. pressure, incline the tubes, and allow the agar medium to solidify.	40	1 tube

Reagent	Experiment number	Required per student
Stock medium		

Potassium sodium tartrate (NaKC$_4$H$_4$O$_6$·4H$_2$O) . . . . 5 g.
Sodium nitrate (NaNO$_3$). . . . . 4 g.
Potassium dihydrogen phosphate (KH$_2$PO$_4$). . . . . 1 g.
Magnesium sulfate (MgSO$_4$·7H$_2$O) . . . . 0.5 g.
Sodium chloride (NaCl). . . . . 0.1 g.
Calcium chloride, anhydrous (CaCl$_2$). . . . . 0.1 g.
Glycerol (CH$_2$OHCHOHCH$_2$OH). . . . . 0.02 g.
Casein (vitamin-free) hydrolysate (10 per cent)[a] . . . . . . 2.5 ml.
Yeast extract (Difco). . . . . 5 g.
Malt extract (Difco). . . . . 5 g.

[a]See Special under Reagents and Supplies.

Reagent	Experiment number	Required per student
Agar tube (for *Lactobacillus arabinosus* 17-5). Dissolve 20 g. of agar in 1 liter of boiling distilled water. Add 10 g. of yeast extract (Difco) and 10 g. of C.P. D-glucose. Stir the mixture until the solids dissolve, transfer 10-ml. portions of the hot solution to 6-in. test tubes, stopper the tubes, autoclave them for 15 min. at 15 p.s.i. pressure, and allow the tubes to stand until the agar medium solidifies.	39	1 tube
AGU solution. Dissolve 120 mg. each of adenine sulfate [(C$_5$H$_5$N$_5$)$_2$·H$_2$SO$_4$·2H$_2$O], guanine hydrochloride (C$_5$H$_5$N$_5$O·HCl·2H$_2$O), and uracil (C$_4$H$_4$N$_2$O$_2$)in 100 ml. of 0.5 N HCl with stirring and heating.	39	0.7 ml.
DL-Alanine	36	0.3 g.
Albumin, egg or bovine plasma	46	100 mg.
Amino acids (see Experiments, Appendix)	9,10,21	
Amino acid solution. Add 3.2 g. of L-tryptophan, 1.2 g. of L-cysteine hydrochloride, and 6.0 g. of U.S.P. ammonium chloride to 100 ml. of distilled water. Stir and heat the mixture until the solids dissolve.	39	1.25 ml.
1-Amino-2-naphthol-4-sulfonic acid, 0.2 per cent solution. Dissolve 30 g. of sodium acid sulfite (NaHSO$_3$) in 200 ml. of distilled water in a 250-ml. volumetric flask. Add 0.5 g. of 1-amino-2-naphthol-4-sulfonic acid and 6 g. of sodium sulfite. Stir until the solids dissolve and dilute with distilled water to the mark. Mix thoroughly. Allow the solution to stand overnight and filter. This reagent is stable for about 4 weeks if protected from strong light.	43	3.5 ml.
Ammonium carbonate, technical	2	162 g.
Ammonium hydroxide, 0.01 M (standard)	20	10 ml.
Ammonium hydroxide—ammonium carbonate reagent. Dissolve 5 g. of ammonium carbonate in 50 ml. of distilled water, add 100 ml. of concentrated ammonium hydroxide, and mix the solutions.	21	2 ml.
Ammonium molybdate [(NH$_4$)$_2$MoO$_4$·4H$_2$O], 5 per cent solution in 7 N (20 per cent by volume) sulfuric acid	43	7 ml.
Ammonium molybdate [(NH$_4$)$_2$MoO$_4$·4H$_2$O], 9 per cent solution	22	2 ml.
Ammonium sulfate, powder	36	7.6 g.
Ammonium sulfate, standard solution (0.08 mg. of nitrogen per milliliter). Dissolve 0.38 g. (weighed to ±1 mg.) of ammonium sulfate in distilled water in a 1-liter volumetric flask, dilute to the mark, and mix thoroughly.	46	30 ml.

Reagent	Experiment number	Required per student
Ammonium sulfate, standard solution (0.25 mg. of nitrogen per milliliter). Dissolve 1.13 g. (weighed to ±1 mg.) of ammonium sulfate in distilled water in a 1-liter volumetric flask, dilute to the mark, and mix thoroughly.	46	15 ml.
Amyl alcohol (b.p. 135–137°) and diethyl ether solution (1:1)	21	65 ml.
L-Arabinose	31	1 mg.
L-Ascorbic acid	38	0.1 mg.
Ball-mill mixture (see Experiments, Appendix)	39	
Barfoed's reagent. Dissolve 24 g. of cupric acetate [$Cu(C_2H_3O_2)_2 \cdot H_2O$] and 210 g. of 85 per cent lactic acid in 500 ml. of distilled water.	36	10–20 ml.
Barium carbonate, powder	30–32	25–40 g.
Barium hydroxide octahydrate, powder (containing less than 0.5 per cent carbonate)	30–32	80–220 g.
Benedict's reagent (for qualitative determination of reducing substances). Dissolve 173 g. of sodium citrate ($Na_3C_6H_5O_7 \cdot 5H_2O$) and 100 g. of sodium carbonate (Na_2CO_3) in 800 ml. of distilled water with stirring and heating. Filter the solution and dilute the filtrate to 850 ml. Dissolve 17.3 g. of cupric sulfate ($CuSO_4 \cdot 5H_2O$) in 100 ml. of distilled water. Mix the two solutions thoroughly and dilute the mixture to 1 liter.	28,36,46	5–15 ml.
Benzaldehyde (b.p. 75–76° at 16 mm. Hg)	8,36	2–20 ml.
Benzhydrazide (benzoylhydrazine), 10 per cent solution in 95 per cent ethanol. The following method is essentially that of Struve [*J. prakt. Chem.*, (2) *50*, 295 (1895)]. Other methods described by Struve are less satisfactory. Place 45 g. (0.57 mole) of practical (85 per cent in water) hydrazine hydrate ($NH_2NH_2 \cdot H_2O$) and 27 g. (0.18 mole) of ethyl benzoate ($C_6H_5COOC_2H_5$) (b.p. 100–102° at 20 mm. Hg) in a 250-ml. flask. Stopper the flask and shake it at frequent intervals. Allow the flask to stand overnight at room temperature, filter the suspension, and recrystallize the product from the minimum volume of hot water. The yield of product (m.p. 112–113°) is 14 g. (57 per cent of the theoretical amount).	36	10 ml.
Benzidine (m.p. 126–127°) 4 per cent solution in glacial acetic acid	36	0.5 mg.
Benzoyl chloride (m.p. −0.5°)	7	25 ml.
Benzoylhydrazine (see Benzhydrazide)		
Bial's reagent. Dissolve 0.2 g. of orcinol (m.p. 106–108°) and 0.025 g. of ferric chloride ($FeCl_3 \cdot 6H_2O$) in 100 ml. of 12 N HCl and 16 ml. of distilled water.	36	3 ml.
Biotin solution, 5 µg per ml.	40	1 ml.
Bromine	37	1 ml.
Bromine–acetic acid reagent. Dissolve 1 g. (0.34 ml. of bromine in a solution of 33 ml. of glacial acetic acid and 67 ml. of distilled water.	21	1 ml.
Bromine water (saturated solution). Thoroughly mix 5 drops of bromine with 100 ml. of distilled water; remove and use the supernatant solution.	21	1 ml.

Reagent	Experiment number	Required per student
Bromthymol blue indicator solution (see Indicator, bromthymol blue solution)		
Buffer solution, pH 3.5. Dissolve 10.2 g. of potassium acid phthalate ($KHC_8H_4O_4$) and 7.85 ml. of N HCl in distilled water. Dilute to 1 liter, mix thoroughly, determine the pH with a pH meter, and adjust the pH to 3.5 by adding potassium acid phthalate or HCl as required.	16	1 ml.
Buffer solution, pH 4.5. Dissolve 41 g. of anhydrous sodium acetate (CH_3COONa) in distilled water. Add 83.5 ml. of $6 N$ acetic acid, dilute to 1 liter, mix thoroughly, determine the pH with a pH meter, and adjust the pH to 4.5 by adding sodium acetate or acetic acid as required.	16,44	1–180 ml.
Buffer solution, pH 5.7. Dissolve 10.2 g. of potassium acid phthalate ($KHC_8H_4O_4$) and 41.5 ml. of N NaOH in distilled water. Dilute to 1 liter, mix thoroughly, determine the pH with a pH meter, and adjust the pH to 5.7 by adding potassium acid phthalate or NaOH as required.	12	1 ml.
Buffer solution, pH 6.8. Dissolve 6.95 g. of KH_2PO_4 and 27.35 g. of $Na_2HPO_4 \cdot 12H_2O$ in distilled water. Dilute to 1 liter, mix thoroughly, determine the pH with a pH meter, and adjust the pH to 6.8 by adding KH_2PO_4 or $Na_2HPO_4 \cdot 12H_2O$ as required.	21,46	2–24 ml.
Buffer (sodium chloride-phosphate) solution, pH 6.8. Prepare as described for buffer solution, pH 6.8, except that 2.50 g. of NaCl are dissolved in addition to the two phosphate salts.	42	50 ml.
Buffer solution, pH 7.0. Dissolve 6.80 g. of KH_2PO_4 and 49.4 ml. of $6 N$ NaOH in distilled water. Dilute to 1 liter, mix thoroughly, determine the pH with a pH meter, and adjust the pH to 7.0 by adding KH_2PO_4 or NaOH as required.	6	1 ml.
Buffer solution, pH 8.0. Dissolve 6.80 g. of KH_2PO_4 and 7.8 ml. of $6 N$ NaOH in distilled water. Dilute to 1 liter, mix thoroughly, determine the pH with a pH meter, and adjust the pH to 8.0 by adding KH_2PO_4 or NaOH as required.	21	2 ml.
Buffer solution, pH 8.7. Dissolve 358 g. of $Na_2HPO_4 \cdot 12H_2O$ in distilled water, dilute to 1 liter, and mix thoroughly.	21	10 ml.
n-Butanol (b.p. 116–118°)	30–32,36	1–10 ml.
Caffeine, 0.5 per cent solution in $2 N$ H_2SO_4. Dissolve 50 mg. in 10 ml. of $2 N$ sulfuric acid.	37	0.1 ml.
Calcium chloride, granular anhydrous, 4- to 8-mesh	8,41	1 g.
Calcium hydroxide, carbonate-free	21	0.7 g.
Carbohydrates (see Experiments, Appendix)	36	
Carbon, decolorizing (Norit or Nuchar XXX)	4,8,12,15 16,19,21	0.5–55 g.
Carbon disulfide	8,38	1–10 g.
Casein, commercial	12	100 g.
Casein hydrolysate (vitamin-free), 10 per cent solution. Reflux a mixture of 200 g. of commercial vitamin-free casein and 2 liters of $6 N$ HCl for 24 hr. Distill *in vacuo* until excess HCl is removed, take up the residual sirup	39	5.6 ml.

Reagent	Experiment number	Required per student

in 1,500 ml. of distilled water, and adjust the pH of the solution to 3.0 with 18 *N* NaOH. Add 20 g. of decolorizing carbon, stir the suspension for 10 min., filter the suspension, and dilute the filtrate to 2 liters. Preserve the final solution in a glass-stoppered bottle stored in the refrigerator. The solution is stable under these conditions for 3 months or longer.

Ceric sulfate, 0.02 *M* (standard). Since commercial ceric sulfate varies in purity, an entire lot should be tested and preserved. Dissolve 6 g. of ceric sulfate $[Ce(HSO_4)_4]$ in a solution prepared by mixing (*Cautiously*) 30 ml. of concentrated sulfuric acid with 500 ml. of distilled water. Dilute to 1 liter, mix thoroughly, and store the solution in a glass-stoppered bottle. **Standardization of Ceric Sulfate Solution.** Prepare 0.02 *M* (standard) solution of ferrous ammonium sulfate (Mohr's salt) $[Fe(NH_4)_2(SO_4)_2 \cdot 6H_2O]$ as follows: Dissolve 0.78 g. (weighed to 1 mg.) of Mohr's salt in 50 ml. of a solution containing 1.5 ml. of concentrated H_2SO_4 in a 100-ml. volumetric flask. Dilute to the mark and mix thoroughly. Pipette (*Caution*) 5.0 ml. of the ceric sulfate solution into a 125-ml. conical flask, add 50 ml. of distilled water, and add 1.5 ml of concentrated H_2SO_4. Titrate with the standard Mohr's salt solution until the color of the ceric sulfate is nearly discharged. Add 8 drops of setopaline indicator solution and continue the titration until the color of the solution changes from a golden brown to a light yellow. Before using this reagent, it must be standardized against pure D-glucose by the procedure described in Exp. 29. 1 ml. of 0.02 *N* ceric sulfate is equivalent (approximately) to 1 mg. of D-glucose. — 29, 50 ml.

Reagent	Experiment number	Required per student
Chicks (day-old), starved	41	4–8
Chick diet (see Experiments, Appendix)	41	
Chloroform, U.S.P.	21,36,44	1–40 ml.
Chloroform (dry)	26,45	50–75 ml.
Chloroacetic acid (m.p. 62–64°)	2	35 g.
Cholesterol (m.p. 148°)	45	1 mg.
Cholesterol (m.p. 148°), standard solution (0.12 mg. per ml.)	45	11 ml.

Choline, standard solution (1.20 μg per ml.). Dissolve 0.69 g. (weighed rapidly to ±1 mg.) of choline chloride (dried *in vacuo* over a desiccant) in distilled water and dilute to 1 liter in a volumetric flask. Prepare a standard solution by diluting 2.00 ml. to 1 liter in a volumetric flask. — 40, 15.5 ml.

Chromogenic (arsenomolybdate) reagent. Dissolve 25 g. of ammonium molybdate $[(NH_4)_2MoO_4 \cdot 4H_2O]$ in 450 ml. of distilled water. Add 21 ml. of concentrated H_2SO_4, mix thoroughly, and add a solution of 3 g. of $Na_2HAsO_4 \cdot 7H_2O$ in 25 ml. of distilled water. Mix thoroughly, incubate the mixture for 24 hr. at 37°, and filter if any suspended material is visible. Store the solution in a brown bottle. — 35, 6 ml.

Chromotropic acid (see Acid, chromotropic)

Cobaltous chloride ($CoCl_2 \cdot 6H_2O$), 1 per cent solution — 36, 2 ml.

Congo red indicator solution (see Indicator, congo red solution)

Reagent	Experiment number	Required per student
Corncobs, air-dried	30	100 g.
Corn sirup, commercial	35	0.5 g.
Cotton	39,40,43	1–2 plugs
Creatinine, C.P., standard solution (0.5 mg. per ml.)	46	3 ml.
Cupric carbonate [$CuCO_3 \cdot Cu(OH)_2$]	21	0.3 g.
Cupric-ion reagent. Dissolve 2.8 g. of Na_2HPO_4 and 4.0 g. of Rochelle salt ($KNaC_4H_4O_6 \cdot 4H_2O$) in 70 ml. of distilled water. Add 10 ml. of N NaOH and a solution of 0.8 g. of $CuSO_4 \cdot 5H_2O$ in 10 ml. of distilled water. Dilute to 100 ml. and allow the solution to stand for 24 hr. Filter if suspended material is visible.	35	12 ml.
Cupric sulfate, 0.01 M solution. Dissolve 2.50 g. of $CuSO_4 \cdot 5H_2O$ in distilled water and dilute to 1 liter.	21	1 ml.
L-Cysteine hydrochloride	44	0.6 g.
L-Cystine, standard solution (1 mg. per ml. in 0.5 N H_2SO_4)	18	2 ml.
Cytosine, 0.5 per cent solution in 2 N H_2SO_4. Dissolve 50 mg. in 10 ml. of 2 N sulfuric acid.	37	0.1 ml.
Denigès reagent. Dissolve 150 g. of $HgSO_4$ in 6 N H_2SO_4, dilute to 1 liter with 6 N H_2SO_4, and mix thoroughly.	21	35 ml.
Diazobenzenesulfonic acid reagent. Mix 4 g. of powdered sulfanilic acid, 6 ml. of distilled water, and 4 ml. of concentrated HCl. Stir to a uniform suspension. Add 4 ml. (in 0.5-ml. portions over 2 min.) of a 50 per cent solution of $NaNO_2$ with stirring and cooling in a water bath at room temperature. Allow the mixture to stand for 5 min., filter the suspended white, crystalline diazo derivative, and wash the precipitate on the funnel with 5 ml. of distilled water. Apply suction for 5 min. Weigh the moist solid and dissolve it in a volume of 4 N NaOH sufficient to make a 10 per cent solution (stable for 6 hr.). The diazo compound should not be allowed to dry completely, since the dry material is unstable to light and may explode when touched.	37	1 ml.
Diazouracil. Test with sucrose before issuing.	36	35 mg.
Dibenzylidine-xylose-dimethylacetal (m.p. 211°). Add 9 ml. of the benzaldehyde-methanol-HCl mixture (preparation described in Exp. 36) to 1 g. of D-xylose in a 6-in. test tube. Shake vigorously and allow it to stand overnight. Filter the suspension of needle crystals and wash the crystals first with 200 ml. of distilled water and then with 50 ml. of methanol. Dry the product at 50° for 1 hr. and store it in a dark bottle. The yield is about 1 g.	36	0.1 g.
2,6-Dichlorophenolindophenol (sodium salt), 0.1 per cent solution	38	200 ml.
1,8-Dihydroxynaphthalene-3,6-disulfonic acid (see Acid, chromotropic)		
p-Dimethylaminobenzaldehyde (m.p. 72–73°) 4 per cent solution in 95 per cent ethanol	21	1 ml.
2,4-Dinitrophenylhydrazine (m.p. 199–200°) 0.5 per cent solution in 2.4 N HCl. Heat the mixture to boiling to dissolve the solid, cool, and filter if a residue remains.	21	5 ml.
Diphenylamine, technical	15	60 g.
Diphenylmethane, technical	15	60 g.

Reagent	Experiment number	Required per student
Egg (chicken)	40	1
Ethanol, 95 per cent	8,16,19,21, 24,25,27, 28,31–33, 36,44	5–715 ml.
Ethanol, absolute	15,21,32,36, 44	1–125 ml.
Ethanol–sulfuric acid reagent. Dissolve 40 ml. of concentrated H_2SO_4 in 150 ml. of 85 per cent ethanol.	36	5 ml.
Ether, diethyl	15,21,28,41, 43	1–500 ml.
Ether, isopropyl (b.p. 67–69°)	7	45 ml.
Ether, petroleum (b.p. 60–100°)	16,36,40	1.5–50 ml.
Ethylene glycol, technical	4	80 ml.
Ferric alum indicator solution (see Indicator, ferric alum solution)		
Ferrous sulfate, saturated solution. Dissolve 300 g. of $FeSO_4 \cdot 7H_2O$ in a solution of 25 ml. of 6 N H_2SO_4 in 750 ml. of distilled water. Heat to boiling, remove the flame, and add (during the course of an hour) three very small portions (excess will cause frothing) of powdered iron to reduce any ferric ion. Heat the solution to boiling between each addition of iron. Add 250 ml. of distilled water, allow the solution to cool overnight, and filter.	28	1 ml.
Ferrous sulfate–hydrochloric acid reagent. Dissolve 0.5 g. of $FeSO_4 \cdot 7H_2O$ in 100 ml. of N HCl. The solution is stable for a week.	37	1 ml.
Filter aid (Celite 503)	12,14,16,19, 27,30–33	1–400 g.
Folin's improved reagent [see Acid, phosphotungstic (Folin's improved reagent)]		
Fuller's earth	45	3 g.
Gelatin, purified	29	0.5 g.
α-D-Glucose, anhydrous	39,46	1–1.5 g.
α-D-Glucose, anhydrous, standard solution (0.035 mg. per ml.)	35	2 ml.
α-D-Glucose, anhydrous, standard solution (0.060 mg. per ml.)	35	2 ml.
α-D-Glucose, anhydrous, standard solution (0.10 mg. per ml.)	35	2 ml.
α-D-Glucose, anhydrous, standard solution (0.15 mg. per ml.)	35	2 ml.
β-Glycerophosphate (substrate) reagent. Dissolve 2.5 g. of sodium β-glycerophosphate, 2.12 g. of monosodium diethylbarbiturate (veronal sodium, barbital sodium), and 1 g. of $MgCl_2 \cdot 6H_2O$ in distilled water. Dilute to 500 ml., transfer to a glass-stoppered bottle, add sufficient petroleum ether (b.p. 30–36°) to form a 2-cm. layer, and preserve in the refrigerator.	43	17 ml.
Glycine, purified	3	15 g.
Glycine, technical	4,7	15 g.
Grapefruit juice, commercial canned	38	210 ml.
Guanine, 0.5 per cent solution in 2 N H_2SO_4. Dissolve 50 mg. of guanine hydrochloride ($C_5H_5NO \cdot HCl \cdot 2H_2O$) in 10 ml. of 2 N sulfuric acid.	37	0.1 ml.

Reagent	Experiment number	Required per student
Hair (crude), men's	16	600 g.
Hanus solution. Suspend 13.2 g. of iodine in 800 ml. of glacial acetic acid. Stir and heat until the iodine dissolves. Allow the solution to cool (in air or under running water) to room temperature. Add 3.0 ml. (9 g.) of bromine to 200 ml. of glacial acetic acid. Mix thoroughly. Mix the iodine and bromine solutions.	26	125 ml.
Hippuric acid (benzoylglycine)	8	36 g.
Hopkins-Cole-Benedict reagent. Place 10 g. of magnesium powder in a 2-liter flask. Add enough distilled water to cover the powder and add slowly (while cooling the flask under running water) 250 ml. of a cold saturated solution of oxalic acid ($H_2C_2O_4 \cdot 2H_2O$). Stir, filter if any suspended material is visible, acidify with acetic acid, and dilute to 1 liter with distilled water.	21	1 ml.
Hydriodic acid (see Acid, hydriodic)		
Hydrochloric acid (see Acid, hydrochloric)		
Hydrogen peroxide, 6 per cent solution	21	1 ml.
Hydrogen peroxide, 30 per cent solution	46	1 ml.
Hydrogen sulfide (from house line or generator)	36,37	Gas
Hydroquinone, (m.p. 168–169°), 1 per cent solution. Add sulfuric acid to acid reaction with litmus paper.	23	25 ml.
p-Hydroxydiphenyl (m.p. 164–165°)	21,36	20 mg.
Hydroxylamine hydrochloride (m.p. 153–155°), 20 per cent solution	21	4 ml.
8-Hydroxyquinoline sulfate, 5 per cent solution	38	4 ml.
*Indicator, bromthymol blue, 0.5 per cent solution. Dissolve 0.5 g. of bromthymol blue (dibromthymolsulfonphthalein) in 33 ml. of 95 per cent ethanol, add 67 ml. of distilled water, and mix thoroughly.	21,29,39,40	1 ml.
Indicator, congo red paper	7,16,21	10 strips
*Indicator, congo red, 0.04 per cent solution. Dissolve 0.04 g. of congo red (sodium tetrazodiphenylnaphthionate) in 20 ml. of 95 per cent ethanol, add 80 ml. of distilled water, and mix thoroughly.	30–32	1 ml.
*Indicator, ferric alum, 10 per cent solution. Dissolve 10 g. of ferric ammonium sulfate [$Fe(NH_4)SO_4)_2 \cdot 12H_2O$] in 95 ml. of distilled water and dilute to 100 ml. with 16 N HNO_3. Mix thoroughly.	11	1 ml.
Indicator, litmus paper	21,27,32,36	10 strips
Indicator, methyl red paper	8,12	10 strips
*Indicator, methyl red, 0.1 per cent solution. Dissolve 0.1 g. of methyl red (dimethylaminoazobenzene-o-carboxylic acid) in 50 ml. of 95 per cent ethanol and dilute to 100 ml. Mix thoroughly.	21	1 ml.
*Indicator, mixed (methyl red and p-nitrophenol) 0.02 per cent solution of methyl red and 0.1 per cent solution of p-nitrophenol. Dissolve 0.02 g. of methyl red in 20 ml. of 95 per cent ethanol and dilute to 100 ml. with distilled water. Dissolve 0.10 g. of p-nitrophenol (m.p. 112–113°) in the solution. Mix thoroughly.	9,20	1 ml.

Reagent	Experiment number	Required per student
Indicator, nitrazine (sodium dinitrophenylazonaphtholdisulfonate) paper, pH range 4.5 to 7.5	6	5 strips
*Indicator, phenolphthalein (dihydroxyphthalophenone), 0.1 per cent solution. Dissolve 0.1 g. of phenolphthalein in 100 ml. of 95 per cent ethanol.	1,23–25	1 ml.
*Indicator, setopaline C, 0.1 per cent solution in water	29	1 ml.
*Indicator, thymolphthalein, 0.1 per cent solution. Dissolve 0.1 g. of thymolphthalein in 100 ml. of 95 per cent ethanol.	7	1 ml.
Indicator, universal paper, pH range 1 to 13	44	5 strips
Ink, india	40	0.1 ml.
Inoculum medium. Dissolve 40 g. of glucose, 24 g. of anhydrous sodium acetate, 20 ml. of AGU solution, 10 ml. of salts A solution, 10 ml. of salts B solution, 10 ml. of vitamins solution, 20 g. of peptone (Difco), and 20 g. of yeast extract (Difco) in distilled water and dilute to 1 liter. Mix thoroughly, add sufficient toluene to form a layer on the surface of the liquid, and store the solution in the refrigerator.	39	10 ml.
Iodine–potassium iodide, 0.01 N iodine solution in 0.01 N KI solution	36	1 ml.
Iodine–potassium iodide, 0.005 M solution in 0.005 M KI solution	42	15 ml.
Isatin	21	1 mg.
Isatin, 1 per cent solution in water (freshly prepared)	21	2 ml.
Ivory-nut meal	32	100 g.
Kjeldahl digestion mixture. Dissolve 10 g. of $CuSO_4 \cdot 5H_2O$ and 80 g. of anhydrous Na_2SO_4 in 1 liter of 18 N H_2SO_4	9	125 ml.
Lactobacillus arabinosus 17-5 culture, American Type Culture Collection, No. 8014	30	1 culture
α-D-Lactose monohydrate, crystalline	33,34,36	0.02–2.5 g.
Lead acetate, 2 N. Dissolve 379.4 g. of $Pb(C_2H_3O_2)_2 \cdot 3H_2O$ in distilled water and dilute to 1 liter.	21	1 ml.
Lead dioxide	21	0.2 g.
Lupinus albus seeds	19	100 g.
L-Lysine picrate, crystalline. Prepare as described in Step XI, Test 10.	21	0.1 g.
Magnesium chloride, M solution. Dissolve 203.3 g. of $MgCl_2 \cdot 6H_2O$ in distilled water and dilute to 1 liter.	36	1 ml.
Magnesium sulfate, anhydrous. Dry $MgSO_4 \cdot 7H_2O$, U.S.P., at 150 to 200°. Heat slowly with occasional stirring to prevent melting or caking.	45	9 g.
Maltose	36	20 mg.
α-D-Mannose, crystalline	32	20 mg.
Mercuric acetate, 2.5 per cent solution in glacial acetic acid	26	50 ml.
Mercuric sulfate, 1.5 per cent solution in 6 N H_2SO_4	14	35 ml.
Mercuric sulfate, 15 per cent solution in 6 N H_2SO_4	13,14	20 ml.
Mesquite gum	31	100 g.
Methanol	2,4–6,12,22, 30–32,36	16–975 ml.
Methanol, anhydrous	3,30,36	1–100 ml.

Reagent	Experiment number	Required per student
Methanol in 2.4 N HCl solution. Pass dry HCl gas (generated as described in Exp. 3) into 100 ml. (79 g.) of anhydrous methanol until the weight increases 8.5 g. Check normality by titration with standard base.	36	1 ml.
Methanol, 75 per cent solution	30	25 ml.
Methanol in 95 per cent ethanol solution (1:3)	32	1 ml.
*Methylamine hydrochloride, 5 per cent solution in water	36	1 ml.
5-methylcytosine, 0.5 per cent solution in 2 N H_2SO_4. Dissolve 50 mg. in 10 ml. of 2 N H_2SO_4.	37	0.1 ml.
Methyl red indicator solution (see Indicator, methyl red solution)		
Milk, skim	22	100 ml.
Millon's reagent. Dissolve 100 g. of mercury in 100 g. (140 ml.) of cold concentrated nitric acid in a large pyrex or porcelain vessel. (*Caution*: Use hood and handle with extreme care. Do not prepare larger quantities in a single run.) Cool the solution and dilute with twice its volume of distilled water. After several hours decant the clear supernatant liquid.	16,21	1 ml.
Mixed indicator solution [see Indicator, mixed (methyl red and *p*-nitrophenol)]		
Molybdic acid—sulfuric acid reagent. Dissolve 25 g. of ammonium molybdate [$(NH_4)_6Mo_7O_{24} \cdot 4H_2O$] in 300 ml. of distilled water. Add 200 ml. of a solution containing 75 ml. of concentrated H_2SO_4. Mix thoroughly.	23	25 ml.
α-Naphthol, 0.02 per cent solution in 20 per cent ethanol. Dissolve in 95 per cent ethanol and dilute to volume.	21	1 ml.
1,2-Naphthoquinone-4-sulfonate (sodium salt), 0.5 per cent solution in water. Discard after second day and prepare fresh solution.	21	1 ml.
Nessler reagent. Dissolve 30 g. of KI in 20 ml. of distilled water. Dissolve 22.5 g. of iodine in this solution. Add 30 g. of mercury (purified) and shake vigorously while cooling the container under running water. Continue until yellow (iodine) color of supernatant liquid disappears. Decant the supernatant liquid (from the mercury) and test for free iodine by adding a few drops of the solution to 1 ml. of 1 per cent soluble starch solution. If the test is negative, add 10 per cent iodine solution to the potassium-mercuric iodide until the starch test is positive (blue color). Dilute the solution to 200 ml., mix thoroughly, and add to 975 ml. of 10.0 per cent NaOH. Mix thoroughly and allow to stand until a clear supernatant solution forms.	21,46	5—90 ml.
Neurospora crassa cholineless mutant No. 34486 (American Type Culture Collection No. 9277)	40	1 culture
Nicotinic acid	39	0.1 g.
Nicotinic acid, standard solution (0.060 μg per ml.)	39	11.5 ml.
Ninhydrin, 0.1 per cent solution in water	21	1 ml.
Ninhydrin, 1 per cent solution in water	21	2 ml.
Nitrating agent, 10 per cent solution of KNO_3 in concentrated H_2SO_4	21	2 ml.
Nitrobenzene (m.p., 5—6°)	11	50 ml.

Reagent	Experiment number	Required per student
Nucleic acid (ribo), yeast	37	0.1 g.
Organic acids (see Experiments, Appendix)	1	
Oxalic acid (see Acid, oxalic)		
Papain, commercial powder	44	2 g.
Paraffin	42	10 g.
Perchloric acid (see Acid, perchloric)		
Periodic acid (see Acid, periodic)		
Permutit, dry activated ("Decalso"—prepared according to Folin)	46	4 g.
Phenolphthalein indicator solution (see Indicator, phenolphthalein solution)		
DL-Phenylalanine	44	10 g.
Phenylhydrazine hydrochloride	36	0.6 g.
Phosphate standard solution (0.015 mg. of phosphorus per milliliter). Dilute 15 ml. of the stock solution (see below) to 1,000 ml. in a volumetric flask with water. This solution is subject to bacterial contamination after about a week. **Stock Solution.** Dissolve 2.2 g. of KH_2PO_4 (weighed to ±1 mg.) in water, add 5 ml. of 6 N H_2SO_4, and dilute to 500 ml. in a volumetric flask. The stock solution is stable.	23	10 ml.
Phosphate standard solution (0.02 mg. of phosphorus per milliliter). Dilute 10 ml. of the phosphate stock solution to 500 ml. in a volumetric flask with water. This solution is subject to bacterial contamination after about a week.	43	6 ml.
Phosphorus, red	8	20 g.
Phosphotungstic acid (see Acid, phosphotungstic)		
Phosphotungstic acid—phosphomolybdic acid reagent (Folin-Ciocalteu). Place 100 g. of sodium tungstate ($Na_2WO_4 \cdot 2H_2O$), 25 g. of sodium molybdate ($Na_2MoO_4 \cdot 2H_2O$), 700 ml. of distilled water, 50 ml. of 85 per cent phosphoric acid, and 100 ml. of concentrated HCl in a 2-liter standard-taper, round-bottomed flask. Attach a reflux condenser. Heat to boiling and maintain gentle boiling for 10 hr. Add 150 g. of lithium sulfate ($LiSO_4 \cdot H_2O$), 50 ml. of distilled water, and 5 drops of bromine. Heat to boiling (without condenser) and maintain boiling for about 15 min. to remove the excess bromine. Cool, dilute to 1 liter, and filter. The reagent should be free of any greenish cast which would indicate the presence of blue-colored reduction products. The latter would lessen the range of true proportionality between different amounts of tyrosine or tryptophan.	2	0.5 ml.
o-Phthalaldehyde. Place 10 g. of o-tetrabromoxylene [$C_6H_4(CHBr_2)_2$], 9 g. of potassium oxalate ($K_2C_2O_4 \cdot H_2O$), 62 ml. of distilled water, and 62 ml. of 95 per cent ethanol in a flask equipped with a reflux condenser. Heat to boiling and maintain gentle boiling for 40 hr. Remove 50 ml. of liquid (ethanol) by distillation and	21	5 ml.

Reagent	Experiment number	Required per student
add to the residual solution 21.3 g. of $Na_3PO_4 \cdot 10H_2O$ and 300 ml. of distilled water. Distill the solution and collect the first 300 ml. which comes over. Store the reagent in an amber bottle. It is stable almost indefinitely. [Patton and Foreman, *Science*, 109, 339 (1949).] The method of Chaudhuri [*J. Am. Chem. Soc.*, 64, 315 (1942)] has been found less satisfactory. Wawzonek and Karll [*J. Am. Chem. Soc.*, 70, 1666 (1948)] have described a synthesis of o-tetrabromoxylene.		
Picric acid (see Acid, picric)		
Potassium bismuth iodide reagent. Suspend 2.4 g. of $Bi(NO_3)_3 \cdot 5H_2O$ in 50 ml. of distilled water. Add 7.2 g. of KI and stir the mixture until the resulting black precipitate dissolves to a clear bright-red solution.	37	1 ml.
Potassium carbonate solution (50 g. per 100 ml.)	21	6 ml.
*Potassium chromate, 5 per cent solution	36	1 ml.
Potassium ferricyanide (alkaline) solution. Dissolve 8.25 g. of potassium ferricyanide $[K_3Fe(CN)_6]$ and 10.6 g. of anhydrous sodium carbonate in distilled water and dilute to 1 liter. Transfer to a dark bottle and preserve in the refrigerator (stable for 6 weeks).	29	30 ml.
Potassium fluoride (KF), 10 per cent solution in water	28	2 ml.
Potassium hydroxide, 0.1 N (standard) solution	24	50 ml.
Potassium hydroxide, 0.5 N solution in 95 per cent ethanol	27	50 ml.
Potassium hydroxide, 0.5 N (standard) solution in 95 per cent ethanol	25	75 ml.
Potassium iodate, 0.001 M (standard) solution. Dissolve 0.21 g. of KIO_3 (weighed to ±1 mg.) in water and dilute to 1 liter in a volumetric flask.	38	150 ml.
Potassium iodide (iodine-free), 0.1 N solution. Dissolve 16.6 g. of KI in 1 liter of water.	38,42	4–20 ml.
Potassium iodide (iodine-free), 15 per cent solution in water	26	50 ml.
Potassium permanganate	21	1 g.
Potassium permanganate (alkaline) solution, 4 per cent in 0.5 N NaOH	10	150 ml.
Potassium thiocyanate, 0.05 N (standard) solution in water. Dissolve 4.86 g. of KCNS (weighed to ±1 mg.) in water and dilute to 1 liter in a volumetric flask.	11	250 ml.
Potato (irish), fresh	28	600 g.
Purines (see Experiments, Appendix)	37	
Pyridine (b.p. 113.5–115.5°)	21	3 ml.
Pyrimidines (see Experiments, Appendix)	37	
Rats	43,45	1
Resorcinol, 0.2 per cent solution in 95 per cent ethanol	36	10 ml.
Salicylaldehyde (m.p. 1–2°), 6 per cent in absolute ethanol. Prepare fresh each week.	21	7 ml.
Salicylaldehyde (m.p. 1–2°), 10 per cent in 95 per cent ethanol. Prepare fresh each week.	46	1 ml.
Salts (microconstituents) solution. Dissolve in 5 liters of distilled water 6.0 mg. of H_3BO_3, 4.0 mg. of $(NH_4)_6Mo_7O_{24} \cdot 4H_2O$, 90 mg. of $Fe_2(SO_4)_3 \cdot 6H_2O$, 80 mg. of	40	10 ml.

Reagent	Experiment number	Required per student
CuSO$_4$·5H$_2$O, 7 mg. of MnSO$_4$·H$_2$O, and 880 mg. of ZnSO$_4$·7H$_2$O. Shake the mixture before using to resuspend any insoluble material formed.		
Salts solution. Prepare 2 liters of solution containing 2 per cent ammonium tartrate [(NH$_4$)$_2$C$_4$H$_4$O$_6$], 0.4 per cent ammonium nitrate (NH$_4$NO$_3$), 0.4 per cent K$_2$HPO$_4$, 0.2 per cent MgSO$_4$·7H$_2$O, 0.04 per cent NaCl, and 0.08 per cent CaCl$_2$·6H$_2$O. Sterilize (by autoclaving) this solution in aliquots of a volume which will be utilized in a day or so to avoid bacterial contamination of solutions exposed to air for longer time.	40	50 ml.
Salts A solution, 10 per cent K$_2$HPO$_4$ and 10 per cent KH$_2$PO$_4$ solution in water	39	0.38 ml.
Salts B solution. Prepare 100 ml. of a solution containing 4 per cent of MgSO$_4$·7H$_2$O, 0.2 per cent of FeSO$_4$·7H$_2$O, and 0.2 per cent of MnSO$_4$·4H$_2$O, in 0.1 N HCl.	39	0.38 ml.
Setopaline C indicator solution (see Indicator, setopaline C solution)		
Silk waste	12	100 g.
Silver nitrate, 1 per cent solution in water	37	1 ml.
Silver nitrate, 5 per cent solution in 2 N nitric acid	16	1–5 ml.
Silver nitrate, 0.1 N (standard) solution in water	11	450 ml.
Sodium acetate, anhydrous	8,36,39	0.3–17 g.
Sodium arsenite, 0.1 N solution in 2 per cent sodium bicarbonate solution. Dissolve 2.6 g. of sodium arsenite (NaAsO$_2$) in 100 ml. of 2 per cent NaHCO$_3$ solution.	21,36	17 ml.
Sodium arsenite, 5 per cent solution	21	1 ml.
Sodium bicarbonate, 0.5 M solution in water. Dissolve 42 g. of NaHCO$_3$ in distilled water and dilute to 1 liter.	21	5 ml.
Sodium bicarbonate, N solution in water. Dissolve 84 g. of NaHCO$_3$ in distilled water and dilute to 1 liter.	36	10 ml.
Sodium bicarbonate, saturated solution. Dissolve 103 g. of NaHCO$_3$ in a liter of distilled water.	18	40 ml.
Sodium carbonate	21	0.2 g.
Sodium chloride	36	0.5 g.
Sodium chloride, 0.9 per cent solution	39	50 ml.
Sodium chloride buffer (pH 6.8) solution [See Buffer (sodium chloride-phosphate) solution]		
Sodium cyanide, 5 per cent solution in N NaOH. Prepare fresh each week.	21	1 ml.
Sodium cyanide, 12 per cent solution in water. Prepare fresh each week.	46	50 ml.
Sodium hydrosulfite, 2 per cent solution of Na$_2$S$_2$O$_4$·2H$_2$O in water. Prepare fresh each week.	21	1 ml.
Sodium hydroxide, pellets	46	0.5 g.
Sodium hydroxide, 0.03 N (standard) solution in water	39	500 ml.
Sodium hydroxide, 0.1 N solution in water	21	1 ml.
Sodium hydroxide, 0.1 N (standard) solution in water	1,9,20	100–300 ml.
Sodium hydroxide, 0.5 N solution in water	46	20 ml.
Sodium hydroxide, N solution in water	21,29,35,40	20–25 ml.

Reagent	Experiment number	Required per student
Sodium hydroxide, 2 N solution in water	36	5 ml.
Sodium hydroxide, 3 N solution in water	12,21,46	4–400 ml.
Sodium hydroxide, 5 N solution in water	14	10 ml.
Sodium hydroxide, 19 N (saturated) solution in water	9,21	4–150 ml.
Sodium hypobromite (NaOBr), 2 per cent bromine in 1.5 N NaOH	21	1 ml.
Sodium (metal), freshly cut	21,28	50 mg.
Sodium β-naphthoquinone-4-sulfonate [see 1,2-naphthoquinone-4-sulfonate (sodium salt)]		
Sodium nitrite, 0.2 per cent solution in water	13	20 ml.
Sodium nitrite, 0.8 per cent solution in water	14	4 ml.
Sodium nitrite, 30 per cent solution in water	10,21	1–175 ml.
Sodium nitroprusside, 1 per cent solution of $Na_2Fe(CN)_5 NO \cdot 2H_2O$ in water. Prepare fresh daily.	21	1 ml.
Sodium sulfide, 10 per cent solution in water	36	20 ml.
Sodium sulfite, 10 per cent solution in 0.5 N NaOH. Discard after 1 day.	21	5 ml.
Sodium sulfite, 10 per cent solution in water. Discard after 1 day.	18	8 ml.
Sodium thiosulfate, 0.1 N (standard) solution	26	125 ml.
Solution A. Dissolve 50 mg. each of the following in 10 ml. of 2 N H_2SO_4 with the aid of heat: cytosine, hypoxanthine, 5-methylcytosine, thymine, and uracil. On standing, a precipitate will form which can be readily redissolved by warming.	37	0.1 ml.
Solution B. Dissolve the following in 10 ml. of 2 N H_2SO_4 with the aid of heat: adenine sulfate [$(C_5 H_5 N_5)_3 \cdot H_2SO_4 \cdot 2H_2O$], 50 mg.; caffeine, 50 mg.; guanine hydrochloride dihydrate, 50 mg.; theobromine, 50 mg.; theophylline, 50 mg.; and xanthine, 25 mg. If a precipitate forms, redissolve it by heating.	37	0.1 ml.
Solvent, commercial cleaning	16	1.5 liters
Spinal cords (fresh beef). Obtain from meat slaughtering company.	27	400 g.
Starch (purified)	28,29	0.5 g.
Starch (purified, whole, *not soluble*, starch), 0.20 per cent, 0.50 per cent, 1.0 per cent, 1.5 per cent, 2.0 per cent, and 2.5 per cent solutions in water. Freshly prepared solutions are stable for 48 hr. if preserved in refrigerator.	42	5 ml. each
Starch (soluble), 0.5 per cent solution in water. Triturate 5 g. of soluble starch in sufficient distilled water to make a paste. Add the paste to 900 ml. of boiling distilled water with stirring. Cool, dilute to 1 liter in a graduate, and dispense into a number of containers plugged with cotton (not rubber stopper or cork). Autoclave for 10 min. at 15 p.s.i. pressure. Starch solution in unplugged containers may be used for 3 to 4 days before gross bacterial contamination occurs. Commercial soluble-starch solutions may be used satisfactorily.	26,38	8–10 ml.
Stones, boiling	20,21	10
Sucrose, crystalline	40	4 g.
Sulfuric acid (see Acid, sulfuric)		
Sulfuric acid–nitric acid reagent (1:1 of concentrated acids)	23	4 g.

Reagent	Experiment number	Required per student
Sulfuric acid–*n*-propanol reagent (1 pt. 2 *N* H_2SO_4 to 3 pt. *n*-propanol)	37	100 ml.
Theobromine, 0.5 per cent solution in 2 *N* H_2SO_4. Dissolve 50 mg. in 10 ml. of 2 *N* H_2SO_4.	37	0.1 ml.
Theophylline, 0.5 per cent solution in 2 *N* H_2SO_4. Dissolve 50 mg. in 10 ml. of 2 *N* H_2SO_4.	37	0.1 ml.
Thread, stout	9	1 piece
Thymine, 0.5 per cent solution in 2 *N* H_2SO_4. Dissolve 50 mg. in 10 ml. of 2 *N* H_2SO_4.	37	0.1 ml.
*Thymol, 5 per cent solution in 95 per cent ethanol	36	1 ml.
Thymolphthalein indicator solution (see Indicator, thymolphthalein solution)		
Toluene	19,39,40,46	5–20 ml.
p-Toluidine (m.p. 42–43°)	44	5 g.
Toweling (Boote), test-tube-rack cover	39	1
Trichloroacetic acid (see Acid, trichloroacetic)		
Turkey red oil (sulfonated castor-bean oil)	21,31	5 ml.
L-Tyrosine, standard solution (0.5 mg. per ml. in 0.5 *N* H_2SO_4)	13	1 ml.
L-Tyrosine, technical	15	10 g.
Uracil, 0.5 per cent solution in 2 *N* H_2SO_4. Dissolve 50 mg. in 10 ml. of 2 *N* H_2SO_4.	37	0.1 ml.
Urea, 50 per cent solution in water	46	50 ml.
Urease, commercial powder	46	40 mg.
Urease, tablets (containing phosphate buffer salts)	46	2 tablets
Uric acid reagent [see Acid, phosphotungstic (Folin's improved reagent)]		
Uric acid (purified), standard solution (0.004 mg. per ml.).	46	30 ml.

Stock Solution (1 Mg. per Ml.). Transfer 0.25 g. (weighed to ±1 mg.) of purified uric acid to a 250-ml. volumetric flask. Dissolve 0.30 g. of lithium carbonate in 35 ml. of distilled water, warm the solution to 60°, warm the volumetric flask, transfer the warm lithium carbonate solution to the flask, and shake the flask until the uric acid dissolves (5 min.). Cool under running water. Add 4 ml. of 40 per cent formaldehyde solution (formalin), 70 ml. of distilled water, and (gradually) 10 ml. of *N* H_2SO_4. Dilute to the mark, mix thoroughly, and store in a glass-stoppered bottle in the dark. Dilute 1 ml. of the stock solution to 250 ml. with water in a volumetric flask and mix thoroughly.

Vitamin-D–deficient diet (see Chick diet)		
Vitamin D oil, commercial (with approximate concentration of vitamin D known)	41	20 g.
Vitamin D oil, standard (see Experiments, Appendix)	41	1 g.
Vitamin solution. Dissolve the following quantities of vita-	39	1.25 ml.

mins [or corresponding aliquots of stock vitamin solutions (in 50 per cent ethanol)] in 50 ml. of water and dilute to 100 ml. (in a graduate) with 95 per cent ethanol: thiamine chloride, 6 mg.; calcium *d*-pantothenate, 6 mg.; pyridoxine hydrochloride, 12 mg.; riboflavin, 12 mg.; *p*-aminobenzoic acid, 0.6 mg.; and biotin, 0.03 mg. Resuspend the solid, which separates, before using.

Reagent	Experiment number	Required per student
Vitamin tablet (containing nicotinic acid)	39	1
Water, special distilled	20	500 ml.
Whey powder, sweet	33	25 g.
Xanthine, 0.25 per cent solution in 2 N H_2SO_4. Dissolve 25 mg. of xanthine (with heating) in 10 ml. of 2 N H_2SO_4.	37	0.1 ml.
D-Xylose, crystalline	30,36	0.1 g.
Yeast, baker's, active dehydrated	36	1 g.
Zinc, granular	9	3 g.

Aeration. See Fig. 5 for the aeration assembly used in Exps. 21 and 36.

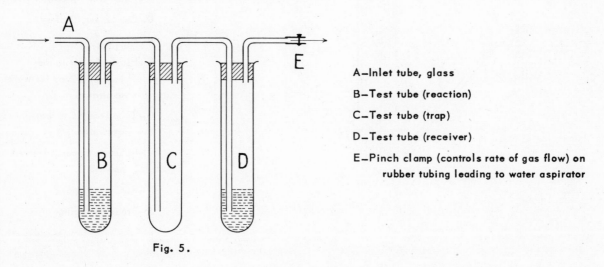

A—Inlet tube, glass

B—Test tube (reaction)

C—Test tube (trap)

D—Test tube (receiver)

E—Pinch clamp (controls rate of gas flow) on
    rubber tubing leading to water aspirator

Fig. 5.

Distillation. See Figs. 6 and 7 for the apparatus to be used in distilling liquids under atmospheric

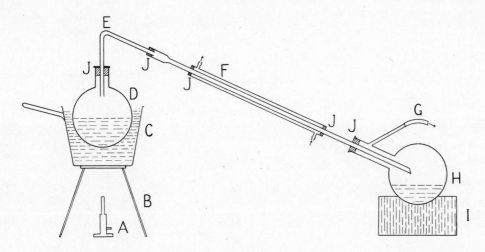

Fig. 6.

A—Burner

B—Tripod

C—Water bath

D—Flask, 2-liter round-bottomed

E—Tube, 10-mm. glass

F—Condenser, water-cooled

G—Rubber tubing (leading to sink)

H—Flask, 2-liter distilling

I —Flask support (wood or cork)

J —Corks (do not use rubber stoppers)

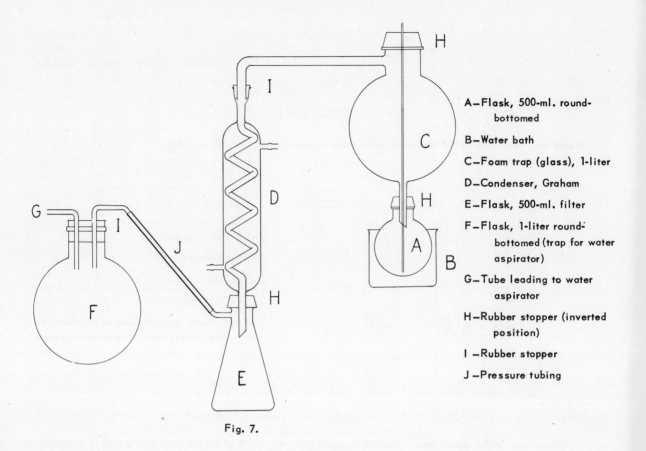

A—Flask, 500-ml. round-
        bottomed

B—Water bath

C—Foam trap (glass), 1-liter

D—Condenser, Graham

E—Flask, 500-ml. filter

F—Flask, 1-liter round-
        bottomed (trap for water
        aspirator)

G—Tube leading to water
        aspirator

H—Rubber stopper (inverted
        position)

I —Rubber stopper

J —Pressure tubing

Fig. 7.

A—Conical flask, 125-ml.

B—Test tube, 6-in. (with protruding ring of glass
        as shown)

C—Rubber stopper

D—Glass tube, inlet

E—Glass tube, outlet

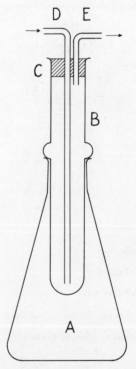

Fig. 8.

pressure and under reduced pressure. The Hopkins condenser shown in Fig. 8 is to be used in Exps. 21, 25, and 35 for refluxing liquids. Distilling apparatus should be set up properly especially to avoid closed systems which would explode during distillation. In distilling under reduced pressure, turn on the water aspirator *before* applying heat, disconnect the tubing leading to the water aspirator before removing the source of heat when discontinuing distillation, and employ only round-bottomed flasks.

Inflammable solvents (diethyl ether, acetone, and petroleum ether) should be distilled at atmospheric pressure, using steam from the house line or hot water heated some distance away but *never* with an open flame. Other solvents (benzene, alcohols, and higher boiling ethers) may be distilled safely by means of an electric hot plate or mantle with covered heating elements or with a flame-heated water bath.

Filtration. Relatively large amounts of suspensions may be filtered most conveniently under reduced pressure on a Buchner funnel and relatively small amounts on a Hirsch funnel. A precipitate on the funnel should be washed by disconnecting the tube leading from the filter flask to the water aspirator, adding the wash liquid to the funnel, stirring the precipitate and wash liquid in such a manner that no fibers are detached from the filter paper, and reapplying suction.

Filtration of colloidal materials, which filter slowly because of clogging of the pores of the filter paper, may be facilitated by depositing a layer (by filtering a suspension) of filter aid on the filter paper before introducing the colloidal product. Colloidal material may also be filtered effectively by gravity on a fluted filter (Robertson, 1943).

Cleaning Glassware. All glassware, especially that in special apparatus, is expensive and difficult to replace. It should be handled with great care to avoid inconvenience to the class and the assessment of breakage bills.

In cleaning glassware, *first* remove as much of the foreign material as possible with the aid of soap solution and a brush or other mechanical means. Following this preliminary cleaning, dissolve remaining deposits in tap water, acetone or methanol, tap water, and distilled water, in the order given. Allow the washed apparatus to drain and dry. If desired, traces of moisture may be removed quickly by passing hot air from a dryer (gas-heated, with compressed-air attachment) through the apparatus.

If the apparatus is not clean after the water has drained, add sufficient (avoid excess) stock cleaning solution to wet the entire inner surface of the flask, pour any excess cleaning solution into the stock bottle, add 1 to 5 ml. of water to the apparatus, rotate the apparatus so that the (now hot) cleaning liquid will come into contact with the entire surface, and allow the cleaning liquid to stand in the apparatus for 5 min. Rinse the apparatus thoroughly with tap water and then with distilled water. Discard the spent (reduced) cleaning solution, which has changed color from the initial reddish brown to a dark green.

Stock cleaning solution is prepared by mixing (*Cautiously*) 200 ml. of concentrated sulfuric acid with 7 ml. of saturated sodium dichromate solution. It is extremely corrosive and should be handled with great caution. Rags soaked with cleaning solution may ignite spontaneously and should not be stored in the locker.

Melting Point. The purity of the substance prepared in Exp. 27 and the identity of the substances investigated in Exps. 21 and 36 may be determined by means of their melting points.

Melting-point tubes are prepared by heating a test tube or thin-walled glass tubing uniformly over a small area until the glass is thoroughly softened, removing the heated area from the flame, immediately drawing the glass until the heated part is drawn to the desired diameter, cutting the tube to the proper length, and sealing one end in the edge of the flame. Use an oxygen or compressed-air gas flame to soften pyrex glass.

A quantity of the dried material sufficient to form a layer 6 to 8 mm. deep is placed in a 1 to 2-mm. capillary tube (prepared as described) 8 to 10 cm. in length. It is convenient to pack the powder by drawing a triangular file across the tube and by tapping the tube sharply on the desk. Attach the tube to a thermometer with the sample directly opposite the bulb by means of a small rubber band or a helix constructed from resistance wire (B. & S. gauge No. 28).

The student's thermometer should be checked against a calibrated thermometer by the following procedure: Immerse both thermometers to the same depth in a suitable liquid heated at least 10° above the temperature at which the substance melts, allow the bath to cool in air, and observe simultaneously the temperatures recorded on the two thermometers. Prepare a table of these data, which should be used as the basis of temperature corrections to be applied to the student's thermometer. Fixed points for thermometer calibration are given in chemical handbooks.

pH. pH defined by Sörensen in 1909 as the negative logarithm of the hydrogen-ion concentration ($-\log[H^+]$, or $\log 1/[H^+]$), is commonly determined by photometric and electrometric methods. The approximate pH may be determined photometrically by comparing the colors (intensities and tints) of an unknown and standard buffer solutions of known pH values to which the same small volumes of an indicator solution have been added. Bromthymol blue, which changes color from yellow to blue over the pH range 6.0 to 7.6, is an example of an indicator used for this purpose.

pH is determined electrometrically with the hydrogen electrode, the quinhydrone electrode, and the glass electrode. The principle of all electrometric methods is the determination (with a voltmeter) of the potential difference between two half cells joined by a salt bridge. One half cell is a standard cell of constant potential, usually the calomel cell (saturated $HgCl_2$ solution in contact with metallic mercury by means of a KCl bridge). The other half cell is the solution of unknown pH (that is, potential). pH is calculated from the equation, $pH = (E - 0.243)/0.059$, where E is volts measured as potential difference between the two half cells.

The glass electrode consists of a glass bulb which (a) contains a fixed solution of constant pH and a metal– metal salt (such as Ag-AgCl) electrode of constant potential and which (b) is immersed in a solution of unknown pH with liquid-junction contact to a calomel (or other cell). Sensitive vacuum-tube potentiometers are required to measure the potential, since glass bulbs of relatively high resistance are commonly used. The accuracy of the measurement is limited to about 0.02 pH unit, primarily because of variations in the liquid-junction potential. It is also necessary to shield the glass membranes from the effects of induced currents. The glass electrode method is widely used, since it is convenient, rapid, and adaptable to colored, turbid, and viscous solutions. pH values below 0 and above 10 cannot be determined accurately with the glass electrode because of the variable hydration of the hydrogen ion on the one hand and the varying permeability of the glass for metal ions on the other. The operation of the pH meter to be used in the present experiments will be explained and demonstrated by the instructor.

Photometry. For discussions of the principles and applications of photometry see reviews by Strafford (1936), Drabkin in Glasser (1944), Gibb (1942), Snell and Snell (1948), Yoe (1928), Summerson (1939), Müller (1939), and Vredenburg (1950).

Photometry is the technique employed in determining the concentration of a substance dissolved in water or other solvent by means of the ultraviolet (200 to 400 mμ[1]), infrared (800 to 1,500 mμ) or visible (410 to 810 mμ) light which is transmitted. In photometric analysis, light (preferably nearly monochromatic of a particular wave length) is passed through a solution of a colored substance, the amount of absorbed light is compared with that absorbed by a known concentration of the pure substance in a standard solution, and the concentration of the substance in the unknown solution is calculated from these data. Visual photometric analysis is performed with a visual colorimeter (named, more correctly, comparator), such as that shown in Fig. 9 (shown on following page), by determining the depth (thickness) of the unknown colored solution required to give the same color intensity as that of a fixed depth of a standard solution. This is accomplished by lengthening or shortening the light path (lowering or raising the glass plunger in the colorimeter cup) and matching the color fields (one half from the unknown and the other from the standard solution).

The absorption and transmission of light by an absorbing medium are expressed by the Beer-Lambert equation, $\log I_0/I = kcl$, where I_0 is the incident light, I is the transmitted light, k is the extinction coefficient, c is the concentration of the absorbing material, and l is the thickness (in centimeters) of the absorbing solution. Some of the light which is passed into an absorbing layer is absorbed and a fraction $(1/x)$ is transmitted. The intensity of the light transmitted is $I_0(1/x)$ when the absorbing layer is of unit thickness, $I_0(1/x)(1/x)$ for two layers, $I_0(1/x^3)$ for three layers, and $I_0(1/x^1)$ for l layers. Taking $\log_x$ of both sides of the equation $I = I_0(1/x^1)$ gives $l = \log_x I_0/I$. Since the logarithm of any number to the base 10 is related to the logarithm of this number to another base by a constant, $\log_{10} I_0/I = k \log_x I_0/I$, and $\log_{10} I_0/I = kl$. The last expression is the Beer-Lambert relation at unit concentration.

[1] 1 mμ (millimicron) = 10 A. (angstrom units) = 10^{-9}cm.

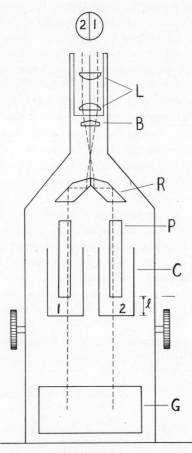

L — Lens system

B — Biprism

R — Rhomboid prism

P — Glass plunger

C — Cup

G — Reflector, mirror (one side) and frosted
    glass plate (other side)

l — Light path

Fig. 9.

For solutions of different concentrations, light transmissions may be made equal by adjusting the length of the light paths (depths of the solutions). Under these conditions

$$\log_{10} I_0/I_1 = \log_{10} I_0'/I_2 = k_1 c_1 l_1 = k_2 c_2 l_2.$$

Since $k_1 = k_2$ (for the same solute), $c_1 l_1 = c_2 l_2$ This relation (Beer's law) is commonly employed in visual photometric procedures, but it holds strictly only when the light source is monochromatic (or composed of narrow spectral band obtained with a filter). The relationship is invalidated also for solutes which associate, dissociate, or shift in equilibrium on dilution. At similar concentrations (where l_1 and l_2 differ by only about 5 mm.) of solute in the unknown and standard solutions, the relationship holds approximately. The concentration of solute in the unknown may be determined by determining the color intensities of different concentrations of the pure solute in a series of solutions, plotting these experimental values, drawing a smooth curve, and interpolating this standard curve.

A diagram of the Duboscq visual colorimeter is shown in Fig. 9. In carrying out a photometric analysis with a visual colorimeter, attention should be given to the following points:

1. Wash the cups and glass plungers with distilled water and dry them carefully with lens paper to avoid scratching the glass surfaces. Be careful not to crack or chip these glass parts.

2. Place the cups in position in the instrument and raise each cup by rotating its control wheel until the plunger makes gentle but firm contact with the bottom of the cup. The reading on each scale should be zero. If not, consult the instructor, who will adjust the scales.

3. Observe the circular field through the eyepiece. The entire field should be nearly colorless and of uniform appearance. If one half of the field differs perceptibly from the other, change the angle of the mirror, the focus of the lenses by adjusting the eyepiece, or the position of the colorimeter with reference to the source of light.

4. Lower the cups to their original positions, remove the cups, and rinse them with the standard solution. Half fill each cup with the standard solution and place the cups in position in the instrument.

5. Raise the left cup until the scale reading is 20.0 mm. (thickness of the solution from the bottom of the cup to the bottom of the plunger). Make certain that all air bubbles have been displaced.

6. Raise the right cup until the color intensity of one half field, observed through the eyepiece, appears to match exactly that of the other half field. Note that the color of the right half field reflects the solution in the left cup, and *vice versa*. Record the scale reading. Repeat these manipulations four times and record each scale reading. Raise the right cup until the scale reading is 1 or 2 mm. less than that observed when the color intensities appeared to be matched. Lower the cup until the color intensities of the two half fields appear to match exactly. Repeat these manipulations four times and record the scale readings. The averages of the two sets of scale readings should agree within 0.1 mm., and the average value should differ from the scale reading of the left cup by not more than 0.1 mm. If the values disagree more than this amount, repeat the described procedures.

7. Lower the right cup and discard the solution. Rinse the cup twice with the unknown solution and half fill the cup with this solution. Adjust the right cup until the half fields of the unknown and the standard match. Record and average the readings approached from above and below the matching point as described. If the average scale reading of the unknown differs from that of the standard by more than 5 mm., repeat the determination using a standard solution of different concentration.

8. Discard the solutions, rinse the cups and plungers with distilled water, and wipe the cups and plungers with lens paper and the metal parts of the instrument with a towel. Replace the instrument in its container.

Photoelectric colorimeters (see Figs. 10 and 11) are usually graduated to give optical density (absorbance) amd per cent transmission (transmittance). The light, rendered essentially monochromatic

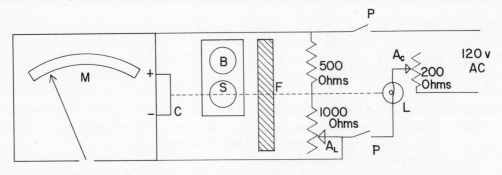

Fig. 10.

M—Microammeter (calibrated as optical density and per cent transmission)

C—Photovoltaic cell

S—Sample tube

B—Blank tube

F—Filter

P—Push button (on and off switch)

A_c—Coarse adjustment (controls light intensity)

A_e—Fine adjustment (controls light intensity)

L—Projector lamp

by passage through a filter, is passed through water or a blank solution containing all unknown components except the chromogenic substance, and the instrument is adjusted for zero optical density, or 100 per cent transmission. Solutions containing the chromogen at various concentrations are placed in turn in the light path, and the optical density is read from the scale. Measurements are made usually with light of the wave length at which the unknown colored compound exhibits maximum absorption.

Optical density is defined as $\log I_0/I$ and per cent transmission as $100I/I_0$. Since $\log I_0/I = kcl$, $c = (1/kl)_x(\log I_0/I)$, and a plot of c against $\log I_0/I$ on millimeter coordinate paper gives a straight line of slope $1/kl$. The light-path length is kept constant by use of matched glass containers (cuvettes) in the form of test tubes or rectangular glass cells. In measurements of per cent transmission $(100I/I_0)$, $c = -1/kl (\log 100I/I_0)$, and a straight line results if c is plotted against $100I/I_0$ on semilogarithmic

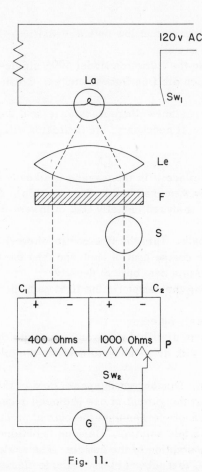

120 v AC

L_a —Projector lamp

L_e —Lens

F —Filter

S —Sample or blank

C_1 —Photovoltaic cell (standard)

C_2 —Photovoltaic cell (variable resistance)

P —Potentiometer (logarithmic scale units)

G —Galvanometer (indicator when balancing circuit)

Sw_1 —Light switch

Sw_2 —Galvanometer switch (when closed galvanometer is shunted from circuit)

Fig. 11.

paper (transmission as the vertical logarithmic axis). Optical density and per cent transmission may be compared at any concentration of a chromogen since

$$\frac{1}{kl}\log\frac{I_0}{I} = -\frac{1}{kl}\log\frac{I}{I_0} = -\frac{1}{kl}\log\left(100\,\frac{I}{I_0}\,\frac{1}{100}\right) = -\frac{1}{kl}\left(\log 100\,\frac{I}{I_0} - \log 2\right)$$

or   Optical density = log 2 − log per cent transmission

  Single-photocell colorimeters[2] are designed so that light passing through a colored solution and impinging upon a photoelectric cell generates a current proportional to the intensity of the light. The current is measured by means of a microammeter. The difference in currents produced by two photocells (one receiving light directly from the source and the other after it has passed through the colored solution) is measured by means of the two-photocell instruments.[3]

  Two principal types of photocells, the barrier-layer or photovoltaic cell and the high-vacuum cell, are used in the two-cell photometers. The former consists of a photosensitive surface (cuprous oxide or selenium semiconducting layer on a plate of copper or iron covered by a light-transmitting layer of metal) which, on exposure to light, liberates electrons and produces current. This cell requires a simple circuit for measurement of the current, which is nearly proportional to the intensity of the light. The latter type of photocell consists of a highly evacuated cell with a composite cesium cathode. When a potential is applied, the cathode becomes photosensitive and a current is generated which is proportional to the intensity of the light received by the cell. This current (in contrast to that generated by barrier-layer

[2] Lumetron Model 400A, Cenco-Sheard, Sanford, Evelyn, Fisher, Hellige-Diller, Kromatrol, Leitz, Pfaltz and Bauer, and Yoe and Crumpler.

[3] Aminco Type F, Klett-Summerson, Lumetron Model 402, Spekker, and Waco.

cells) may be amplified, making possible accurate measurements at low optical densities. More complicated circuits are required for operation of the high-vacuum cell.

The following points should be observed when using the Lumetron Model 400A single-cell photometer

1. Obtain at least two matched 6-in. test tubes which are free from scratches. Clean and dry the tubes.

2. Plug the power cord of the instrument into the constant-voltage transformer and the power cord of the transformer into a 105- to 125-volt, 60-cycle, a-c line. If necessary, the instructor will adjust the (lower scale) zero setting of the microammeter.

3. Insert the proper filter in the light path.

4. Fill a matched tube with the blank solution and place it in the opening (marked B in Fig. 10) so that the mark near the lip of the tube faces you (the tubes were matched in this position). Similarly, fill a second matched tube with the standard or sample to be analyzed (usually that of lowest intensity) and place the tube in the opening (marked S) as described.

5. Move the holder to bring the blank in the light path. Turn the fine-control (lower) knob to a central position. Press the push button and turn first the coarse-control knob and then the fine-control knob until the needle rests on the line of the scale indicating zero optical density.

6. Release the push button, move the holder to bring the sample in the light path, press the button, and observe the reading.

7. Repeat steps 5 and 6 until the readings are closely agreeing.

8. Remove the sample tube, rinse the tube twice with distilled water and once with the sample solution of next higher intensity, or rinse the tube twice with distilled water and dry the tube, and fill the tube with the sample solution.

9. Rinse the matched tubes and allow them to drain. Disconnect the power cord of the instrument.

The Klett-Summerson photometer is designed so that the current of one photocell receiving light directly from the source is balanced (by a null-point galvanometer) against the current produced a second photocell receiving light which has passed through the sample solution. Balance is obtained by means of a potentiometer which indicates on a scale the light absorption of the sample. The scale is graduated in optical density (multiplied by 500) units; matched 5-in. test tubes (14-mm. outside diameter) are used; and three filters are employed [No. 42, blue range (400 to 465 mμ); No. 54, green range (500 to 570 mμ); and No. 66, red range (640 to 700 mμ)].

Observe the following points when using the Klett-Summerson photometer.

1. Clean and dry 5-in. matched test tubes.

2. Plug the power cord of the instrument into a 110- to 120-volt, 60-cycle, a-c or d-c power line.

3. Insert the proper light filter into the holder and place the latter in the space provided between the lamp housing and the tube holder.

4. Adjust the pointer (by means of the knob directly above) until it coincides with the line (*only* with the lamp off).

5. Turn the large-scale knob until the scale reading is zero. Turn on the light switch and place a matched tube containing the blank solution in the tube holder with the mark on the tube facing you. Open the galvanometer switch (right side of instrument), adjust the pointer (which swings when the switch is on) to coincide with the line by means of the knob (left side of test-tube holder), and, after waiting several minutes, readjust the pointer.

6. Replace the tube with one containing a standard or unknown solution, turn the large-scale knob until the pointer coincides with the line, and record the scale reading. Adjust the instrument again, using blank and unknown solutions to obtain check readings, which should agree within 1 per cent.

7. Remove the sample tube and replace it with one containing solution of next higher intensity and repeat the described manipulations.

8. Rinse the matched tubes and turn off the switches to the lamp and the galvanometer.

The concentrations of colored substances are to be determined photometrically in Exps. 13 and 1 (tyrosine), 18 (cystine), 23 and 43 (phosphate), 35 (glucose), 45 (cholesterol), and 46 (ammonia).

Polarimetry. The principles and applications of polarimetry have been reviewed by Bates and associates (1942), Brown and Zerban (1941), Weissberger (1946), and Forrest in Glasser (1944).

Polarimetry is the technique used in measuring the number of angular degrees to which the plane of polarized light is rotated by a solution of an optically active substance. Polarized light (vibrates in a single plane) is produced by passing white light through a nicol prism [two wedge-shaped pieces of calcite (crystalline calcium carbonate) cemented together with canada balsam]. The plane of polarization may be rotated to the right (dextro) or the left (levo) depending upon the structure and spatial configuration of the optically active substance. The rotations of the antipodes of an optically active substance are equal in magnitude but opposite in sign.

Optical rotation is measured with a polarimeter under arbitrary conditions, and the specific rotation, characteristic of each optically active substance, is calculated from the equation

$$[\alpha]_D^t = \frac{\alpha \times 100}{l \times p \times d} = \frac{\alpha \times 100}{l \times c}$$

where α = observed angle of rotation
t = temperature, $^\circ$C
D = wave length (5,890 A.) of sodium line
l = length of polarimetric tube, dm.
p = grams of solute per 100 g. of solution
d = density of solution
c = grams of solute per 100 ml. of solution ($c = p \times d$)

The principle of the polarimeter is shown in Fig. 12. The light (L) entering the polarimeter is divided into two rays; one (shown) emerges from the polarizer (P) polarized, and the other (not shown)

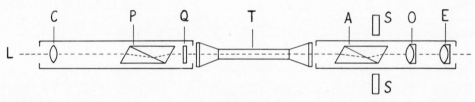

Fig. 12.

A—Analyzer	O—Objective
C—Condensing lens	P—Polarizer
E—Eyepiece	Q—Quartz plate
L—Light source (sodium-vapor lamp, electric)	S —Scale
	T—Tube

is bent, reflected, and absorbed. The phase of the plane-polarized light is altered half a wave length by the quartz plate (Q) which covers half the field in causing the field to be half shadowed.

The Spencer polarimeter with Lippich half-shade polarizer (Spencer Lens Company, Buffalo, New York) has been found satisfactory for use by students under the conditions described in this manual. The analyzer and polarizer consist of Polaroid disks in place of the usual nicol prisms. The polarizer is made of two pieces of Polaroid sheet, one covering the entire aperture and the other (narrow strip) covering the central part. There is produced by this means a central dark field with which the two adjacent fields (produced by light passing through the solution) are matched when the end point is reached. Polaroid, a polarizing material in sheet form, consists of microscopic needles of iodoquinone embedded in cellulose nitrate or other matrix. All the needles are orientated in the same direction.

Pressure. Atmospheric-pressure values of use in Exp. 10 are obtained by reading a barometer in the laboratory. In determining the corrected reading, subtract the appropriate value interpolated from the following list of corrections at the indicated temperatures: 15° (2 mm.), 20° (2.5 mm.), 25° (3.0 mm.), and 30° (3.5 mm.). The corrections are to reduce readings of a mercurial barometer with a brass scale to 0°C.

BIBLIOGRAPHY

Abderhalden, E., and Gebelein, F. 1926. Über Decarboxylierung von Aminosäuren unter Bildung der entsprechenden Amine und über die Darstellung der Enolform von, 2,5-Dioxo-piperazinen. *Z. physiol. Chem.*, *152*, 125.

—— and Schmidt, H. 1911. Über die Verwendung von Triketohydrindenhydrat zum Nachweis von Eiweiss-stoffen und deren Abbaustufen. *Z. physiol. Chem. 72*, 37.

—— and ——. 1913. Einige Beobachtungen und Versuche mit Triketohydrindenhydrat (Ruhemann). *Z. physiol. Chem.*, *85*, 143.

—— and Weil, A. 1911. Über den Gehalt ägyptischer Mumien an Eiweiss und Eiweissabbauprodukten. *Z. physiol. Chem.*, *72*, 15.

Abrams, R., Hammarsten, E., and Shemin, D. 1948. Glycine as a precursor of purines in yeast. *J. Biol. Chem.*, *173*, 429.

Abul-Fadl, M. A. M., and King, E. J. 1949. Properties of the acid phosphatases of erythrocytes and of the human prostate gland. *Biochem. J.*, *45*, 51.

Acree, S. F., 1906—1907. On the detection of formaldehyde in milk. *J. Biol. Chem.*, *2*, 145.

——. 1921. Mucic acid, etc. *Brit. Pat. 160,777 (1921). Chem. Abstracts, 15*, 2545.

Adamkiewicz, A. 1874. Farbenreaktionen des Albumin. *Arch. ges. Physiol.*, *9*, 156.

Adams, J., Acker, M., and Frediani, H. S. 1947. Iodimetric titrimetric determination of ascorbic acid. *J. Am. Pharm. Assoc.*, *36*, 170.

Agulhon, H. 1911. Recherche colorimetrique de l'alcool en présence de l'acetone. Réactions colorées de certains groupements organiques en présence d'acides mineraux et de bichromate de potassium. *Bull. soc. chim.* (4) *9*, 881.

Albanese, A. A., and Irby, V. 1944. Determination of urinary amino nitrogen by the copper method. *J. Biol. Chem.*, *153*, 583.

Alexander, B., Landwehr, G., and Seligman, A. M. 1945. A specific micromethod for the colorimetric determination of glycine in blood and urine. *J. Biol. Chem.*, *160*, 51.

—— and Seligman, A. M. 1945. A colorimetic method for the microdetermination of α-alanine in blood. *J. Biol. Chem.*, *159*, 9.

Almquist, H. J. 1946. Interrelations between choline, betaine, and methionine. *Science*, *103*, 722.

American Can Company. 1943. The Canned Food Reference Manual, 2d ed. American Can Company, New York.

Andersch, M. A. 1946. The determination of serum amylase, with particular reference to the use of β-amylose as the substrate. *J. Biol. Chem.*, *166*, 705.

Anderson, E., and Otis, L. 1930. The composition and structure of mesquite gum. *J. Am. Chem. Soc.*, *52*, 4461.

—— and Sands, L. 1925. Preparation of *l*-arabinose from mesquite gum. *Ind. Eng. Chem.*, *17*, 1257.

—— and ——. 1926. The composition of mesquite gum; the isolation of *d*-galactose and *l*-arabinose. *J. Am. Chem. Soc.*, *48*, 3172.

—— and ——. 1941. *l*-Arabinose. *Org. Syntheses*, Coll. Vol. 1, 67.

——, ——, and Sturgis, N. 1925. Some plant gums of the Southwestern United States. *Am. J. Pharm.*, *97*, 589.

Andrews, J. C., and Andrews, K. C. 1937. Substances which inhibit color development in the Sullivan method for cystine. *J. Biol. Chem.*, *118*, 555.

Anson, M. L. 1937. Estimation of papain with hemoglobin. *J. Gen. Physiol.*, *20*, 561.

Arhimo, A. A. 1939. The determination of small amounts of aspartic acid by the malic acid method of Pucher. *Suomen Kemistilehti, 12B*, 6.

Armitage, F. D. 1943. A systematic identification of starches. *Ind. Chemist, 19*, 383, 398.

Arnow, L. E. 1937. Colorimetric determination of the components of 3,4-dihydroxyphenylalanine-tyrosine mixtures. *J. Biol. Chem.*, *118*, 531.

Association of Official Agricultural Chemists. 1945. Official and Tentative Methods of Analysis, 6th ed. Washington, D.C.

Association of Vitamin Chemists. 1947. Methods of Vitamin Assay, Interscience Publishers, New York.

Bacher, J. E., and Allen, F. W. 1950. Mild dephosphorylation of pyrimidine nucleotides. *Federation Proc.*, *9*, 148.

Bailey, K., Chibnall, A. C., Rees, M. W., and Williams, E. F. 1943. Critique of the Foreman method for the estimation of the dicarboxylic acids in protein hydrolysates. *Biochem. J.*, *37*, 360.

Bailey, W. H., and Roe, J. H. 1944. Studies of the metabolism of mannose. The influence of mannose administration on blood sugar, blood lactic acid, and liver glycogen in the adult rabbit. *J. Biol. Chem., 152*, 135.

Baker, J. L., and Hulton, H.F. E. 1910. The estimation of lactose in the presence of the commonly-occurring sugars. *Analyst, 35*, 512.

Balch, R. T. 1941. Rapid determination of starch (root) with sodium hypochlorite. *Ind. Eng. Chem., Anal. Ed., 13*, 246.

Bálint, P. 1938. Stufenphotometrische Tyrosin-, Tryptophan-, and Cystinbestimmung (auf Grund des kolorimetrischen Verfahrens von Folin und Marenzi). *Biochem. Z., 299*, 133.

Ballou, G. A., and Luck, J. M. 1941. The effects of different buffers on the activity of β-amylase. *J. Biol. Chem., 139*, 233.

Balls, A. K., and Lineweaver, H. 1939. Isolation and properties of crystalline papain. *J. Biol. Chem., 130*, 669.

——, Swenson, T. L., and Stuart, L. S. 1935. Assay of papain. *J. Assoc. Offic. Agr. Chemists, 18*, 140.

——, Thompson, R. R., and Jones, W. W. 1940. Crude papain, preparation and properties. *Ind. Eng. Chem., 32*, 1144.

——, ——, and Walden, M. K., 1946. A crystalline protein with β-amylase activity, prepared from sweet potatoes. *J. Biol. Chem., 163*, 571.

Bang, I. 1906. Zur Methodik der Zuckerbestimmung. *Biochem. Z., 2*, 271.

Barfoed, C. 1873. Über die Nachweisung des Traubenzuckers neben Dextrin und verwandten Körpern. *Z. anal. Chem., 12*, 27.

Barger, G. 1930. Some Applications of Organic Chemistry to Biology and Medicine, Chap. V, Blue adsorption compounds of iodine. McGraw-Hill Book Company, Inc., New York.

Barham, H. N., Kramer, G., and Reed, G. N. 1943. Influence of various factors on the starch content of Kansas-grown potatoes and sweet potatoes. *J. Agr. Research, 67*, 395.

——, Wagoner, J. A., Campbell, C. L., and Harclerode, E. H. 1946. The chemical composition of some sorghum grains and the properties of their starches. *Kans. State Coll. Agr. Expt. Sta., Tech. Bull. 61*, p. 5.

Barker, S. B. 1949. Metabolic functions of the endocrine systems. *Ann. Rev. Physiol., 11*, 45.

—— and Summerson, W. H. 1941. The colorimetric determination of lactic acid in biological material. *J. Biol. Chem., 138*, 535.

Barton-Wright, E. C. 1944. The microbiological assay of nicotinic acid in cereals and other products. *Biochem. J., 38*, 314.

——. 1945. The theory and practice of the microbiological assay of the vitamin-B complex; together with the assay of selected amino acids and potassium. *Analyst, 70*, 283.

Bates, F. J., and associates. 1942. Polarimetry, Saccharimetry and the Sugars. U.S. Government Printing Office, Washington, D. C.

Bates, F. L., French, D., and Rundle, R. E. 1943. Amylose and amylopectin content of starches determined by their iodine complex formation. *J. Am. Chem. Soc., 65*, 142.

Bauer, C. W., and Martin, W. F. 1948. Stability and activity of salivary amylase. *J. Am. Pharm. Assoc., 37*, 188.

Baumann, E. 1886. Über eine einfache Methode der Darstellung von Benzöesäureäthern. *Ber., 19*, 3218.

Baumstark, F. 1885. Über eine neue Methode, das Gehirn chemisch zu erforschen, und deren bisherige Ergebnisse. *Z. physiol. Chem., 9*, 145.

Baur, H. 1949. Tierische Phosphatasen. *Z. Vitamin-, Hormon- u. Fermentforsch., 2*, 507.

Beach, E. F., Bernstein, S. S., Hoffman, O.D., Teague, D. M., and Macy, I.G. 1941. Distribution of nitrogen and protein amino acids in human and in cow's milk. *J. Biol. Chem., 139*, 57.

Bear, R. S. 1942. The significance of the "V" X-ray diffraction patterns of starches. *J. Am. Chem. Soc., 64*, 1388.

——. 1944. Complex formation between starch and organic molecules. *J. Am. Chem. Soc., 66*, 2122.

Beard, H. H. 1935. Coefficients of correlation between the nitrogenous constituents of the urine after ingestion of low, normal and high protein diets. *Human Biology, 7*, 419.

Beerstecher, E., Jr., and Shive, W. 1947. Tryptophan as a competitive growth inhibiting analog of phenylalanine. *J. Am. Chem. Soc., 69*, 461.

Behre, J. A. 1928. A clinical test for urinary acetone and diacetic acid. *J. Lab. Clin. Med., 13*, 770.

——. 1940. A modified salicylaldehyde method for the determination of acetone bodies in blood and urine. *J. Biol. Chem., 136*, 25.

—— and Benedict, S. R. 1926. A colorimetric method for the determination of acetone bodies in blood and urine. *J. Biol. Chem., 70*, 487.

Behrens, O. K., Doherty, D. G., and Bergmann, M. 1940. Resolution of DL-phenylalanine by asymmetric enzymatic synthesis. *J. Biol. Chem., 136*, 61.

Bell, R. D., and Doisy, E. A. 1920. Rapid colorimetric methods for the determination of phosphorus in urine and blood. *J. Biol. Chem.*, *44*, 55.

Benedict, S. R. 1907. The detection and estimation of reducing sugars. *J. Biol. Chem.*, *3*, 101.

——. 1908–1909. A reagent for the detection of reducing sugars. *J. Biol. Chem.*, *5*, 485.

——. 1911. The detection and estimation of glucose in urine. *J. Am. Med. Assoc.*, *57*, 1193.

——. 1915. On the colorimetric determination of uric acid in blood. *J. Biol. Chem.*, *20*, 629.

——. 1918. A modification of the Lewis-Benedict method for the determination of sugar in the blood. *J. Biol. Chem.*, *34*, 203.

——. 1931. The analysis of whole blood. II. The determination of sugar and of saccharoids (non-fermentable copper-reducing substances). *J. Biol. Chem.*, *92*, 141.

—— and Behre, J. A. 1936. Some applications of a new color reaction for creatinine. *J. Biol. Chem.*, *114*, 515.

—— and Franke, E. 1922. A method for the direct determination of uric acid in urine. *J. Biol. Chem.*, *52*, 387.

—— and Hitchcock, E. H. 1915. On the colorimetric estimation of uric acid in urine. *J. Biol. Chem.*, *20*, 619.

—— and Osterberg, E. 1918. A method for the determination of sugar in normal urine. *J. Biol. Chem.*, *34*, 195.

Berggren, R. E. L. 1932. The application of the Fiske-Subbarow colorimetric method to the determination of phosphorus in casein. *J. Biol. Chem.*, *95*, 461.

Bergmann, M., and Fruton, J. S. 1941. The specificity of the proteinases. *Advances in Enzymol.*, *1*, 63.

—— and Niemann, C. 1937. On the structure of proteins: cattle hemoglobin, egg albumin, cattle fibrin, and gelatin. *J. Biol. Chem.*, *118*, 301.

—— and ——. 1938. On the structure of silk fibroin. *J. Biol. Chem.*, *122*, 577.

Bertrand, G. 1891. Recherches sur quelques dérives du xylose. *Bull. soc. chim.* (3), *5*, 554.

Bessey, O. A. 1938a. Vitamin C. Methods of assay and dietary sources. *J. Am. Med. Assoc.*, *111*, 1290.

——. 1938b. A method for the determination of small quantities of ascorbic acid and dehydroascorbic acid in turbid and colored solutions in the presence of other reducing substances. *J. Biol. Chem.*, *126*, 771.

—— and King, C. G. 1933. The distribution of vitamin C in plant and animal tissues, and its determination. *J. Biol. Chem.*, *103*, 687.

Best, C. H., Hershey, J. M., and Huntsman, M. E. 1932. The effect of lecithin on fat deposition in the liver of the normal rat. *J. Physiol.*, *75*, 56.

Bethke, R. M., Steenbock, H., and Nelson, M. T. 1923–1924. Fat-soluble vitamins. XV. Calcium and phosphorus relations to growth and composition of blood and bone with varying vitamin intake. *J. Biol. Chem.*, *58*, 71.

Bial, M. 1902. Die Diagnosie der Pentosurie. *Deut. med. Wochschr.*, *28*, 253.

Bills, C. E. 1935. Physiology of the sterols, including vitamin D. *Physiol. Revs.*, *15*, 1.

——. 1947. Vitamin D assay — line test and chemical methods. *Biol. Symposia*, *12*, 409.

Bish, E. J. B. 1929. The determination of small quantities of starch in vegetable tissue. *Biochem. J.*, *23*, 31.

Bishop, J. P. 1944. Extending the use of products from corn in postwar processed foods. *Proc. Inst. Food. Technol.*, 5th conf., 125.

Blanchetière. A. 1927. Séparation et dosage des 2,5-diacipiperazines en présence des amino-acides et des péptides. *Bull. soc. chim.* (4), *41*, 101.

Blanksma, J. J. 1909. Over de constitutie van het oxymethylfurfural. *Chem. Weekblad*, *6*, 1047; Cent. *1910*, I, 539.

Blatherwick, N. R., Bradshaw, P. J., Cullimore, O. S., Ewing, M. E., Larson, H. W., and Sawyer, S. D. 1936. The metabolism of d-xylose. *J. Biol. Chem.*, *113*, 405.

Bloch, K., and Schoenheimer, R. 1941. The biological precursors of creatine. *J. Biol. Chem.*, *138*, 167.

Block, R. J. 1946. The isolation and synthesis of the naturally occurring α-amino acids. *Chem. Revs.*, *38*, 501.

—— and Bolling, D. 1939. Chemical metabolic studies on phenylalanine. I. The nitration of phenylalanine. *J. Biol. Chem.*, *129*, 1.

—— and ——. 1940. The Determination of the Amino Acids. Burgess Publishing Company, Minneapolis, Minn.

—— and ——. 1945. The Amino Acid Composition of Proteins and Foods. Charles C. Thomas, Publisher, Springfield, Ill.

——, ——, and Kondritzer, A. A. 1940. Microestimation of leucine, isoleucine, and valine. *Proc. Soc. Exptl. Biol. Med.*, *45*, 289.

Bloor, W. R. 1943. Biochemistry of the Fatty Acids. Reinhold Publishing Corporation, New York.

Bodansky, A. 1933. Phosphatase studies. II. Determination of serum phosphatase. Factors influencing the accuracy of the determination. *J. Biol. Chem.*, *101*, 93.

—— and Jaffe, H. L. 1934. Phosphatase. Serum phosphatase in diseases of the bone: interpretation and significance. *Arch. Internal Med.*, *54*, 88.

Bodansky, M., and Bodansky, O. 1940. Biochemistry of Disease. The Macmillan Company, New York.

Bollinger, A. J. 1944. Color reactions for sugars. I. Identification and determination of monosaccharides with thymol, HCl and FeCl₃. *Proc. Roy. Soc., N. S., Wales*, *77*, 109.

Bolomey, R. A., and Kemmerer, A. R. 1947. Spectrophotometric studies of the Roe method for the determination of dehydroascorbic acid. *J. Biol. Chem.*, *167*, 781.

Bonsnes, R. W., and Taussky, H. H. 1945. On the colorimetric determination of creatinine by the Jaffe reaction. *J. Biol. Chem.*, *158*, 581.

Bopp, F. 1849. Einiges über Albumin, Casein, und Fibrin. *Ann.*, *69*, 16.

Borglin, N. E. 1947. Excretion of choline in urine. *Acta Pharmacol. Toxicol.*, 3, Suppl. 1.

Borkel, C. 1903. Über Pepsin — Fibrinpepton. *Z. physiol. Chem.*, *38*, 289.

Boswell, V. R., Deonier, M. T., Carolus, R. L., Edmond, J. B., Garrison, O. B., Cochran, H. L., Woodard, O., Anderson, W. S., Miller, J. C., and Wright, R. E. 1944. Place and season effects on yields and starch content of 38 kinds of sweet potatoes. *U. S. Dept. Agr. Circ.* 714.

Boulet, M., Nelson, J. A., and McFarlane, W. D. 1947. A rapid colorimetric method for the determination of lysine in protein hydrolysates. *Can. J. Research, 25B*, 540.

Bourquelot, E., and Hérissey, H. 1899. Sur la dosage du mannose mélangé à d'autres sucres. *Compt. rend.*, *129*, 339.

Boyd, M. J., and Logan, M. A. 1942. Colorimetric determination of serine. *J. Biol. Chem.*, *146*, 279.

Braconnot, H. 1820. Sur la conversion des matières animales en nouvelles substances par le moyen de l'acide sulfurique. *Ann. chim. et phys.*, (2), *13*, 113.

———. 1827. Recherches sur la fermentation du fromage, et sur l'oxide caseeux et l'acide caseique. *Ann. chim. et phys.* (2), *36*, 159.

Bradley, J. A. 1942. Kjeldahl distillation without absorbing acid. *Ind. Eng. Chem., Anal. Ed.*, *14*, 705.

Bradstreet, R. B. 1940. A review of the Kjeldahl determination of organic nitrogen. *Chem. Revs.*, *27*, 331.

Breddy, L. J., and Jones, J. K. N. 1945. The quantitative estimation of xylose. *J. Chem. Soc.*, 738.

Brederick, H. 1931. Zur Molisch-Reaktion. *Ber.*, *64B*, 2856.

———. 1932. Zur Molisch-Reaktion (II. Mitteil.). *Ber.*, *65B*, 1110.

Breslow, D. S., and Hauser, C. R. 1939. Condensations brought about by bases. V. Condensation of the anhydride with the aldehyde in the Perkin synthesis. *J. Am. Chem. Soc.*, *61*, 786.

Briant, A. M., Personius, C. J., and Cassel, E. G. 1945. Physical properties of starch from potatoes of different culinary quality. *Food Research, 10*, 437.

Brigg, A. P. 1922. A modification of the Bell-Doisy phosphate method. *J. Biol. Chem.*, *53*, 13.

Briggs, D. R., and Hanig, M. 1946. Chemical state of phosphorus in starch as indicated by titration curves on electrodialyzed starches. *Cereal Chem.*, *23*, 277.

Brimhall, B., and Hixon, R. M. 1943. Two types of molecules in starch. *Wallerstein Labs. Communs.*, *6*, 95.

Brockmann, H. 1936. Die Isolierung des antirachitischen Vitamins aus Thunfischleberöl. *Z. physiol. Chem.*, *241*, 104.

——— and Busse, A. 1938. Die Konstitution des antirachitischen Vitamins der Thunfischleber. *Z. physiol. Chem.*, *256*, 252.

Brown, A. H. 1946. Determination of pentose in the presence of large quantities of glucose. *Arch. Biochem.*, *11*, 269.

Brown, C. A., and Zerban, F. W. 1943. Physical and Chemical Methods of Sugar Analysis, 3d ed. John Wiley & Sons, Inc., New York.

Brown, W. L. 1944. The determination of phenylalanine in proteins. *J. Biol. Chem.*, *155*, 277.

Brückner, J. 1943. Über Erkennung und Bestimmung verschiedener Hexosen nebeneinander. *Z. physiol. Chem.*, *277*, 181.

Bruhns, G. 1890. Über Adenin und Hypoxanthin. *Z. physiol. Chem.*, *14*, 533.

Buchanan, O. H., Block, W. D., and Christman, A. A. 1945. The metabolism of the methylated purines. I. The enzymatic determination of urinary uric acid. *J. Biol. Chem.*, *157*, 181.

Bullard, J. G. and others. 1947. Starch for Paper Coating, Monograph No. 3. *Tech. Assoc. Pulp Paper Ind.*

Bunzel, H. H. 1908. The rate of oxidation of sugars in an acid medium. *Am. J. Physiol.*, *21*, 23.

Burgen, A. S. V. 1947. Urinary excretion of phosphatases in man. *Lancet, 252*, 329.

Burian, R. 1904. Diazoaminoverbindungen der Imidazole und der Purinsubstanzen. *Ber.*, *37*, 696.

———. 1907. Weitere Beiträge zur Kenntnis der Diazoaminoverbindungen der Purinbasen. *Z. physiol. Chem.*, *51*, 425.

Burman, M. 1943. Muscular dysfunctions. *Merck Rept.*, *52*, 11.

Bushill, J. H., Lampitt, L. H., and Baker, L. C. 1934. The determination of cystine. Use of the Zeiss photometer *Biochem. J.*, *28*, 1293.

Butenandt, A. 1936a. Biochemistry of the sterol group. Lecture I. Chemistry of sterols, bile acids, and neutral saponins. *J. Soc. Chem. Ind.*, *55*, 753.

———. 1936b. Biochemistry of the sterol group. Lecture II. Cardiac poisons and vitamin D. *J. Soc. Chem. Ind.*, *55*, 891.

———. 1936c. Biochemistry of the sterol group. Lecture III. The sex hormone group. *J. Soc. Chem. Ind.*, 55, 990.

Cahours, A. 1858. Recherches sur les acides amidés. *Compt. rend.*, 46, 1044.

———. 1859. Untersuchungen über die Aminsäuren. *Ann.*, 109, 10.

Caldwell, J. R., and Moyer, H. V. 1935. Determination of chloride. *Ind. Eng. Chem.*, *Anal. Ed.*, 7, 38.

Caldwell, M. L., and Adams, M., in Anderson, J. A. 1946. Enzymes and their Role in Wheat Technology, Chapter II. Interscience Publishers, New York.

———, Booher, L. E., and Sherman, H. C. 1931. Crystalline amylase. *Science*, 74, 37.

———, Weill, C. E., and Weil, R. S. 1945. Further studies of the essential groups of pancreatic amylase. *J. Am. Chem. Soc.*, 67, 1079.

Callan, T. P., and Toennies, G. 1941. Determination of sulfur in organic compounds. *Ind. Eng. Chem.*, *Anal. Ed.*, 13, 450.

Callow, R. K. 1938. Steroids. *Ann. Repts. on Progress Chem. (Chem. Soc. London)*, 35, 281.

Calvery, H. O., in Schmidt, C. L. A. 1938. Methods of analysis and reactions of the amino acids and proteins. Chemistry of the Amino Acids and Proteins. Charles C. Thomas, Publisher, Springfield, Ill.

Cameron, A. T. 1947. The taste sense and the relative sweetness of sugars and other sweet substances. *Sugar Research Foundation*, N.Y., Sci. Rept. Ser. No. 9.

Camien, M. N., and Dunn, M. S. 1948. A composite basal medium for the microbiological assay of leucine. *J. Biol. Chem.*, 173, 137.

———, ———, and Salle, A. J. 1947. The effect of carbohydrates on acid production by twenty-four lactic acid bacteria. *J. Biol. Chem.*, 168, 33.

Cannan, R. K. 1944. The estimation of the dicarboxylic amino acids in protein hydrolysates. *J. Biol. Chem.*, 152, 401.

Cantarow, A., and Trumper, M. 1945. Clinical Biochemistry, 3d ed. W. B. Saunders Company, Philadelphia.

Carter, C. E. 1950. Paper chromatography of purine and pyrimidine derivatives of yeast nucleic acid. *J. Am. Chem. Soc.*, 72, 1466.

Carter, H. E., and Hooper, J. R., in Sahyun, M. 1944. Synthesis and isolation of certain amino acids. Outline of the Amino Acids and Proteins. Reinhold Publishing Corporation, New York, 94 pp.

Cassidy, H. G., (and twelve collaborators). 1948. Chromatography. *Ann. N.Y. Acad. Sci.*, 49, 141.

Chadwick, A. F., and Pacsu, E. 1941. The rates of ammonolysis of some α-halogen acids and α-halogen acyl peptides. *J. Am. Chem. Soc.*, 63, 2427.

Cherbuliez, E., and Schneider, M. L. 1932. Recherches sur la caseine. I. La caseine n'est pas un corps homogene. Etude de son fractionement par le chlorure d'ammonium. *Helv. Chim. Acta*, 15, 597.

Cheronis, N. D., and Spitzmueler, K. H. 1941. Studies in ammonolysis. I. The ammonolysis of halogen fatty acids and preparation of α-amino acids. *J. Org. Chem.*, 6, 349.

Chibnall, A. C. 1924. Investigations on the nitrogenous metabolism of the higher plants. Part VI. The role of asparagine in the metabolism of the mature plant. *Biochem. J.*, 18, 395.

———. 1939. Protein Metabolism in the Plant. Yale University Press, New Haven.

———, Rees, M. W., and Williams, E. F. 1943. The total nitrogen content of egg albumin and other proteins. *Biochem. J.*, 37, 354.

———, ———, ———, and Boyland, E. 1940. The glutamic acid of normal and malignant tissue proteins. *Biochem. J.*, 34, 285.

Christman, A. A., and Ravwitch, S. 1932. The determination of uric acid in human urine. *J. Biol. Chem.*, 95, 115.

Clark, E. P. 1922. Note on the preparation of mannose. *J. Biol. Chem.*, 51, 1.

Clark, W. M., Zoller, H. F., Dahlberg, A. O., and Weimar, A. C. 1920. Studies on technical casein. II. Grain-curd casein. *Ind. Eng. Chem.*, 12, 1163.

Clarke, D. H., and Marney, A. F. 1945. The determination of the free and total cholesterol of plasma with photo-electric colorimeter. *J. Lab. Clin. Med.*, 30, 615.

Clarke, H. T. 1932. The action of sulfite upon cystine. *J. Biol. Chem.*, 97, 235.

——— in Gilman, H. 1943. Organic Chemistry, an Advanced Treatise, Vol. II, 2d ed. John Wiley & Sons, Inc., New York, 1079.

Clay, R. C., Cook, K., and Routh, J. I. 1940. Studies in composition of human hair. *J. Am. Chem. Soc.*, 62, 2709.

Clendenning, K. A., and Wright, D. E. 1945. Composition and specific rotary power of starches in relation to source and type. *Can. J. Research*, 23B, 131.

Cohen, P. P. 1939. Microdetermination of glutamic acid. *Biochem. J.*, 33, 551.

Cohn, E. J., and Hendry, J. L. 1943. Casein. *Org. Syntheses*, Coll. Vol. II, 120.

Cohn, E. W., and Brookes, M. H. 1936. The diastatic activity of rat saliva. *J. Biol. Chem.*, 114, 139.

Cohn, R. 1895. Zur Kenntniss des bei der Pancreasverdauung entstehenden Leucins. *Z. physiol. Chem.*, 20, 203.

Cohn, W. 1950. The anion-exchange separation of ribonucleotides. *J. Am. Chem. Soc.*, 72, 1471.

Cold Spring Harbor Symposia on Quantitative Biology. 1947. Nucleic Acids and Nucleoproteins. *Cold Spring Harbor Symposia Quant. Biol.*, Vol. 12.

Cole, S. W. 1903. On certain colour reactions of proteid due to tryptophan. *J. Physiol.*, 30, 311.

Consden, R., Gordon, A. H., and Martin, A. J. P. 1944. Qualitative analysis of proteins: a partition chromatographic method using paper. *Biochem. J.*, 38, 224.

Conway, E. J. 1933. An absorption apparatus for the micro-determination of certain volatile substances. II. The determination of urea and ammonia in body fluids. *Biochem. J.*, 27, 430.

_____ and Byrne, A. 1933. An absorption apparatus for the microdetermination of certain volatile substances. I. The micro-determination of ammonia. *Biochem. J.*, 27, 419.

Copeland, D. H., and Salmon, W. D. 1946. The occurrence of neoplasms in the liver, lungs, and other tissues of rats as a result of prolonged choline deficiency. *Am. J. Path.*, 22, 1059.

Corley, R. C. 1929. Pentose metabolism. III. A comparison of the rates of disposal of *d*-arabinose and *l*-arabinose in the rabbit. *J. Biol. Chem.*, 82, 269.

Csonka, F. A., and Denton, C. A. 1946. Methionine determination in proteins and foods. *J. Biol. Chem.*, 163, 329.

Curl, A. L., and Nelson, E. K. 1944. A water-soluble mannan from the seeds of *Daubentonia drummondii*. *J. Am. Chem. Soc.*, 66, 1227.

Curtius, T., and Goebel, F. 1888. Darstellung von salzsaurem Glycinäther aus salzsaurem Glycocoll. *J. prakt. Chem.* (2), 37, 159.

Dakin, H. D. 1920. Amino-acids of gelatin. *J. Biol. Chem.*, 44, 499.

Daly, M. M., and Mirsky, A. E. 1949. Chromatography of purines and pyrimidines on starch columns. *J. Biol. Chem.*, 179, 981.

Dann, W. J. 1947. The bioassay for nicotinic acid. *Biol. Symposia*, 12, 181.

Darby, W. J., and Day, P. L. 1940. Blood sugar levels in rats receiving the cataractogenic sugars galactose and xylose. *J. Biol. Chem.*, 133, 503.

Davidson, J. N. 1949. Nucleoproteins, nucleic acids and derived substances. *Ann. Rev. Biochem.*, 18, 155.

Decker, A., and McGinnis, J. 1947. Black pigmentation in feathers of Buff Orpington chicks caused by vitamin D deficiency. *Proc. Soc. Exptl. Biol. Med.*, 66, 224.

Dehn, W. M., Jackson, K. E., and Ballard, D. A. 1932. Identification of common carbohydrates. *Ind. Eng. Chem., Anal. Ed.*, 4, 413.

Denigès, G. 1898a. Sur les functions pouvant se combiner au sulfate mercurique. Cas des acétones. *Compt. rend.*, 126, 1868.

_____. 1898b. Combinaison, recherche et dosage de l'acétone ordinaire avec le sulfate mercurique. *Compt. rend.*, 127, 963.

Denny, F. E. 1934a. Improvements in methods of determining starch in plant tissues. *Contribs. Boyce Thompson Inst.*, 6, 129.

_____. 1934b. Starch-determination methods involving solubility in acids. *Contribs. Boyce Thompson Inst.*, 6, 381.

Dickinson, W. P., and Marshall, P. G. 1929. The isomeric monohydroxyphenylalanines. Part I. A new synthesis of the *o*- and *m*-isomerides and a comparison of their properties with those of tyrosine. *J. Chem. Soc.*, 1495.

Dimler, R. J., Davis, H. A., Rist, C. E., and Hilbert, G. E. 1944. Production of starch from wheat and other cereal flours. *Cereal Chem.*, 21, 430.

Dittmer, K. 1949. The synthesis and microbiological properties of β-3-thienylalanine, a new *anti*-phenylalanine. *J. Am. Chem. Soc.*, 71, 1205.

Dorfman, A., Horwith, M. K., Koser, S. A., and Saunders, F. 1939. The use of the dysentery organism for the quantitative determination of nicotinic acid. *J. Biol. Chem.*, 128, xx.

Drechsel, E. 1877. Zur Volhard'schen Silberbestimmungsmethode. *J. prakt. Chem.*, 15, 191.

Drury, H. F. 1948. Identification and estimation of pentoses in the presence of glucose. *Arch. Biochem.*, 19, 45

Dubnoff, J. W. 1941. A micromethod for the determination of arginine. *J. Biol. Chem.*, 141, 711.

Dulière, W. L., and Raper, H. S. 1930. The tyrosinase-tyrosine reaction. VII. The action of tyrosinase on certai substances related to tyrosine. *Biochem. J.*, 24, 239.

Düll, G. 1895. Die Einwirkung von Oxalsäure auf Inulin. *Chem. Ztg.*, 19, 216; Cent., 1895, I, 534.

Dunn, M. S., 1943. The constitution and syntheses of the amino acids. In Schmidt, C. L. A. Chemistry of Amino Acids and Proteins. Charles C. Thomas, Publisher, Springfield, Ill.

_____. 1949. Casein. *Biochem. Prep.*, 1, 22.

_____, Akawie, S., Yeh, H. L., and Martin, H. 1950. Urinary excretion of amino acids in liver disease. *J. Clin. Invest.*, 29, 302.

_____, Butler, A. W., amd Frieden, E. H. 1941. Quantitative investigations of amino acids and peptides. VI. The function of carbonate in the synthesis of glycine from ammonium carbonate. *J. Phys. Chem.*, 45, 1123.

_____, Camien, M. N., Shankman, S., and Block, H. 1947. Urinary excretion of twelve amino acids by normal male and female subjects measured microbiologically. *Arch. Biochem.*, *13*, 207.

_____ and Porush, I. 1939. Quantitative investigations of amino acids and peptides. V. The function of iodine in amino nitrogen analyses by the nitrous acid method. *J. Biol. Chem.*, *127*, 261.

_____ and Rockland, L. B. 1947. The preparation and criteria of purity of the amino acids. *Advances in Protein Chem.*, *3*, 295.

_____ and Schmidt, C. L. A. 1922. The influence of position and of temperature upon the reaction of aliphatic amino nitrogen with nitrous acid. *J. Biol. Chem.*, *53*, 401.

Dunning, J. W., and Lathrop, E. C. 1945. The saccharification of agricultural residues. A continuous process. *Ind. Eng. Chem.*, *37*, 24.

Earle, J. R., and Milner, R. T. 1944. Improvements in the determination of starch in corn and wheat. *Cereal Chem.*, *21*, 567.

Eckhardt, R. D., Cooper, A. M., Faloon, W. W., and Davidson, C. S. 1948. The urinary excretion of amino acids in man. *Trans. N.Y. Acad. Sci.*, *10*, 284.

Edman, P., Hammarsten, E., Löw, B., and Reichard, P. 1949. Partition chromatographic separation of adenine and guanine. *J. Biol. Chem.*, *178*, 395.

Eegriwe, E. 1933. Reaktionen und Reagenzien zum Nachweis organischer Verbindungen. II. *Z. anal. Chem.*, *95*, 323.

_____. 1937. Reaktionen und Reagenzien zum Nachweis organischer Verbindungen. IV. *Z. anal. Chem.*, *110*, 22.

Ehrensvärd, G., Sperber, E., Salulste, E., Reio, L., and Stjernholm, R. 1947. Metabolic connection between proline and glycine in the amino acid utilization of *Torulopsis utilis*. *J. Biol. Chem.*, *169*, 759.

Ehrlich, F. 1908. Über die Spaltung racemischer Aminosäuren mittels Hefe. II. Mitteilung. *Biochem. Z.*, *8*, 438.

_____. 1917. Die Pektinstoffe, ihre Konstitution und Bedeutung. *Chem. Ztg.*, *41*, 197.

Eisner, A., and Wagner, E. C. 1934. Stability of aqueous solutions of boric acid used in the Kjeldahl method. *Ind. Eng. Chem., Anal. Ed.*, *6*, 473.

van Ekenstein, W. A., and Blanksma, J. J. 1910. Über das ω-Oxymethyl-furfurol als Ursache einiger Farbreaktionen der Hexosen. *Ber.*, *43*, 2355.

Elsdon, G. D. 1926. Edible Oils and Fats. Ernest Benn, Ltd., London.

Elvehjem, C. A., Madden, R. J., Strong, F. M., and Woolley, D. W. 1937. Relation of nicotinic acid and nicotinic acid amide to canine black tongue. *J. Am. Chem. Soc.*, *59*, 1767.

Embleton, J., and Collings, A. J. 1947. Transference of vitamin D from the female rat to her young. *Nature, 159*, 341.

Emmerling, O. 1897. Die Zersetzung von Fibrin durch Streptococcen. *Ber.*, *30*, 1863.

_____. 1902. Über die Eiweiss-spaltung durch Papyotin. *Ber.*, *35*, 695.

Engel, R. W. 1942. Modified methods for the chemical and biological determination of choline. *J. Biol. Chem.*, *144*, 701.

Erlenmeyer, E., Jr. 1886. Über die Phenylglycidsäure. *Ber.*, *19*, 2576.

_____. 1887. Zur Kenntniss der Phenyl-α- und der Phenyl-α,β-oxypropionsäure. *Ber.*, *20*, 2465.

_____. 1892. Zur Kenntniss der Phenylbrenztraubensäure und der Phenylglycidsäure. *Ann.*, *271*, 137.

_____. 1893. Über die Condensation der Hippursäure mit phtalsäureanhydrid und mit Benzaldehyd. *Ann.*, *275*, 1.

_____. 1897. Über eine Anscheinend allgemeine Reaction der α-aminosäuren von der Formel RCH(NH$_2$)COOH. *Ber.*, *30*, 2896.

_____. 1899. Zur Kenntniss der α-Amidosäuren. *Ann.*, *307*, 70.

_____. 1904a. Zur Kenntniss der α-Amidosäuren. *Ann.*, *337*, 205.

_____. 1904b. Über Azlactone und ihre Unwandlungsprodukte. *Ann.*, *337*, 265.

Ershoff, B. H. 1946. Studies on the nutritive value of lactose and galactose with the single-food choice method. *Am. J. Physiol.*, *147*, 13.

Etheredge, M. P. 1944. Report on starch in raw and baked cereals. *J. Assoc. Offic. Agr. Chemists*, *27*, 404.

Evans, W. L. 1929. The mechanism of carbohydrate oxidation. *Chem. Revs.*, *6*, 281.

_____. 1942. Less familiar aspects of carbohydrate chemistry. *Chem. Revs.*, *31*, 537.

_____, Nicoll, W. D., Strouse, G. C., and Waring, C. E. 1928. The mechanism of carbohydrate oxidation. IX. The action of copper acetate solutions on glucose, fructose, and galactose. *J. Am. Chem. Soc.*, *50*, 2267.

Fabinyi, R. 1900a. Verfahren zur Darstellung von Farbstoffen aus Salicylaldehyd und Ketonverbindungen. Deut. Reich Pat. 110,520. Cent., II, 301.

_____. 1900b. Verfahren zur Darstellung eines neuen Seidenfarbstoffes. Deut. Reich Pat. 110,521. Cent., II, 302.

Fearon, W. R. 1942. Detection of lactose and maltose by means of methylamine. *Analyst*, *67*, 130.

_____. 1944. The detection and estimation of uric acid by 2,6-dichloroquinone-chloromide. *Biochem. J.*, *38*, 399.

_____, and Mitchell, D. M. 1932. The nitrochromic acid reaction for the detection of primary and secondary alcohols with special reference to saccharides. *Analyst,* 57, 372.

Fehling, H. 1849. Die quantitative Bestimmung von Zucker und Stärkmehl mittelst Kupfervitriol. *Ann.,* 72, 106.

_____. 1858. Die quantitative Bestimmung von Zucker. *Ann.,* 106, 75.

von Fellenberg, T. 1947. Separation of sugars. *Mitt. Gebiete Lebensm. Hyg.,* 38, 265; *Chem. Abstracts,* 42, 3288 (1948).

Ferger, M. A., and du Vigneaud, V. 1949. The antiphenylalanine effect of β-2-thienylalanine for the rat. *J. Biol. Chem.,* 179, 61.

Fieser, L. F., and Fieser, M. 1949. Natural Products Related to Phenanthrene, 3d ed. Reinhold Publishing Corporation, New York.

_____ and _____. 1944. Organic Chemistry. D. C. Heath and Company, Boston, 351.

Firstenberger, B. G. 1943. The data, design, and specifications for a plant to produce xylose from corn stalks. *Iowa State Coll. J. Sci.,* 18, 27.

Fischer, E. 1884. Verbindungen des Phenylhydrazins mit den Zubkerarten. *Ber.,* 17, 579.

_____. 1887. Verbindungen des Phenylhydrazins mit den Zuckerarten. II. *Ber.,* 20, 821.

_____. 1901. Über die Hydrolyse des Caseins durch Salzsäure. *Z. physiol. Chem.,* 33, 151.

_____. 1906. Synthese von Polypeptiden. XV. *Ber.,* 39, 2893.

_____ and Fourneau, E. 1901. Über einige Derivate des Glykocolls. *Ber.,* 34, 2868.

_____ and Hirschberger, J. 1888. Über Mannose. I. *Ber.,* 21, 1805.

_____ and _____. 1889a. Über Mannose. II. *Ber.,* 22, 365.

_____ and _____. 1889b. Über Mannose, IV. *Ber.,* 22, 3218.

_____ and Mouneyrat, A. 1900. Spaltung einiger racemischer Aminosäuren in die optisch aktiven Komponenten. IV. *Ber.,* 33, 2383.

_____ and Schoeller, W. 1907. Synthese von Polypeptiden. XXII. Derivate des *l*-Phenylalanin. *Ann.,* 357, 1.

Fischer, H. 1909. Zur Frage der Bindung der Purinbasen im Nucleinsäuremolekül. *Z. physiol. Chem.,* 60, 69.

Fischer, M. M., and Hooker, M. O. 1918. A note on the colloid chemistry of Fehling's sugar test. *J. Lab. Clin. Med.,* 3, 368.

Fiske, C. H., and Subbarow, Y. 1925. The colorimetric determination of phosphorus. *J. Biol. Chem.,* 66, 375.

Fletcher, J. P., Best, C. H., and Solandt, O. M. 1935. The distribution of choline. *Biochem. J.,* 29, 2278.

Flock, E. V., and Bollman, J. L. 1948. Alkaline phosphatase in the intestinal lymph of the rat. *J. Biol. Chem.,* 175, 439.

Foldes, F. F., and Murphy, A. J. 1946a. Distribution of cholesterol, cholesterol esters and phospholipid phosphorus in normal blood. *Proc. Soc. Exptl. Biol. Med.,* 62, 215.

_____ and _____. 1946b. Distribution of cholesterol, cholesterol esters and phospholipid phosphorus in blood in thyroid disease. *Proc. Soc. Exptl. Biol. Med.,* 62, 218.

Folin, O. 1903. The acidity of urine. *Am. J. Physiol.,* 9, 25.

_____. 1905. Approximately complete analyses of thirty "normal" urines. *Am. J. Physiol.,* 13, 45.

_____. 1910. On the preparation of cystin. *J. Biol. Chem.,* 8, 9.

_____. 1914. On the determination of creatinine and creatine in urine. *J. Biol. Chem.,* 17, 469.

_____. 1922a. A system of blood analysis. Supp. III. A new colorimetric method for the determination of the amino-acid nitrogen in blood. *J. Biol. Chem.,* 51, 377.

_____. 1922b. A colorimetric determination of the amino-acid nitrogen in normal urine. *J. Biol. Chem.,* 51, 393.

_____. 1933. Standardized methods for the determination of uric acid in unlaked blood and in urine. *J. Biol. Chem.,* 101, 111.

_____. 1934. The preparation of sodium tungstate free from molybdate, together with a simplified process for the preparation of a correct uric acid reagent (and some comments). *J. Biol. Chem.,* 106, 311.

_____ and Bell, R. D. 1917. Applications of a new reagent for the separation of ammonia. *J. Biol. Chem.,* 29, 329.

_____ and Berglund, H. 1922. A colorimetric method for the determination of sugars in normal human urine. *J. Biol. Chem.,* 51, 209.

_____ and Ciocalteu, V. 1927. On tyrosine and tryptophane determinations in proteins. *J. Biol. Chem.,* 73, 627.

_____ and Denis, W. 1912. Tyrosine in proteins as determined by a new colorimetric method. *J. Biol. Chem.,* 12, 245.

_____ and _____. 1913a. A new (colorimetric) method for the determination of uric acid in blood. *J. Biol. Chem.,* 13, 469.

_____ and _____. 1913b. On the colorimetric determination of uric acid in urine. *J. Biol. Chem.,* 14, 95.

_____ and _____. 1914. The quantitative determination of albumin in urine. *J. Biol. Chem.,* 18, 273.

_____ and Looney, J. M. 1922. Colorimetric methods for the separate determination of tyrosine, tryptophane, and cystine in proteins. *J. Biol. Chem.,* 51, 421.

_____ and Marenzi, A. D. 1929a. Tyrosine and tryptophane determinations in one-tenth gram of protein. *J. Biol. Chem.*, 83, 89.

_____ and _____. 1929b. An improved colorimetric method for the determination of cystine in proteins. *J. Biol. Chem.*, 83, 103.

_____ and McEllroy, W. S. 1918. Copper-phosphate mixtures as sugar reagents. *J. Biol. Chem.*, 33, 513.

_____ and Svedberg, A. 1926. The sugar in urine and in blood. *J. Biol. Chem.*, 70, 405.

_____ and Wu, H. 1919. A revised colorimetric method for determination of uric acid in urine. *J. Biol. Chem.*, 38, 459.

_____ and Youngberg, G. E. 1919. Note on the determination of urea in urine by direct nesslerization. *J. Biol. Chem.*, 38, 111.

Foreman, F. W. 1914. Quantitative estimation of aspartic and glutamic acids in the products of protein hydrolysis. *Biochem. J.*, 8, 463.

Foulger, J. H. 1931. The use of the Molisch (α-naphthol) reactions in the study of sugars in biological fluids. *J. Biol. Chem.*, 92, 345.

Fraenkel-Conrat, H., Cooper, M., and Olcott, H. S. 1945. Action of aromatic isocyanates on proteins. *J. Am. Chem. Soc.*, 67, 314.

Frankel, M., and Katchalski, E. 1942. Poly-condensation of alanine ethyl ester. *J. Am. Chem. Soc.*, 64, 2268.

Frankl, W., and Dunn, M. S. 1947. The apparent concentration of free tryptophan, histidine, and cystine in normal human urine measured microbiologically. *Arch. Biochem.*, 13, 93.

_____ , Martin, H., and Dunn, M. S. 1947. The apparent concentration of free tryptophan, histidine, and cystine in pathological human urine measured microbiologically. *Arch. Biochem.*, 13, 103.

Fraps, G. S. 1932. Estimation of starch in feeding stuffs. *J. Assoc. Offic. Agr. Chemists*, 15, 304.

Fred, E. B., Peterson, W. H., and Anderson, J. A. 1921a. The relation of lactic acid bacteria to corn silage. *J. Biol. Chem.*, 46, 319.

_____ , _____ , and _____ . 1921b. The characteristics of certain pentose-destroying bacteria, especially as concerns their action on arabinose and xylose. *J. Biol. Chem.*, 48, 385.

Fresenius, W., and Grünhut, L. 1896. IV. Specielle analytische methoden. 1. Auf Lebensmittel, Gesundheitspflege, Handel, Industrie und Landwirthschaft bezügliche. *Z. anal. Chem.*, 35, 606.

Friedberg, F., Winnick, T., and Greenberg, D. M. 1947. Incorporation of labeled glycine into the protein of tissue homogenates. *J. Biol. Chem.*, 171, 441.

Friedemann, T. E., and Graeser, J. B. 1933. The determination of lactic acid. *J. Biol. Chem.*, 100, 291.

Friedmann, E. 1937. The Sterols and Related Compounds. Chemical Publishing Company, Inc., Brooklyn.

Fromageot, C., and Heitz, P. 1939. Méthode de dosage spécifique de la valine et de la leucine dans un mélange d'acides amines quelconques. *Enzymologia*, 6, 258.

Fromm, F. 1935. Die stufenphotometrische Bestimmung kleiner Pyrrolmengen. *Mikrochemie*, 17, 141.

Furman, N. H., and Evans, O. M. 1929. Applications of ceric sulfate in volumetric analysis. V. Potentiometric study of the reaction between ferrocyanide and ceric ions. *J. Am. Chem. Soc.*, 51, 1128.

Fürth, O., and Fleishmann, W. 1922. Über die Ermittelung des Tyrosingehaltes von Proteinen. *Biochem. Z.*, 127, 137.

Gál, I. 1936. Estimation of ascorbic acid (vitamin C) by titration. *Nature*, 138, 799.

Gale, E. F., and Epps, H. M. R. 1945. Studies on bacterial amino-acid decarboxylases. *Biochem. J.*, 38, 250.

Garrod, A. E. 1923. Inborn Errors of Metabolism, 2d ed. H. Frowde, Hodder, and Stoughton, London.

Geddes, W. F. 1946. The amylases of wheat and their significance in milling and baking technology. *Advances in Enzymol*, 6, 415.

Gentele, J. G. 1859. Über die Bestimmung des Traubenzuckers, Rohrzuckers und Dextrins in ihren Mischungen. *Dinglers polytech. J.*, 152, 68.

Gerrard, A. W. 1893. New method for the estimation of grape sugar. *Pharm. J. Trans.* (3), 52, 208. Abstracted in *J. Chem. Soc.*, 64, II, 248.

Gibb, T. R. P., Jr. 1942. Optical Methods of Chemical Analysis. McGraw-Hill Book Company, Inc., New York.

Gibbs, H. D. 1926. Phenol tests. I. A classification of the tests and a review of the literature. *Chem. Revs.*, 3, 291.

_____ . 1927. Phenol tests. II. Nitrous acid tests. The Millon and similar tests. Spectrophotometric investigations. *J. Biol. Chem.*, 71, 445.

Giesy, P. M. 1920. The preparation of cholesterol in quantity. *Science*, 51, 350.

Gillespie, H. B., and Snyder, H. R. 1943. dl-β-Phenylalanine. *Org. Syntheses*, Coll. Vol. II, 489.

Glasser, O. 1944. Medical Physics. Year Book Publishers, Inc., Chicago.

Goodwin, T. W., and Morton, R. A. 1946. The spectrophotometric determination of tyrosine and tryptophan in proteins. *Biochem. J.*, 40, 628.

Gortner, R. A., and Hoffman, W. F. 1941. L-Cystine. *Org. Syntheses*, Coll. Vol. I, 194.

Gottschalk, R. G.   1945. Microdetermination of acid phosphatase. A study of the reaction of King and Armstrong. *Biochim. et Biophys. Acta.* 2, 582.

Grassman, W., and von Arnim, K.   1934. Über die Reaktion des Ninhydrins und Isatins mit Prolin und Oxyprolin. *Ann.,* 509, 288.

_____ and _____.   1935. Über neue Farbreaktionen des Pyrrolidins und Prolins. II. *Ann.,* 519, 192.

Graziani, F.   1915. Anhydrides and amines of α-amino acids. *Atti accad. nazl. Lincei,* 24, I, 822, 936; *Chem. Abstracts,* 9, 3065.

Greenbaum, F. R.   1935. Method of separation of large amounts of tyrosine from cystine. *Am. J. Pharm.,* 107, 162.

Greenwald, I.   1925. Chemistry of Jaffe's reaction for creatinine. II. Effect of substitution in the creatinine molecule and a possible formula for the red tautomer. *J. Am. Chem. Soc.,* 47, 1443.

_____.   1928. The chemistry of Jaffe's reaction for creatinine. V. The isolation of the red compound. *J. Biol. Chem.,* 80, 103.

_____ and Gross, J.   1924. The chemistry of Jaffe's reaction for creatinine. A red tautomer of creatinine picrate. *J. Biol. Chem.,* 59, 601.

Greenwood, D. A., Kraybill, H. R., Feaster, J. F., and Jackson, J. M.   1944. Vitamin retention in processed meat. *Ind. Eng. Chem.,* 36, 922.

Griffith, W. H.   1926. Benzoylated amino acids in the animal organism. III. A method for the determination of hippuric acid and a study of the synthesis of hippuric acid in rabbits. *J. Biol. Chem.,* 69, 197.

_____.   1941. The nutritional importance of choline. *J. Nutrition,* 22, 239.

_____ and Wade, N. J.   1940. Choline metabolism. II. The interrelationship of choline, cystine, and methionine in the occurrence and prevention of hemorrhagic degeneration in young rats. *J. Biol. Chem.,* 132, 627.

Guest, G. H.   1939. A note on the colorimetric determination of proline. *Can. J. Research,* 17B, 143.

_____ and MacFarlane, W. D.   1939. A study of the colorimetric determination of pyrrole with isatin and the application of the method to biological materials. *Can. J. Research,* 17B, 133.

Gunness, M., Dwyer, I. M., and Stokes, J. L.   1946. Microbiological methods for the determination of amino acids. III. Extension of the uniform assay method for the ten essential amino acids to include tyrosine. *J. Biol. Chem.,* 163, 159.

György, P.   1950. Vitamin Methods, Vol. I. Academic Press, New York.

van der Haar, A. W.   1920. Nachweis zur Trennung und Bestimmung der reinen und aus Glukosiden usw. erhaltenen Monosaccharide und Aldehydsäuren. Verlagsbuchhandlung Gebrüder Borntraeger, Berlin.

Habermann, J., and Ehrenfeld, R.   1902. Eine quantitative Methode zur Trennung des Leucins und Tyrosins. *Z. physiol. Chem.,* 37, 18.

Hagedorn, H. C., and Jensen, B. N.   1923a. Zur Mikrobestimmung des Blutzuckers mittels Ferricyanid. *Biochem. Z.,* 135, 46.

_____ and _____.   1923b. Die Ferricyanidmethode zur Blutzuckerbestimmung. II. *Biochem. Z.,* 137, 92.

Haines, W. S., Pond, G. P., and Webster, R. W.   1920. An improved test for the detection of glucose, especially in urine. *J. Am. Med. Assoc.,* 74, 301.

Hale, E. B., Davis, G. K., and Baldwin, H. R.   1942. The distribution of nicotinic acid in feeds. *J. Biol. Chem.,* 146, 565.

Hall, W. K., Bowles, L. L., Sydenstricker, V. P., and Schmidt, H. L., Jr.   1948. Cataracts due to deficiencies of phenylalanine and of histidine in the rat. A comparison with other types of cataracts. *J. Nutrition,* 36, 277.

_____, Sydenstricker, V. P., and Rawls, K.   1948. Factors affecting the excretion of metabolites of phenylalanine and tyrosine in alkaptonuria. *Federation Proc.,* 7, 289.

Hamilton, P. B.   1945. Gasometric determination of glutamine amino acid carboxyl nitrogen in plasma and tissue filtrates by the ninhydrin-carbon dioxide method. *J. Biol. Chem.,* 158, 375.

_____ and Van Slyke, D. D.   1943. The gasometric determination of free amino acids in blood filtrates by the ninhydrin-carbon dioxide method. *J. Biol. Chem.,* 150, 231.

Hammarsten, O.   1873–1874. Upsala Läkareforen. Förh. 9, 363. Quoted by Hammarsten, O., and Hedin, S. G., Textbook of Physiological Chemistry, 7th ed. trans. by J. A. Mandel, John Wiley & Sons, Inc., New York (1914).

_____.   1883. Zur Frage, ob des Casein ein einheitlicher Stoff sei. *Z. physiol. Chem.,* 7, 227.

Handler, P.   1947a. The biochemical defect underlying the nutritional failure of young rats on diets containing excessive quantities of lactose or galactose. *J. Nutrition,* 33, 221.

_____.   1947b. The determination of choline in biological material. *Biol. Symposia,* 12, 361.

_____ and Perlzweig, W. A.   1945. Detoxication mechanisms. *Ann. Rev. Biochem.,* 14, 617.

Hanes, C. S.   1929. An application of the method of Hagedorn and Jensen to the determination of larger quantities of reducing sugars. *Biochem. J.,* 23, 99.

_____.   1936. The determination of starch in plant tissue, with particular reference to the apple fruit. *Biochem. J.* 30, 168.

_____. 1937. The action of amylases in relation to the structure of starch and its metabolism in the plant. Parts I—III. *New Phytologist, 36*, 101.

Hanke, M. E. 1948. Conditions necessary for complete decarboxylation of pure L-lysine and L-tyrosine by amino acid decarboxylases. *Federation Proc., 7*, 158.

Hanke, M. T. 1925. The quantitative estimation of tyrosine and histidine in protein. A method for estimating tyramine in protein-containing mixtures. *J. Biol. Chem., 66*, 475.

_____. 1928. Determination of the tyrosine content of protein. *J. Biol. Chem., 79*, 587.

Hann, R. M., and Hudson, C. S. 1944. The action of copper sulfate on phenylosazones of the sugars. Phenyl-D-glucosotriazole. *J. Am. Chem. Soc., 66*, 735.

Hanus, J. 1901. Die Anwendung von Iodmonobromid bei der Analyse von Fetten und Ölen. *Z. Untersuch. Nahr. U. Genussm., 4*, 913.

Harding, T. S. 1922. The discovery and production of arabinose. *Sugar, 24*, 656.

_____. 1923a. History of xylose, its discovery and methods of preparation. *Sugar, 25*, 124.

_____. 1923b. History of mannose, its discovery and method of preparation. *Sugar, 25*, 583.

Harding, V. J., and MacLean, R. M. 1915. A colorimetric method for the estimation of amino acid α-nitrogen. *J. Biol. Chem., 20*, 217.

_____ and _____. 1916. The ninhydrin reaction with amines and amides. *J. Biol. Chem., 25*, 337.

Harding, V. S., and Warneford, F. H. S. 1916. The ninhydrin reaction with amino acids and ammonium salts. *J. Biol. Chem., 25*, 319.

Harington, C. R., and McCartney, W. 1927. Note on the Erlenmeyer amino-acid synthesis. *Biochem. J., 21*, 852.

Harries, C., and Weiss, M. 1903. Über das Hydantoin und Isomerien bei den Methylhydantoinen. *Ann., 327*, 355.

Harris, L. J. 1922—1923. On the existence of an unidentified sulphur grouping in the protein molecule. Part II. On the estimation of cystine in certain proteins. *Proc. Roy. Soc. (London), 94B*, 441.

Harris, R. H., and Jesperson, E. 1946a. A study of the effect of various factors on the swelling of certain cereal starches. *J. Colloid Sci., 1*, 479.

_____ and _____. 1946b. Factors affecting some physicochemical properties of starch. *Food Research, 11*, 216.

Harris, W. F. 1921. Anthony von Leeuwenhoek, the first bacteriologist. *Sci. Monthly, 12*, 150.

Harrison, G. A. 1947. Chemical Methods in Clinical Medicine, 3d ed. J. and A. Churchill Ltd., London.

Hart, E. B., Kline, O. L., and Keenan, J. A. 1931. A ration for the production of rickets in chicks. *Science, 73*, 710.

Hartmann, B. G., and Hillig, F. 1931. The determination of starch in flour by diastase-acid hydrolysis. *J. Assoc. Offic. Agr. Chemists, 14*, 112.

Harvey, D. G., Miller, E. J., and Robson, W. 1941. The Adamkiewicz, Hopkins and Cole, and Rosenheim tests for tryptophan. *J. Chem. Soc.*, 153.

Hassid, W. Z. 1936. Determination of reducing sugars and sucrose in plant materials. *Ind. Eng. Chem., Anal. Ed., 8*, 138.

_____. 1937. Determination of sugars in plants. *Ind. Eng. Chem., Anal. Ed., 9*, 228.

_____. 1943. The molecular constitution of starch and the mechanism of its formation. *Quart. Rev. Biol., 18*, 311.

_____. 1945a. The molecular constitution of starch. *Wallerstein Labs. Communs., 8*, 34.

_____. 1945b. Recent advances in the molecular constitution of starch and glycogen. *Federation Proc., 4*, 227.

_____, McCready, R. M., and Rosenfels, R. S. 1940. Determination of starch in plants. *Ind. Eng. Chem., Anal. Ed., 12*, 142.

Hawk, P. B., Oser, B. L., and Summerson, W. H. 1947. Practical Physiological Chemistry, 12th ed. The Blakiston Company, Philadelphia.

Hawkins, J. A. 1929. A micro time method for determination of reducing sugars, and its application to analysis of blood and urine. *J. Biol. Chem., 84*, 69.

_____ and Van Slyke, D. D. 1929. A time method for determination of reducing sugars, and its application to analysis of blood and urine. *J. Biol. Chem., 81*, 459.

Haworth, W. N. 1933. The constitution of ascorbic acid. *J. Soc. Chem. Ind., 52*, 482.

_____. 1946. Starch. *J. Chem. Soc.*, 543.

_____ and Hirst, E. L. 1933. Synthesis of ascorbic acid. *J. Soc. Chem. Ind., 52*, 645.

_____, Peat, S., and Sagrott, P. E. 1946. A new method for the separation of the amylose and amylopectin components of starch. *Nature, 157*, 19.

Heberlein, D. G., and Clifcorn, L. E. 1944. Vitamin content of dehydrated foods. Effect of packaging and storage. *Ind. Eng. Chem., 36*, 912.

Heilbron, I. M. 1936. Recent developments in the chemistry of the sterols and related compounds. *J. Soc. Chem. Ind., 55*, 129T.

Henderson, L. J., and Palmer, W. W. 1914. On the several factors of acid excretion. *J. Biol. Chem., 17*, 305.

Henneberg, W. 1903. Zur Kenntniss der Milchsäuren Bakterien. Paul and Parey, Berlin.

Henriques, V., and Sörensen, S. P. L. 1910. Über die quantitative Bestimmung der Aminosäuren, Polypeptide und der Hippursäure im Harne durch Formoltitration. *Z. physiol. Chem.*, *64*, 120.

Hepburn, J. S., and Kotlikoff, R. 1943. Comparative study of certain methods for the determination of serum cholesterol. *Rev. Gastroenterol.*, *10*, 170.

Hershberg, E. B. 1936. A new type of laboratory stirrer. *Ind. Eng. Chem., Anal. Ed.*, *8*, 313.

Herstein, B. 1911. The centenary of glucose and the early history of starch. *Ind. Eng. Chem.*, *3*, 158.

Hess, W. C. 1933. The gasometric determination of cysteine and cystine. *J. Biol. Chem.*, *103*, 449.

—— and Sullivan, M. X. 1943. The cysteine, cystine, and methionine content of proteins. *J. Biol. Chem.*, *151*, 635.

Hestrin, S., and Mager, J. 1947. Color test for identification of glucose. *Ind. Eng. Chem., Anal. Ed.*, *19*, 1032.

Heyl, F. W., Caryl, C. R., and Staley, J. F. 1914. Standardization of commercial papain. *Am. J. Pharm.*, *86*, 542.

Highet, D. M., and West, E. S. 1942. A procedure for the determination of ascorbic acid based upon the use of a standardized solution of 2,6-dichlorophenol indophenol in xylene. *J. Biol. Chem.*, *146*, 655.

Hilbert, G. E., and MacMasters, M. M. 1946. Pea starch, a starch of high amylose content. *J. Biol. Chem.*, *162*, 229.

Hiller, A., Greif, R. L., and Beckman, W. W. 1948. Determination of protein in urine by the biuret method. *J. Biol. Chem.*, *176*, 1421.

Hinkel, F. C., and Sherman, H. C. 1907. Experiments upon Barfoed's acid cupric acetate solution as a means of distinguishing glucose from maltose, lactose and sucrose. *J. Am. Chem. Soc.*, *29*, 1744.

Hinterberger, F. 1849. Untersuchung des Ochsenhorns. *Ann.*, *71*, 70.

Hirst, E. L. 1933. The structure of ascorbic acid. *J. Soc. Chem. Ind.*, *52*, 221.

—— , Jones, J. K. N., and Woods, E. A. 1947. The quantitative determination of galactose, mannose, arabinose, and rhamnose. *J. Chem. Soc.*, 1048.

Hitchings, G. H., and Fiske, C. H. 1941. The determination of the purines. *J. Biol. Chem.*, *140*, 491.

Hixon, R. M., and Rundle, R. E. 1944. Recent advances in starch chemistry. In Alexander, J., Colloid Chemistry, Theoretical and Applied, Reinhold Publishing Corporation, New York, *5*, 667.

—— and Sprague, G. F. 1942. Waxy starch of maize and other cereals. *Ind. Eng. Chem.*, *34*, 959.

Hlasiwetz, H., and Habermann, J. 1873. Über die Proteinstoffe. *Ann.*, *169*, 150.

Hobson, W. 1939. Urinary output of creatine and creatinine associated with physical exercise, and its relationship to carbohydrate metabolism. *Biochem. J.*, *33*, 1425.

Hodge, H. C. 1944. Acute toxicity of choline hydrochloride administered intraperitoneally to rats. *Proc. Soc. Exptl. Biol. Med.*, *57*, 26.

Hodges, R. C., Sperry, W. M., and Andersen, D. H. 1943. Serum cholesterol values for infants and children. *Am. J. Diseases Children*, *65*, 858.

Hodson, A. Z. 1945. The use of *Neurospora* for the determination of choline and biotin in milk products. *J. Biol. Chem.*, *157*, 383.

Hoffman, W. S. 1937. A rapid photoelectric method for the determination of glucose in blood and urine. *J. Biol. Chem.*, *120*, 51.

Hoffman, R. 1853. Reaktion auf Leucin und Tyrosin. *Ann.*, *87*, 123.

Hoffmeyer, J. 1944. Cholesterol content in rabbit serum. *Acta Physiol. Scand.*, *7*, 313.

Holiday, E. R., and Johnson, E. A. 1949. Location of paper chromatogram spots of purine and pyrimidine derivatives in ultra-violet light. *Nature*, *163*, 216.

Hopkins, C. Y. 1934. Polarimetric estimation of starch. *Can. J. Research*, *11*, 751.

Hopkins, F. G., and Cole, S. W. 1901a. Adamkiewicz's proteid reaction, chemistry of glyoxylic acid. *Proc. Roy. Soc. (London)*, *68*, 21.

—— and ——. 1901b. A contribution to the chemistry of proteids. Part I. *J. Physiol.*, *27*, 418.

—— and ——. 1903. A contribution to the chemistry of proteids. Part II. *J. Physiol.*, *29*, 451.

Hopkins, R. H. 1946. The action of the amylases. *Advances in Enzymol.*, *6*, 389.

Horn, M. J., Jones, D. B., and Blum, A. E. 1946. Colorimetric determination of methionine in proteins and foods. *J. Biol. Chem.*, *166*, 313.

Horowitz, N. H., and Beadle, G. W. 1943. A microbiological method for the determination of choline by use of a mutant of *Neurospora*. *J. Biol. Chem.*, *150*, 325.

Horton, P. M. 1921. Preparation of mannose from ivory-nut shavings. *Ind. Eng. Chem.*, *13*, 1040.

Hotchkiss, R. D. 1948. The quantitative separation of purines, pyrimidines and nucleosides by paper chromatography. *J. Biol. Chem.*, *175*, 315.

Huber, C. 1867. Vorläufige Notiz über einige Derivate des Nicotins. *Ann.*, *141*, 271.

Hübl, B. 1884. Eine allgemein anwendbare Methode zur Untersuchung der Fette. *Dinglers polytech. J.*, *253*, 281.

Hudson, C. S., and Harding, T. S. 1917. The preparation of xylose. *J. Am. Chem. Soc.*, *39*, 1038.

_____and ____. 1918. The preparation of xylose from corn cobs. *J. Am. Chem. Soc.*, *40*, 1601.

_____and Jackson, E. L. 1934. Improvements in the preparation of crystalline *d*-mannose. *J. Am. Chem. Soc.*, *56*, 958.

_____and Sawyer, H. L. 1917. The preparation of pure crystalline mannose and a study of its mutarotation. *J. Am. Chem. Soc.*, *39*, 470.

Hunter, G. 1936. A test for thymine, with observations on the keto-enolic type of diazo-test. *Biochem. J.*, *30*, 745.

_____and Hlynka, I. 1937. Note on the preparation of purines and pyrimidines from nucleic acid. *Biochem. J.*, *31*, 486.

Ihl, A. 1885. Phenole als Reagenzien für Kohlehydrate. *Chem. Ztg.*, *9*, 281; *Cent.*, *1885*, 761.

_____. 1887. Farbenreaktionen des Rübenzuckers. *Chem. Ztg.*, *11*, 2.

_____and Pechmann, A. 1884. Phenol und Diphenylamin als Reagenzien für Kohlehydrate. *Ber. d. österr. Ges. z. Förd. d. chm. Ind.*, 106; *Cent.*, *1885*, 761.

Ikawa, M., and Niemann, C. 1949. A spectrophotometric study of the behavior of carbohydrates in seventy-nine per cent sulfuric acid. *J. Biol. Chem.*, *180*, 923.

Isbell, H. S. 1941. Preparation of *d*-mannose. *J. Research, Natl. Bur. Standards*, *26*, 47.

Jamieson, G. S. 1943. Vegetable Fats and Oils, 2d ed., Reinhold Publishing Corporation, New York.

Jirak, L. W. 1935. Control of the washing-out process in potato starch manufacture. *Z. Spiritusind.*, *58*, 81; *Chem. Abstracts*, *30*, 2791 (1936).

Johnson, A. H., and Green, J. R. 1930. Modified methyl red and sodium alizarin sulfonate indicators. *Ind. Eng. Chem., Anal. Ed.*, *2*, 2.

Johnson, B. C. 1945. The microbiological determination of nicotinic acid, nicotinamide, and nicotinuric acid. *J. Biol. Chem.*, *159*, 227.

_____, Hamilton, T. S., and Mitchell, H. H. 1945a. The effect of choline intake and environmental temperature on the excretion of choline from the human body. *J. Biol. Chem.*, *159*, 5.

_____, ____, and ____. 1945b. The excretion of nicotinic acid, nicotinamide, nicotinuric acid, and N^1-methyl-nicotinamide by normal individuals. *J. Biol. Chem.*, *159*, 231.

Johnson, T. B. 1943. A sensitive color reaction for the detection of uracil and cytosine. *Science*, *98*, 90.

_____and Clapp, S. H. 1908–1909. Researches on pyrimidines: the action of diazobenzene sulfonic acid on thymin, uracil and cytosine. *J. Biol. Chem.*, *5*, 163.

_____and Coghill, R. D. 1925. Researches on pyrimidines. The discovery of 5-methylcytosine in tuberculinic acid, the nucleic acid of the tubercle bacillus. *J. Am. Chem. Soc.*, *47*, 2838.

_____and Daschavsky, P. G. 1924–1925. Researches on amines. X. The formation of tyramine by decarboxylation of tyrosine produced from silk. *J. Biol. Chem.*, *62*, 725.

_____and Kohmann, E. F. 1915a. I. Determination of the structure of nitrotyrosine. *J. Am. Chem. Soc.*, *37*, 1863.

_____and ____. 1915b. II. Synthesis of 3,5-dinitrotyrosine. *J. Am. Chem. Soc.*, *37*, 2164.

Jones, D. B., and Moeller, O. 1928. Some recent determinations of aspartic and glutamic acids in various proteins. *J. Biol. Chem.*, *79*, 429.

Jonnard, R. 1945. Determination of total nitrogen in proteins and their hydrolyzates. *Ind. Eng. Chem., Anal. Ed.*, *17*, 246.

Jukes, T. H., and Sanford, T. D. 1939. The vitamin D requirements of young turkeys. *J. Nutrition*, *18*, 71.

Kapeller-Adler, R. 1932. Über eine neue Reaktion zur qualitativen und quantitativen Bestimmung des Phenyl-alanins. *Biochem. Z.*, *252*, 185.

_____. 1934. Über eine stufenphotometrische Bestimmung des Histidins. *Biochem. Z.*, *271*, 206.

Kapfhammer, J., and Eck, R. 1927. *l*-Oxyprolin und *l*-Prolin. Ihre Darstellung aus Eiweiss mit Hilfe der Reineckesäure. *Z. physiol. Chem.*, *170*, 294.

Karrer, P., and Keller, R. 1943. Die Natur der Waser'schen spezifischen Farbreaktion auf α-Aminosäuren. *Helv. Chim. Acta*, *26*, 50.

Kassell, B., and Brand, E. 1938. The photometric determination of cystine, cysteine, ascorbic acid, and related compounds with phosphotungstic acid. *J. Biol. Chem.*, *125*, 115.

Kawai, K. 1916. *p*-Hydroxyphenylethylamine from tyrosine. Jap. Pat. 30,334; *Chem. Abstracts*, *11*, 2027 (1917).

Kelling, A. H. 1944. Starch from corn. U. S. Pats. 2,324,849, and 2,324,850.

Kendrick, A. B., and Hanke, M. E. 1937. The use of iodine and other modifications in the Van Slyke manometric amino nitrogen method. *J. Biol. Chem.*, *117*, 161.

_____and ____. 1940. The effect of iodine and mercury on amino nitrogen values with nitrous acid. *J. Biol. Chem.*, *132*, 739.

Kennedy, N. F. 1946. Corn starch — a versatile commodity. *Food Inds.*, *18*, 685.

Kent, W. H., and Tollens, B. 1884. Vorläufige Notiz über Galactose und Schleimsäure. *Ber.*, *17*, 668.

_____ and _____. 1885. Untersuchungen über Milchzucker und Galactose. *Ann., 227,* 221.

Kermack, W. O. 1946. Recent advances in science: biochemistry. *Science Progress, 34,* 778.

Kerr, R. W., and Trubell, O. R. 1943. Spectrophotometric analysis of starches. *Paper Trade J., 117,* 25.

Kiermayer, J. 1895. Über ein Furfurolderivat aus Lävulose. *Chem. Ztg., 19,* 1003; Cent., *1895,* II, 214.

Kimbrough, W. D. 1942. Production of sweet potatoes for starch or other purposes. *Louisiana Agr. Expt. Sta. Bull.* 348.

King, C. G. 1936. Vitamin C, ascorbic acid. *Physiol. Revs., 16,* 238.

_____. 1941. Chemical methods for determination of vitamin C. *Ind. Eng. Chem., Anal. Ed., 13,* 225.

King, E. J. 1932. The colorimetric determination of phosphorus. *Biochem. J., 26,* 292.

Kingsbury, F. B., Clark, C. P., Williams, G., and Post, A. L. 1926. The rapid determination of albumin in urine. *J. Lab. Clin. Med., 11,* 981.

Kingsley, G. R., and Schaffert, R. R. 1949. Determination of free and total cholesterol by direct chloroform extraction. *J. Biol. Chem., 180,* 315.

Kirk, E. 1948. The acid phosphatase concentration of the prostatic fluids in young, middle-aged and old individuals. *Gerentol., 3,* 98.

Kitson, R. E., and Mellon, M. G. 1944a. Colorimetric determination of phosphorus as molybdivanadophosphoric acid. *Ind. Eng. Chem., Anal. Ed., 16,* 379.

_____ and _____. 1944b. Further studies of the molybdenum blue reaction. *Ind. Eng. Chem., Anal. Ed., 16,* 466.

Kjeldahl, J. 1883. Neue Methode für Bestimmung des Stickstoffs in organischen Körpern. *Z. anal. Chem., 22,* 366.

Klein, G., and Linser, H. 1932a. Colorimetrische Methode zur quantitativen Bestimmung von Glykokoll. *Z. physiol. Chem., 205,* 251.

_____ and _____. 1932b. Cholinstoffwechsel bei Pflanzen. *Biochem. Z., 250,* 220.

_____ and _____. 1933. Cholinstoffwechsel bei Pflanzen. II. *Biochem. Z., 260,* 215.

Kleiner, I. S. 1945. Human Biochemistry. The C. V. Mosby Company, Medical Publishers, St. Louis.

Kltazkin, C., Norris, F. W., and Wokes, P. 1948. Nicotinic acid in cereals. I. The effect of germination. *Biochem. J., 42,* 414.

Kneen, E., and Beckord, L. D. 1946. Quantity and quality of amylose produced by various bacterial isolates. *Arch. Biochem., 10,* 41.

Knight, C. A., and Stanley, W. M. 1941. Aromatic amino acids in strains of tobacco mosaic virus and in the related cucumber viruses 3 and 4. *J. Biol. Chem., 141,* 39.

Knoop, F. 1908. Kürzere Mitteilungen. VIII. Eine Farbenreaktion des Histidins. *Beitr. Chem. Physiol. Pathol., 11,* 356.

_____ and Blanco, J. G. 1925. Über die Acetylierung von Aminosäuren im Tierkörper. *Z. physiol. Chem., 146,* 267.

Koch, F. 1886. Experimentelle Prüfung des Holzgummi und dessen Verbreitung im Pflanzenreiche. *Pharm. Z. Russland, 25,* 619; Cent., *1886,* 932.

Koch, F. C., and McMeekin, T. L. 1924. A new direct nesslerization micro-Kjeldahl method and a modification of the Nessler-Folin reagent for ammonia. *J. Am. Chem. Soc., 46,* 2066.

Koenigsfeld, H. 1912. Untersuchungen über die physikalisch-chemischen Grundlagen der Seliwanoffschen Lävulosereaktion. *Biochem. Z., 38,* 310.

Koettstorfer, J. 1879. Neue Methode zur Untersuchung der Butter auf fremde Fette. *Z. anal. Chem., 18,* 199, 431.

Kolthoff, I. M. 1935. Adsorption indicators. *Chem. Revs., 16,* 87.

Konig, W. 1904. Über eine neue, vom Pyridin derivierende Klasse von Farbstoffen. *J. prakt. Chem., 69,* 105.

Korenman, I. M. 1934. Über die Empfindlichkeit der Jodstärkereaktion. *Mikrochemie, 15,* 25.

Koser, S. A., and Rettger, L. F. 1919. Studies on bacterial nutrition. The utilization of nitrogenous compounds of definite chemical composition. *J. Infectious Diseases, 24,* 301.

Kossel, A. 1898. Über die Constitution der einfachsten Eiweiss-stoffe. *Z. physiol. Chem., 25,* 165.

Kraut, K. 1890. Über die Bildung von Glycocoll aus Monochloressigsäure. *Ber., 23,* 2577.

_____. 1891. Glycocoll und Derivate. *Ann., 266,* 292.

Kreger, D. 1946. X-Ray fibre pattern of part of a single starch grain: powder photographs of potato, wheat, and arrowroot (maranta) starch. *Nature, 158,* 199.

Krehl, W. A., Elvehjem, C. A., de la Huerga, J., and Hart, E. B. 1946. The distribution of niacinamide and niacin in natural materials. *J. Biol. Chem., 166,* 53.

_____, _____, and Strong, F. M. 1943. Determination of nicotinic acid. *Ind. Eng. Chem., Anal. Ed., 15,* 471.

Krocker, Dr. 1846. Bestimmung des Starkmehlgehaltes in vegetabilischen Nahrungsmitteln. *Ann., 58,* 212.

Kuhn, R., and Desnuelle, P. 1937. Über die Aminosäuren des gelben Ferments. *Ber., 70,* 1907.

Kulp, W. L., and Rettger, L. F. 1924. Comparative study of *Lactobacillus acidophilus* and *Lactobacillus bulgaricus. J. Bact., 9,* 357.

LaForge, F. B., and Hudson, C. S. 1918. The preparation of several useful substances from corn cobs. *Ind. Eng. Chem.*, 10, 925.

Lamb, F. W. 1943. Direct quantitative determination of nicotinamide in vitamin mixtures. *Ind. Eng. Chem., Anal. Ed.*, 15, 352.

____, Mueller, A., and Beach, G. W. 1946. Quantitative determination of ergosterol, cholesterol and 7-dehydrocholesterol. *Ind. Eng. Chem., Anal. Ed.*, 18, 187.

Lamb, J., and Robson, W. 1931. The Erlenmeyer synthesis of amino-acids. *Biochem. J.*, 25, 1231.

Lampitt, L. H., Fuller, C. H. F., and Goldenberg, N. 1948. The fractionation of potato starch. II. The reducing powers, mean molecular weights, and solubilities of the fractions. *J. Soc. Chem. Ind.*, 67, 38.

Lang, K. 1933. Eine Mikromethode zur Bestimmung des Prolins und des Oxyprolins. *Z. physiol. Chem.*, 219, 148.

Langley, W. D., and Evans, M. 1936. The determination of creatinine with sodium 3,5-dinitrobenzoate. *J. Biol. Chem.*, 115, 333.

Lanyar, F. 1942. Degradation of the *d-* and *l*-forms of phenylalanine and the *dl-* and *l*-forms of tyrosine by alkaptonurics. *Z. physiol. Chem.*, 275, 217.

Larson, H. W. 1932. A colorimetric method for the determination of allantoin. *J. Biol. Chem.*, 94, 727.

Lawrow, D. 1899. Über die Spaltungsprodukte des Histons von Leucocyten. *Z. physiol. Chem.*, 28, 388.

Leiboff, S. L. 1942. The determination of total cholesterol and cholesterol esters in blood. *J. Lab. Clin. Med.*, 28, 219.

Levene, P. A. 1903. Darstellung und Analyse einiger Nucleinsäuren (vierte Mitteilung). *Z. physiol. Chem.*, 39, 4.

____. 1923. Preparation of α-mannose. *J. Biol. Chem.*, 57, 329.

____. 1924. Preparation of α-mannose. Second paper. *J. Biol. Chem.*, 59, 129.

____. 1925. Phenylhydrazine derivatives of pyrimidines. *J. Biol. Chem.*, 63, 653.

____. 1935. Note on the preparation of crystalline *d*-mannose and of crystalline *d*-ribose. *J. Biol. Chem.*, 108, 419.

____ and Bass, L. W. 1931. Nucleic Acids. Chemical Catalog Company, Inc., New York.

Levin, L. 1945. The effect of several varieties of stress on the cholesterol content of the adrenal glands and of the serum of rats. *Endocrinology*, 37, 34.

Levine, V. E. 1929–1930. A general test for carbohydrates. *Proc. Soc. Exptl. Biol. Med.*, 27, 830.

Leviton, A. 1949. Methanol extraction of lactose and soluble proteins from skim milk powder. *Ind. Eng. Chem.*, 41, 1351.

____ and Leighton, A. 1938. Separation of lactose and soluble proteins of whey by alcohol extraction. *Ind. Eng. Chem.*, 30, 1305.

Lewis, H. B. 1941. End products of nitrogen metabolism in animals. *Biol. Symposia*, 5, 20.

Lewis, R. C., and Benedict, S. R. 1915. A method for the estimation of sugar in small quantities of blood. *J. Biol. Chem.*, 20, 61.

Lewis, T., and Woodward, E. F. 1948. Papain. *Drug & Cosmetic Ind.*, 63, 734.

Lewkowitsch, J. 1901. The Laboratory Companion to Fats and Oils Industries. Macmillan & Co., Ltd., London.

____. 1921. Chemical Technology and Analysis of Oils, Fats and Waxes, Vol. I. Macmillan & Co., Ltd., London.

____. 1922. Chemical Technology and Analysis of Oils, Fats and Waxes, Vol. II. Macmillan & Co., Ltd., London.

Lieben, F., and Müller, R. 1928. Über die Bromaufnahme von Casein, sowie von Casein- und Keratinhydrolysaten. *Biochem. Z.*, 197, 119.

Liebig, J. 1846. Über die Abwesenheit der Kohlensäuren Alkalien im Blute. *Ann.*, 57, 127.

____. 1847. Über die Bestandtheile der Flüssigkeiten des Fleisches. *Ann.*, 62, 257.

Linderstrøm-Lang, K. 1928. Über die Einheitlichkeit des Kaseins. Vorläufige Mitteilung. *Z. physiol. Chem.*, 176, 76.

____. 1929. Studies on casein. III. On the fractionation of casein. *Compt. rend. lab. Carlsberg*, 17, No. 9.

____ and Kodama, S. 1925. Studies on casein. I. On the solubility of casein in hydrochloric acid. *Compt. rend. lab. Carlsberg*, 16, No. 1.

Lineweaver, H., and Schwimmer, S. 1941. Some properties of crystalline papain. *Enzymologia*, 10, 81.

Ling, A. R., and Nanji, D. R. 1923. The preparation of xylose from maize cobs. *J. Chem. Soc.*, 123, 620.

Lintner, C. 1907. Determination of starch in barley by means of polarization. *Z. ges. Brauw.*, 30, 109; *Chem. Abstracts*, 1, 2740 (1907).

von Lippmann, E. O. 1921. Einige pflanzenchemische Beobachtungen. *Ber.*, 54, 3111.

Loftfield, R. B. 1947. Preparation of C[14]-labeled hydrogen cyanide, alanine and glycine. *Nucleonics*, 1, 54.

Looney, J. M. 1926. The colorimetric estimation of tyrosine, tryptophane, and cystine in proteins. II. *J. Biol. Chem.*, 69, 519.

Löwe, J. 1870. Über die Anwendung des Glycerin-Kupferoxyd-Natrons zur Nachweisung und Bestimmung des Traubenzuckers. *Z. anal. Chem.*, 9, 20.

Lucas, C. C., and Beveridge, J. M. R. 1940. The analysis of hair keratin. I. A method for the quantitative removal of cystine from keratin hydrolysates. *Biochem. J.*, *34*, 1356.

Luecke, R. W., and Pearson, P. B. 1944a. The microbiological determination of free choline in plasma and urine. *J. Biol. Chem.*, *153*, 259.

_____ and _____ . 1944b. The determination of free choline in animal tissues. *J. Biol. Chem.*, *155*, 507.

Lugg, J. W. H. 1932a. The application of phospho-18-tungstic acid (Folin's reagent) to the colorimetric determination of cysteine, cystine and related substances. I. The reduction of phospho-18-tungstic acid by various substances. *Biochem. J.*, *26*, 2144.

_____ . 1932b. The application of phospho-18-tungstic acid (Folin's reagent) to the colorimetric determination of cysteine, cystine and related substances. II. The determination of sulphydryl compounds and disulphides already existing in solution. *Biochem. J.*, *26*, 2160.

_____ . 1933. Sullivan's reaction for the quantitative determination of cysteine and cystine. *Biochem. J.*, *27*, 668.

_____ . 1938. Investigations of sources of error in the estimation of tyrosine and tryptophan in complex materials which are associated with hydrolysis. *Biochem. J.*, *32*, 775.

Lund, H., and Lieck, H. 1936. A specific reaction for the qualitative and quantitative determination of ascorbic acid in serum. *Nature*, *137*, 784.

Lwoff, A., and Querido, A. 1938. Dosage de l'amide de l'acide nicotinique au moyen du test *Proteus*. Principe de la méthode. *Compt. rend. soc. biol.*, *129*, 1039.

McArthur, C. S. 1946. Biological incorporation of a choline homologue into liver phospholipids. *Science*, *104*, 222.

McCalla, A. G., and Corns, W. G. 1943. Effects of variety and environment on the starch content of wheat and barley. *Can. J. Research*, *21C*, 307.

McCarthy, T. E., and Sullivan, M. X. 1941. A new and highly specific colorimetric test for methionine. *J. Biol. Chem.*, *141*, 871.

McCollum, E. V., Simmonds, N., and Becker, J. E. 1922. Studies on experimental rickets. XXI. An experimental demonstration of the existence of a vitamin which promotes calcium deposition. *J. Biol. Chem.*, *53*, 293.

_____ , _____ , Shipley, P. G., and Park, E. A. 1922. Studies on experimental rickets. XVI. A delicate biological test for calcium-depositing substances. *J. Biol. Chem.*, *51*, 41.

McCready, R. M., and Hassid, W. Z. 1943. The separation and quantitative estimation of amylose and amylopectin in potato starch. *J. Am. Chem. Soc.*, *65*, 1154.

McFarlane, W. D., and Guest, G. H. 1939. A new colorimetric method for the determination of hydroxyproline and its application to gelatin hydrolysates. *Can. J. Research*, *17B*, 139.

McGuigan, H. 1907. The oxidation of various sugars and the oxidizing power of different tissues. *Am. J. Physiol.*, *19*, 175.

McIntire, J. M., Schweigert, B. S., and Elvehjem, C. A. 1944. The choline and pyridoxine content of meats. *J. Nutrition*, *28*, 219.

McKittrick, D. S., and Schmidt, C. L. A. 1945. Elimination of error in the Volhard analysis for chloride by titration in acetic acid. *Arch. Biochem.*, *6*, 273.

McLean, F. C., and Van Slyke, D. D. 1915a. A method for the determination of chlorides in small amounts of body fluids. *J. Biol. Chem.*, *21*, 361.

_____ and _____ . 1915b. A method for the titration of small amounts of halides. *J. Am. Chem. Soc.*, *37*, 1128.

McRary, W. L., and Slattery, M. C. 1945. The colorimetric determination of pentoses and pentosans. *Arch. Biochem.*, *6*, 151.

MacFadyen, D. A. 1942. Determination of amino acids in plasma by the ninhydrin—carbon dioxide reaction without removal of proteins. *J. Biol. Chem.*, *145*, 387.

_____ . 1944. Determination of ammonia evolved from α-amino acids by ninhydrin. *J. Biol. Chem.*, *153*, 507.

_____ . 1945. Estimation of formaldehyde in biological mixtures. *J. Biol. Chem.*, *158*, 105.

MacMasters, M. M., and Hilbert, G. E. 1944. Glutinous corn and sorghum starches. *Ind. Eng. Chem.*, *36*, 958.

Macpherson, H. T. 1942. Modified procedures for the colorimetric estimation of arginine and histidine. *Biochem. J.*, *36*, 59.

Maher, F. T., and Wirth, E. H. 1946. The assay of papain with suggestion for the modification of the tentatively accepted assay. *Bull. Natl. Formulary Comm.*, *14*, 56.

Maillard, L. C. 1914a. Synthese de polypeptides par action de la glycerine sur le glycocolle. *Ann. chim.* (9), *1*, 519.

_____ . 1914b. Synthese de polypeptides par action de la glycerine sur le glycocolle: étude dynamique. *Ann. chim.* (9), *2*, 210.

Malaprade, M. L. 1934. Etude de l'action des polyalcools sur l'acide périodique et les périodates alcalins. *Bull. soc. chim.* (5), *1*, 833.

Malpress, F. H., and Morrison, A. B. 1949. The semi-micro estimation of lactose alone and in the presence of other sugars. *Biochem. J.*, *45*, 455.

Mannich, C., and Lenz, K. 1920. Über eine Methode zur polarimetrischen Bestimmung der Stärke in Calcium-chloridlösung. *Z. Untersuch. Nahr. U. Genussm.*, *40*, 1.

Maquenne, L., and Roux, E. 1903. Sur la rétrogradation de l'empois d'amidon. *Compt. rend.*, *137*, 88.

Markham, R., and Smith, J. D. 1949. Chromatographic studies of nucleic acids. *Biochem. J.*, *45*, 294.

Marquardt, P. 1947. Über eine Arbeitstheorie zu den Beziehungen zwischen dem Stadium einer Infektionskrankheit und der Höhe des Cholesterinspiegels im Blut. *Experientia*, *3*, 203.

Marshall, E. K., Jr. 1926. The secretion of urine. *Physiol. Revs.*, *6*, 440.

Mathews, A. P. 1930. Physiological Chemistry, 5th ed. William Wood & Company, New York.

_____ and McGuigan, H. 1907. A study of the oxidizing power of cupric acetate solutions. *Am. J. Physiol.*, *19*, 199.

Mellanby, E. 1919. A further demonstration of the part played by accessory food factors in the aetiology of rickets. *J. Physiol.*, *52*, LIII.

Melnick, D., and Oser, B. L. 1943. Chemical differentiation between niacinamide and niacin in pharmaceutical products. *Ind. Eng. Chem., Anal. Ed.*, *15*, 355.

Merck and Co. 1939. Nicotinic Acid. Rahway, N. J.

Meredith, W. O. S. 1946. Analysis of data for A.A.C.C. check sample service. II. Protein and thiamine results, 1944–1945. *Cereal Chem.*, *23*, 585.

Meyer, K. H. 1942. Recent developments in starch chemistry. In Kroemer, E. O., Advances in Colloid Science, New York, I, 143.

_____ , Fischer, E. H., and Bernfeld, P. 1947. Physical and chemical properties of crystalline α-amylase of hog pancreas. *Arch. Biochem.*, *14*, 149.

_____ , Wertheim, M., and Bernfeld, P. 1941. Recherches sur l'amidon XIII. Contribution à l'étude de l'amidon de pommes de terre. *Helv. Chim. Acta*, *24*, 378.

Militzer, W. E. 1941. The qualitative chemical identification of the natural sugars. *J. Chem. Education*, *18*, 25.

_____ . 1946. Note on the orcinol reagent. *Arch. Biochem.*, *9*, 85.

_____ , Ikeda, C., and Kneen, E. 1946a. The preparation and properties of an amylase inhibitor of wheat. *Arch. Biochem.*, *9*, 309.

_____ , _____ , and _____ . 1946b. The mode of action of an amylase inhibitor from wheat. *Arch. Biochem.*, *9*, 321.

Miller, B. F., and Muntz, J. A. 1938. A method for the estimation of ultramicroquantities of lactic acid. *J. Biol. Chem.*, *126*, 413.

Miller, G. L., and Miller, E. E. 1948. Determination of nitrogen in biological materials. Improved Kjeldahl-Nessler method. *Anal. Chem.*, *20*, 481.

Miller, L., and Houghton, J. A. 1945. The micro-Kjeldahl determination of the nitrogen content of amino acids and proteins. *J. Biol. Chem.*, *159*, 373.

Millon, E. 1849. Sur un réactif propre aux composés protéiques. *Compt. rend.*, *28*, 40.

Mills, M. B., and Roe, J. H. 1947. A critical study of proposed modifications of the Roe and Kuether method for the determination of ascorbic acid, with further contributions to the chemistry of this procedure. *J. Biol. Chem.*, *170*, 159.

Mitchell, H. K., and Niemann, C. 1947. The competitive inhibition of the metabolism of α-amino acids by their halogenated analogs. *J. Am. Chem. Soc.*, *69*, 1232.

_____ and Nyc, J. F. 1948. Hydroxyanthranilic acid as a precursor of nicotinic acid in *Neurospora*. *Proc. Natl. Acad. Sci., U.S.* *34*, 1.

Mohr, D. 1856. Neue massanalytische Bestimmung des Chlors in Verbindungen. *Ann.*, *97*, 335.

Molisch, H. 1886a. Eine neue Methode zur Unterscheidung der Pflanzen- von der Thierfaser. *Dinglers polytech. J.*, *261*, 135.

_____ . 1886b. Zwei neue Zuckerreaktionen. *Monatsh.*, *7*, 198.

Monnier, M., Farchadi, A., and Maulbetsch, A. 1941. Blood cholesterol in the rat. *Compt. rend. soc. phys. hist. nat. Genève*, *58*, 244; *Chem. Abstracts*, *38*, 2379 (1944).

Monroe, K. P. 1919. The preparation of xylose from corn cobs. *J. Am. Chem. Soc.*, *41*, 1002.

Moore, S., and Stein, W. H. 1949. Chromatography of amino acids on starch columns. Solvent mixtures for the fractionation of protein hydrolysates. *J. Biol. Chem.*, *178*, 53.

Morgan, A. F. 1943. Conditions affecting the toxicity of the D vitamins. *Pacific Sci. Congr., Pacific Sci. Assoc.*, *6*, 555.

Mörner, K. A. H. 1899. Cystin, ein Spaltungsprodukt der Hornsubstanz. *Z. physiol. Chem.*, *28*, 595.

_____ . 1901–1902. Zur Kenntniss der Bindung des Schwefels in den Proteinstoffen. *Z. physiol. Chem.*, *34*, 207.

Morrow, C. A., and Sandstrom, W. M. 1935. Biochemical Laboratory Methods. John Wiley & Sons, Inc., New York, 87.

Morse, W., 1933. Chemistry of the integument. V. A new color reaction for hydroxyproline and its use in distinguishing the scleroproteins. *J. Biol. Chem.*, *100*, 373.

Mueller, J. H. 1922. Studies on cultural requirements of bacteria. *J. Bact.*, 7, 309.

———. 1935a. Studies on cultural requirements of bacteria. V. The diphtheria bacillus. *J. Bact.*, 29, 515.

———. 1935b. Studies on cultural requirements of bacteria. VI. The diphtheria bacillus. *J. Bact.*, 30, 513.

Müller, R. H. 1939. Photoelectric methods in analytical chemistry. *Ind. Eng. Chem., Anal. Ed.*, 11, 1.

Murneek, A. E. 1935. Physiological role of asparagine and related substances in nitrogen metabolism of plants. *Plant Physiol.*, 10, 447.

Myers, V. C. 1909–1910. On the salts of cytosine, thymine and uracil. *J. Biol. Chem.*, 7, 249.

———. 1943. Blood amylase in diseases of the pancreas. *Gastroenterology*, 1, 617.

National Research Council, 1943. Reprint and Circular Series No. 115.

Nef, J. U. 1908. Dissoziationsvorgänge in der Zuckergruppe, I. *Ann.*, 357, 214.

———. 1914. Dissoziationsvorgänge in der Zuckergruppe, III. *Ann.*, 403, 204.

Nelson, N. 1944. A photometric adaptation of the Somogyi method for the determination of glucose. *J. Biol. Chem.*, 153, 375.

Neuberg, C., and Strauss, E. 1946. Quantitative formation of osazones. *Arch. Biochem.*, 11, 457.

Neumann, A. 1902–1903. Einfache Veraschungsmethode (Säuregemisch-Veraschung) und vereinfachte Bestimmungen von Eisen, Phosphorsäure, Salzsäure und anderen Aschenbestandtheilen unter Benutzung dieser Säuregemisch-Veraschung. *Z. physiol. Chem.*, 37, 115.

Newton, J. M., Hixon, R. M., and Naylor, N. M. 1943. Soybean amylase. II. Further purification of crude soybean beta-amylase concentrates. *Cereal Chem.*, 20, 23.

Nicolet, B. H., and Shinn, L. A. 1939. Action of periodic acid on α-amino alcohols. *J. Am. Chem. Soc.*, 61, 1615.

——— and ———. 1941. The determination of methylpentoses in the presence of pentoses. *J. Am. Chem. Soc.*, 63, 1456.

Nicolle, J. 1944. Growth of certain bacteria on the optical isomers of arabinose. *Compt. rend.*, 218, 482; *Chem. Abstracts*, 39, 2528 (1945).

Nielsen, J. P., and Gleason, P. C. 1945. Rapid determination of starch. *Ind. Eng. Chem., Anal. Ed.*, 17, 131.

Norris, F. A., and Buswell, R. J. 1943. Rapid iodine number determinations. *Ind. Eng. Chem., Anal. Ed.*, 15, 258.

Northrop, J. H. 1923. Note on the purification and precipitation of casein. *J. Gen. Physiol.*, 5, 749.

———. 1926. A convenient method for the formol titration. *J. Gen. Physiol.*, 9, 767.

Noyes, W. A., Crawford, G., Juniper, C. H., Flory, E. L., and Arnold, R. B. 1904. The hydrolysis of maltose and of dextrin by dilute acids and the determination of starch. *J. Am. Chem. Soc.*, 26, 266.

Nutr. Rev. 1948a. Influence of choline in megaloblastic anemias. *Nutrition Revs.*, 6, 89.

Nutr. Rev. 1948b. Lipotropic substances in cirrhosis of the liver. *Nutrition Revs.*, 6, 298.

Okabe, L. 1928. Studies on the solubility of cystine under various conditions and a new method of cystine preparation. *J. Biochem. (Japan)*, 8, 441; *Chem. Abstracts*, 22, 2958 (1928).

Okey, R. 1945. Cholesterol content of foods. *J. Am. Dietet. Assoc.*, 21, 341.

Okuda, Y. 1925. A new method for the determination of cystine in protein (the iodine method). *J. Biochem. (Japan)*, 5, 217; *Chem. Abstracts*, 20, 1252 (1926).

Orla-Jensen, S. 1919. The Lactic Acid Bacteria. K. Danske videnskabernes selskab, Copenhagen, Denmark.

Orten, J. M., and Hill, R. M. 1931. A simple method for the preparation of glycine. *J. Am. Chem. Soc.*, 53, 2797.

Osborne, T. B., and Guest, H. H. 1911. Hydrolysis of casein. *J. Biol. Chem.*, 9, 333.

Osterberg, A. E., and Helmholz, H. F. 1934. Determination whether ketonurine has bactericidal action. *J. Am. Med. Assoc.*, 102, 1831.

Ostwald, R. 1948. Synthesis of chloroacetic acid and glycine labeled with radioactive carbon in the carboxyl group. *J. Biol. Chem.*, 173, 207.

Paal, H. 1929. Über die Spaltbarkeit der Lecithine. *Biochem. Z.*, 211, 244.

Page, J. E., and Waller, J. G. 1946. Polarographic studies: IV. A note on the determination of ascorbic acid. *Analyst*, 71, 65.

Patterson, J. 1928. The determination of chlorides in body fluids. *Biochem. J.*, 22, 758.

Patton, A. R. 1935. The determination of glycine in proteins. *J. Biol. Chem.*, 108, 267.

Paul, W. D. 1946. Toxic manifestations of large doses of vitamin D as used in the treatment of arthritis. *J. Iowa State Med. Soc.*, 36, 141.

———, Daum, K., and Kemp, C. R. 1947. The action of choline on the blood lipide fractions in cirrhosis of the liver, diabetes mellitus and related conditions of disturbed fat metabolism. *J. Iowa State Med. Soc.*, 37, 146.

Paul Lewis Laboratories. 1948. Method of Performing and Interpretation of Results of Serum Phosphatase Test. Chicago, Ill.

Pavy, F. W. 1880. Eine neue Method der Zuckertitrirung mit ammoniakalischer Kupferlösung. *Z. anal. Chem.*, 19, 98.

Payen, A., and Persoz, J. 1833. Mémoire sur la diastase, les principaux produits de ses réactions, et leurs applications aux arts industriels. *Ann. chim. et phys.* (2), 53, 73.

Pederson, J. 1913. Milk-sugar. *J. Soc. Chem. Ind.*, *32*, 247.

Perkin, W. H., and Duppa, B. F. 1858. Über die Einwirkung des Broms auf Essigsäure. *Ann.*, *108*, 106.

Perlzweig, W. A. 1947. The chemical methods of determination of nicotinic acid and derivatives. *Biol. Symposia*, *12*, 204.

_____ and Huff, J. W. 1945. The fate of N^{1}-methylnicotinamide in man. *J. Biol. Chem.*, *161*, 417.

Peters, J. H. 1942. The determination of creatinine and creatine in blood and urine with the photoelectric colorimeter. *J. Biol. Chem.*, *146*, 179.

Peters, J. P., and Van Slyke, D. D. 1946. Quantitative Clinical Chemistry. Interpretations. Vol. I., 2d ed. The Williams & Wilkins Company, Baltimore.

Pinoff, E. 1905. Über einige Farben- und Spektralreaktionen der wichtigsten Zuckerarten. *Ber.*, *38*, 3308.

Pircio, A., and Cerecedo, L. R. 1948. Application of a new colorimetric method in the determination of the uracil and cytosine fractions of nucleic acid. *Abstr. Papers, Div. Biol. Chem., Am. Chem. Soc.*, September, 43C.

Piria, R. 1848. Recherches sur la constitution chimique de l'asparagine et de l'acide aspartique. *Ann. chim. et phys.* (3), *22*, 160.

Plimmer, R. H. A. 1913. The separation of cystine and tyrosine. *Biochem. J.*, *7*, 311.

_____ and Phillips, H. 1924. The analysis of proteins. III. Estimation of histidine and tyrosine by bromination. *Biochem. J.*, *18*, 312.

Plöchl, J. 1884. Über einige Derivate der Benzoylimidozimmtsäure. *Ber.*, *17*, 1616.

Polit, C. C., and Dhar, N. R. 1925. Induced oxidation of carbohydrates. *J. Phys. Chem.*, *29*, 799.

Poller, K. 1926. Über die Farbenreaktion von Sakaguchi. *Ber.*, *59*, 1927.

Popják, G. 1943. Colorimetric determination of total, free and ester cholesterol in tissue extracts. *Biochem. J.*, *37*, 468.

_____ . 1946. The effect of feeding cholesterol without fat on the plasma-lipids of the rabbit. The role of cholesterol in fat metabolism. *Biochem. J.*, *40*, 608.

Porsche, J. D. 1945. Preparation of cholesterol. U. S. Pat. 2,371,467.

Pratesi, P. 1933. Über Isatin-Kondensationsprodukte der Pyrrole (Pyrrolblaue). *Ann.*, *504*, 258.

Pucher, G. W., Leavenworth, C. S., and Vickery, H. B. 1948. Determination of starch in plant tissues. *Anal. Chem.*, *20*, 850.

_____ and Vickery, H. B. 1936. Determination of starch in plant tissues. *Ind. Eng. Chem., Anal. Ed.*, *8*, 92.

_____ , _____ and Wakeman, A. J. 1934. Determination of malic acid in plant tissue. *Ind. Eng. Chem., Anal. Ed.*, *6*, 288.

Pummerer, R., and Gump, W. 1923. Über die Aufspaltung des Furfuralkohols und den Mechanismus der Lävulinsäure-Bildung aus Hexosen. *Ber.*, *56*, 999.

_____ , Guyot, O., and Birkofer, L. 1935. Über den Mechanismus der Lävulinsäure-Bildung aus Hexosen (II. Mitteil) und über einen hydroxyl-freien glucosanartigen Körper. *Ber.*, *68B*, 480.

Quick, A. J. 1926. The study of benzoic acid conjugation in the dog with a direct quantitative method for hippuric acid. *J. Biol. Chem.*, *67*, 477.

_____ . 1940. The clinical application of the hippuric acid and the prothrombin tests. *Am. J. Clin. Path.*, *10*, 222.

_____ . 1944. Relation of amino acids to biologically important products and the role of certain amino acids in detoxication. In Sahyun, M., Outline of Amino Acids and Proteins. Reinhold Publishing Corporation, New York, 158.

Ramsey, J. B., and Colichman, E. L. 1942. Potentiometric determination of vitamin C. *Ind. Eng. Chem., Anal. Ed.*, *14*, 319.

Raper, H. S. 1927. The tyrosinase-tyrosine reaction. VI. Production from tyrosine of 5:6-dihydroxyindole and 5:6-dihydroxyindole-2-carboxylic acid — the precursors of melanin. *Biochem. J.*, *21*, 89.

Raybin, H. W. 1933. A new color reaction with sucrose. *J. Am. Chem. Soc.*, *55*, 2603.

_____ . 1937. The direct demonstration of the sucrose linkage in the oligosaccharides. *J. Am. Chem. Soc.*, *59*, 1402.

Redfern, S. 1947. Methods for determination of alpha-amylase. IV. A glass end point color standard for use in the dextrinizing method; effect of temperature and starch lot on this method. *Cereal Chem.*, *24*, 259.

Reichard, P. 1948. Partition chromatography on starch of ribonucleotides. *Nature*, *162*, 662.

Reichstein, T., Grüssner, A., and Oppenhauer, R. 1933. Synthesis of d- and l-ascorbic acid (vitamin C). *Nature*, *132*, 280.

Reid, M. E. 1947. Bioassay methods for vitamin C. *Biol. Symposia*, *12*, 373.

Retinger, J. M. 1917. The mechanism of the ninhydrin reaction. A contribution to the theory of color of salts of alloxanthine-like compounds. *J. Am. Chem. Soc.*, *39*, 1059.

Rettger, L. F., and Cheplin, H. A. 1923. The Intestinal Flora. Yale University Press, New Haven.

Rhian, M., Evans, R. J., and St. John, J. L. 1943. The choline content of feeds. *J. Nutrition*, *25*, 1.

Riggs, L. K., and Beaty, A. 1947. Some unique properties of lactose as a dietary carbohydrate. *J. Dairy Sci.*, 30, 939.

Rittenberg, D., and Schoenheimer, R. 1939. Studies in protein metabolism. VI. Hippuric acid formation studies with the aid of the nitrogen isotope. *J. Biol. Chem.*, 127, 329.

Ritthausen, H. 1869a. Asparaginsäure und Glutaminsäure, Zersetzungsprodukte des Legumins beim Kochen mit Schwefelsäure. *J. prakt. Chem.*, 106, 445.

———. 1869b. Asparaginsäure und Glutaminsäure, Zersetzungsprodukte des Legumins und Conglutins beim Kochen mit Schwefelsäure. *J. prakt. Chem.*, 107, 218.

Roberts, E. C., and Snell, E. E. 1946. An improved medium for microbiological assays with *Lactobacillus casei*. *J. Biol. Chem.*, 163, 499.

Robertson, E. B. 1934. Spectrophotometric estimation of ascorbic acid. *J. Soc. Chem. Ind.*, 53, 277.

Robertson, G. R. 1927. The reaction of chloro-acetic acid with ammonia and the preparation of glycine. *J. Am. Chem. Soc.*, 49, 2889.

———. 1943. Laboratory Practices of Organic Chemistry, 2d ed. The Macmillan Company, New York.

Robiquet. 1805. Mémoire sur les acides aspartique et malique. Quoted by Pasteur, L., *Ann. chim. et phys.* (3), 34, 30 (1852).

Roche, J. 1946. Sur la biochimie général des phosphatases. *Helv. Chim. Acta*, 29, 1253.

Roman, W. 1930. Eine chemische Methode zur quantitativen Bestimmung des Cholins und einige physikalische-chemische Daten des Cholins und seiner Salze. *Biochem. Z.*, 219, 218.

Rose, W. C. 1938. The nutritive significance of the amino acids. *Physiol. Rev.*, 18, 109.

Rosenberg, H. R. 1942. Chemistry and Physiology of the Vitamins. Interscience Publishers, New York.

Rosenheim, O. 1906a. On the preparation of cholesterin from brain. *J. Physiol.*, 34, 104.

———. 1906b. A colour reaction of formaldehyde with proteids and its relation to the Adamkiewicz reaction. *Biochem. J.*, 1, 233.

Rosenthaler, L. 1904. Eine titrimetrische Zuckerbestimmung. *Z. anal. Chem.*, 43, 282.

Rosin, H. 1903. Eine Verschärfung der Seliwanoffschen Reaktion. *Z. physiol. Chem.*, 38, 555.

Rothmund, V., and Burgstaller, A. 1909. Über die Genauigkeit der Chlorbestimmung nach Volhard. *Z. anorg. Chem.*, 63, 330.

Rudisch, J., and Celler, H. L. 1907. The quantitative determination of glucose in the urine by a new modification of Fehling's solution. *J. Am. Med. Assoc.*, 48, 324.

Ruhemann, S. 1910. Triketohydrindene hydrate. *J. Chem. Soc.*, 97, 2025.

———. 1911. Triketohydrindene hydrate. Part V. The analogues of uramil and purpuric acid. *J. Chem. Soc.*, 99, 1486.

Rundle, R. E., Foster, J. F., and Baldwin, R. R. 1944. On the nature of the starch-iodine complex. *J. Am. Chem. Soc.*, 66, 2116.

Rydon, H. N. 1948. The synthesis of the nuclear-C-methylated tryptophans. A note on the aldehyde reactions for tryptophan. *J. Chem. Soc.*, 705.

Saifer, A., and Kammerer, O. F. 1946. Photometric determination of total cholesterol in plasma or serum by a modified Liebermann-Burchard reaction. *J. Biol. Chem.*, 164, 657.

Sakaguchi, S. 1925a. A new color reaction of protein and arginine. *J. Biochem. (Japan)*, 5, 25; *Chem. Abstracts*, 19, 3506 (1925).

———. 1925b. The mode of combination and determination of arginine in the protein molecule. *J. Biochem. (Japan)*, 5, 133; *Chem. Abstracts*, 20, 925 (1926).

Sakami, W. 1949. The conversion of glycine into serine in the intact rat. *J. Biol. Chem.*, 178, 519.

———, Evans, W. E., and Gurin, S. 1947. The synthesis of organic compounds labelled with isotopic carbon. *J. Am. Chem. Soc.*, 69, 1110.

Salkowski, E. 1888. Kleinere Mittheilungen. Über die Farbenreaktionen des Eiweiss. *Z. physiol. Chem.*, 12, 215.

Sannié, C. 1942. A simple synthesis of 2,5-diketopiperazines (α-amino acid anhydrides). *Bull. soc. chim.* (5), 9, 487; *Chem. Abstracts*, 37, 5065 (1943).

Sarett, H. P., Bennett, M. J., Riggs, T. R., and Cheldelin, V. H. 1946. Thiamine, riboflavin, nicotinic acid, pantothenic acid and ascorbic acid content of restaurant foods. *J. Nutrition*, 31, 755.

Sasaki, T. 1914. Über die biochemische Umwandlung primärer Eiweiss-spaltprodukte durch Bakterien. *Biochem. Z.*, 59, 429.

Satherfield, G. H. 1947. Chemical methods for the estimation of ascorbic acid. *Biol. Symposia*, 12, 397.

Scheele, C. W. 1780. Kong. Vetenskape Akademiens nya handlinger, 1, 116. Quoted by Sutermeister and Browne (1939).

Schenck, F. 1937. Über die kristallisierte Vitamine D₃. *Naturwissenschaften*, 25, 159.

Schmidt, C. L. A. 1929. The reaction between nitrous acid and certain amino acids and related compounds at 45°. *J. Biol. Chem.*, 82, 587.

_____ and Allen, F. W. 1938. Fundamentals of Biochemistry with Laboratory Experiments, 1st ed. McGraw-Hill Book Company, Inc., New York, 284.

Schöberl, A., and Rambacher, P. 1937—1938. Über die kolorimetrische Bestimmung von Cystein and Cystin mit Phosphorwolframsäure. *Biochem. Z.*, 295, 377.

Schoch, T. J. 1942. Non-carbohydrate substances in the cereal starches. *J. Am. Chem. Soc.*, 64, 2954.

Schoenheimer, R. 1932. Die Spezifitat der Cholesterinresorption und ihre biologische Bedeutung. *Klin. Wochschr.*, 11, 1793.

Schopmeyer, H. H. 1945. Amioca — the starch from waxy corn. *Food Inds.*, 17, 1476.

Schott, H. F., Larkin, J. B., Rockland, L. B., and Dunn, M. S., 1947. Synthesis of *l*(-)leucylglycylglycine. *J. Org. Chem.*, 12, 490.

_____, Rockland, L. B., and Dunn, M. S. 1944. Investigations of amino acids, peptides and proteins. XVI. A source of error in the manometric ninhydrin method for the analysis of amino acids and its suppression by the use of hydrazine. *J. Biol. Chem.*, 154, 397.

Schotten, C. 1888. Die Umwandlung des Piperidins in δ-Amidovaleriansäure und in Oxypiperidin. *Ber.*, 21, 2235.

Schulze, E., and Winterstein, E. 1910. Studien über die Proteinbildung in reifenden Pflanzensamen. *Z. physiol. Chem.*, 65, 431.

Scott, E. M., and Sandstrom, W. M. 1942. The activation of papain. *Arch. Biochem.*, 1, 103.

Scotti, G. 1938. A new method for determining the iodine number of oils and fats. *Olii minerali, grassi e saponi, colori e vernici*, 18, 96; *Chem. Abstracts*, 34, 4291 (1940).

Sebrell, W. H., Jr. 1934. Table showing the pellagra-preventive value of various foods. *Public Health Reports, U.S.P.H.S.*, 49, 754.

Seliwanoff, T. 1887. Notiz über eine Fruchtzuckerreaktion. *Ber.*, 20, 181.

Sen, R. N., and Sinha, N. N. 1923. Condensations of aldehydes with resorcinol and some other aromatic hydroxy compounds. *J. Am. Chem. Soc.*, 45, 2984.

Sendroy, J., Jr. 1937. Microdetermination of chloride in biological fluids, with solid silver iodate. I. Gasometric analysis. *J. Biol. Chem.*, 120, 335.

Seshagirirao, P., and Giri, K. V. 1942. The mechanism of β-amylase inhibition by vitamin C. *Proc. Indian Acad. Sci.*, 16B, 190.

Shafee, M., and Sarin, J. L. 1937. Production of starch from water caltrop. *Ind. Eng. Chem.*, 29, 1436.

Shaffer, P. A., and Hartmann, A. F. 1921. The iodometric determination of copper and its use in sugar analysis. II. Methods for the determination of reducing sugars in blood, urine, milk, and other solutions. *J. Biol. Chem.*, 45, 365.

_____ and Somogyi, M. 1933. Copper-iodometric reagents for sugar determination. *J. Biol. Chem.*, 100, 695.

Sheehan, J. C., and Frank, V. S. 1949. A new synthetic route to peptides. *J. Am. Chem. Soc.*, 71, 1856.

Sheehan, J. T., and Freudenberg, W. 1942. *d*-Mannose. *Org. Syntheses*, 22, 86.

Shemin, D. 1945. The synthesis of glycine in the rat and guinea pig; conversion of serine to glycine. *Federation Proc.*, 4, 103.

_____ and Rittenberg, D. 1947. On the utilization of glycine for uric acid synthesis in man. *J. Biol. Chem.*, 167, 875.

Sherman, H. C., LaMer, V. K., and Campbell, H. L. 1922. The quantitative determination of the antiscorbutic vitamin (Vitamin C). *J. Am. Chem. Soc.*, 44, 165.

Shevky, M. C., and Stafford, D. D. 1923. A clinical method for the estimation of protein in urine and other body fluids. *Arch. Internal Med.*, 32, 222.

Shinn, L. A., and Nicolet, B. H. 1941. The determination of threonine by the use of periodate. *J. Biol. Chem.*, 138, 91.

Shinohara, K., and Kilpatrick, M. 1934. The stability of cystine in acid solution. *J. Biol. Chem.*, 105, 241.

Shipley, P. G., Park, E. A., McCollum, E. V., Simmonds, N., and Parsons, H. T. 1920—1921. Studies on experimental rickets. II. The effect of cod liver oil administered to rats with experimental rickets. *J. Biol Chem.*, 45, 343.

Siegel, L. 1945. The microbiological determination of choline. *Science*, 101, 674.

Sjollema, B., and Rinkes, I. J. 1911. Die Hydrolyse des Kartoffeleiweisses. *Z. physiol. Chem.*, 76, 369.

Sjostrom, O. A. 1936. Microscopy of starches and their modifications. *Ind. Eng. Chem.*, 28, 63.

Smirk, F. H. 1927. The micro-estimation of chlorine in whole blood serum or corpuscles. *Biochem. J.*, 21, 31.

Snell, E. E. 1947. The microbiological determination of nicotinic acid. *Biol. Symposia*, 12, 183.

_____ and Strong, F. M. 1939. A microbiological assay for riboflavin. *Ind. Eng. Chem., Anal. Ed.*, 11, 346.

_____ and Wright, L. D. 1941. A microbiological method for the determination of nicotinic acid. *J. Biol. Chem.*, 139, 675.

Snell, F. D., and Snell, C. T. 1948. Colorimetric Methods of Analysis. D. Van Nostrand Company, Inc., New York.

Sobel, A. E., Hirschman, A., and Besman, L. 1945. A convenient microtitration method for the estimation of amino acids. *J. Biol. Chem.*, *161*, 99.

_____ and Mayer, A. M. 1945. Improvements in the Schoenheimer-Sperry method for the determination of free cholesterol. *J. Biol. Chem.*, *157*, 255.

Sobotka, H. 1938. Chemistry of the Sterids. The Williams & Wilkins Company, Baltimore.

Society for Experimental Biology. 1947. Nucleic Acids. Cambridge University Press, London.

Somogyi, M. 1938. Micromethods for the estimation of diastase. *J. Biol. Chem.*, *125*, 399.

_____ . 1945. A new reagent for the determination of sugars. *J. Biol. Chem.*, *160*, 61.

Soodak, M., Pircio, A., and Cerecedo, L. R. 1949. A colorimetric method for the estimation of uracil and cytosine. *J. Biol. Chem.*, *181*, 713.

Sørenson, M., and Haugaard, G. 1933. Über die Andwendbarkeit der Orcinreaktion zur Bestimmung der Art und Menge von Kohlenhydratgruppen in Eiweiss-stoffen. *Biochem. Z.*, *260*, 247.

Speich, H. 1942. Optical properties of potato starch grains. *Ber. schweiz. botan. Ges.*, *52*, 175; *Chem. Abstracts*, *38*, 2233 (1944).

Stark, I. E. 1942. Equilibria in diastatic reactions. *J. Biol. Chem.*, *142*, 569.

Stein, R. S., and Rundle, R. E. 1948. On the nature of the interaction between starch and iodine. *J. Chem. Phys.*, *16*, 195.

Stein, W. H., and Moore, S. 1949. Amino acid composition of β-lactoglobulin and bovine serum albumin. *J. Biol. Chem.*, *178*, 79.

Steiner, A. 1948. Significance of cholesterol in coronary arteriosclerosis. *N.Y. State J. Med.*, *48*, 1814.

Stekol, J. A. 1941. Detoxication mechanisms. *Ann. Rev. Biochem.*, *10*, 265.

Stephenson, C. H., and Parker, C. E. 1921. Some Microchemical Tests for Alkaloids. J. B. Lippincott Company, Philadelphia, Pa.

Stern, A., Beach, E. F., and Macy, I. G. 1939. Polarographic microdetermination of cystine in protein hydrolysates. *J. Biol. Chem.*, *130*, 733.

Stetten, D., Jr. 1942. Biological synthesis of choline by rats on diets with and without adequate lipotropic methyl. *J. Biol. Chem.*, *142*, 629.

Stewart, A. P., and Sharp, P. F. 1945. Determination of vitamin C in the presence of interfering reducing substances. *Ind. Eng. Chem., Anal. Ed.*, *17*, 373.

Stone, W. E., and Lotz, D. 1891. A new source for xylose. *Am. Chem. J.*, *13*, 348.

Strafford, N. 1936. Quantitative colorimetric analysis. *Ann. Repts. Soc. Chem., on Progress Applied Chem.*, 456.

Strain, H. H. 1942. Chromatographic Adsorption Analysis. Interscience Publishers, New York.

Strain, W. H. 1943. The steroids. In Gilman's Organic Chemistry, Vol. II, 2d ed. John Wiley & Sons, Inc., New York.

Strecker, A. 1849. Beobachtungen über die Galle verschiedener Thiere. *Ann.*, *70*, 149.

Street, H. E., Kenyon, A. E., and Watson, G. M. 1946. Estimation of free choline in plants. *Biochem. J.*, *40*, 869.

Stuart, N. W., and Brimhall, B. 1943. Starch from easter lily bulbs. *Cereal Chem.*, *20*, 734.

Stumpf, P. K., and Green, D. E. 1944. *l*-Amino acid oxidase of *Proteus vulgaris*. *J. Biol. Chem.*, *153*, 387.

Sullivan, J. T. 1935a. The estimation of starch in plants with special reference to woody plants. *J. Assoc. Offic. Agr. Chemists*, *18*, 621.

_____ . 1935b. The estimation of starch. *Ind. Eng. Chem., Anal. Ed.*, *7*, 311.

Sullivan, M. X. 1929a. Studies on the biochemistry of sulphur. IV. The colorimetric estimation of cystine in casein by means of the beta-naphthoquinone reaction. *Public Health Reports, U.S.P.H.S.*, Suppl. No. 78.

_____ . 1929b. Studies on the biochemistry of sulphur. II. Further studies on the distinctive reaction for cysteine and cystine. *Public Health Reports*, U.S.P.H.S., 44, 1421.

_____ and Hess, W. C. 1929. Studies on the biochemistry of sulphur. III. Chemical groups involved in the naphthoquinone reaction for cysteine and cystine. *Public Health Reports, U.S.P.H.S.*, *44*, 1599.

Summerson, W. H. 1939. Simplified test-tube photoelectric colorimeter, and the use of the photoelectric colorimeter in colorimetric analysis. *J. Biol. Chem.*, *130*, 149.

Sumner, J. B. 1921. Dinitrosalicylic acid: a reagent for the estimation of sugar in normal and diabetic urine. *J. Biol. Chem.*, *47*, 5.

_____ . 1925. A more specific reagent for the determination of sugar in urine. *J. Biol. Chem.*, *65*, 393.

_____ and Somers, G. F. 1947. Chemistry and Methods of Enzymes, 2d ed. Academic Press, New York.

Sunderman, F. W. 1942. Phosphatase. Recent advances in the significance and interpretation of phosphate measurement in disease. *Am. J. Clin. Path.*, *12*, 404.

Suomalainen, H., and Arhimo, E. 1947. Oxidative bromination in the determination of malic acid and aspartic acid. *Anal. Chem.*, *19*, 207.

Sutermeister, E., and Browne, F. L. 1939. Casein and Its Industrial Applications. Reinhold Publishing Corporation, New York.

Suzuki, U., Shinamura, T., and Odake, S. 1912. Über Oryzanin, ein Bestandteil der Reiskleie und seine physiologische Bedeutung. *Biochem. Z.*, *43*, 89.

Szent-Györgyi, A. 1928. Observations on the function of peroxidase systems and the chemistry of the adrenal cortex. Description of a new carbohydrate derivative. *Biochem. J.*, *22*, 1387.

Tauber, H. 1937–1938. A color test for pentoses. *Proc. Soc. Exptl. Biol. Med.*, *37*, 600.

———. 1949. The Chemistry and Technology of Enzymes. John Wiley & Sons, Inc., New York.

——— and Kleiner, I. S. 1932–1933. A method for the determination of monosaccharides in the presence of disaccharides and its application to blood analysis. *J. Biol. Chem.*, *99*, 249.

——— and ———. 1935. An enzymic method for the estimation of true vitamin C. *J. Biol. Chem.*, *110*, 559.

Taylor, W. H., and Smith, G. F. 1942. Micro-Kjeldahl nitrogen determination without use of titration procedure. *Ind. Eng. Chem., Anal. Ed.*, *14*, 437.

Tebb, M. C. 1906. The cholesterin of the brain. *J. Physiol.*, *34*, 106.

Teeri, A. E. 1944. The determination of esterified cholesterol. *J. Biol. Chem.*, *156*, 279.

van Thoai, N., and Bernère-Silhol, J. 1946. Sur la purification de l'amylase pancréatique. *Compt. rend.*, *223*, 761.

Thompson, R. L., and Wilkins, M. L. 1948. Inhibition of growth of the vaccinia virus by β-2-thienylalanine and its reversal by phenylalanine. *Proc. Soc. Exptl. Biol. Med.*, *68*, 434.

Tillmans, J., Hirsch, P., and Reinshagen, E. 1928. The use of 2,6-dichlorophenol indophenol as a reduction indicator in the examination of foodstuffs. *Z. Untersuch. Lebensm.*, *56*, 272; *Chem. Abstracts*, *23*, 3277 (1929).

Tinker, J. T., and Brown, G. B. 1948. The characterization of purines and pyrimidines by the method of countercurrent distribution. *J. Biol. Chem.*, *173*, 585.

Todd, J. C., and Sanford, A. H. 1948. Clinical Diagnosis by Laboratory Methods, 11th ed. W. B. Saunders Company, Philadelphia.

Toennies, G., and Bennett, M. A. 1935–1936. Some observations on the isolation of cystine from wool hydrolysates. *J. Biol. Chem.*, *112*, 39.

——— and Lavine, T. F. 1930. On the optical rotation of L-cystine. Determination of its value for the sodium and mercury lines and of the temperature factor. *J. Biol. Chem.*, *89*, 153.

Tompsett, S. L. 1931. A note on the determination of cystine in proteins by the method of Folin and Marenzi. *Biochem. J.*, *25*, 2014.

Tristram, G. R. 1939. The basic amino acids of leaf proteins with a discussion of various methods of analysis. *Biochem. J.*, *33*, 1271.

Tswett, M. 1906. Adsorptionsanalyse und chromatographische Methode. Anwendung auf die Chemie des Chlorophylls. *Ber. deut. botan. Ges.*, *24*, 384; *Cent. 1906*, II, 1286.

Turner, N. C. 1943. Starch blue. *Science*, *108*, 302.

v. Udránsky, L. 1888. Über Furfurolreaktionen. *Z. physiol. Chem.*, *12*, 355.

Underkofler, L. A. Christenson, L. M., and Fulmer, E. I. 1936. Butyl-acetonic fermentation of xylose and other sugars. *Ind. Eng. Chem.*, *28*, 350.

——— and Hunter, J. E., Jr. 1938. Butyl-acetonic fermentation of arabinose and other sugars. *Ind. Eng. Chem.*, *30*, 480.

Uschinsky. 1893. Über eine eiweissfreie Nährlösung für pathogene Bakterien nebst einigen Bemerkungen über Tetanusgift. *Centr. Bakt.*, *14*, 316.

Van Slyke, D. D. 1911. A method for quantitative determination of aliphatic amino groups. Applications to the study of proteolysis and proteolytic products. *J. Biol. Chem.*, *9*, 185.

———. 1912. The quantitative determination of aliphatic amino groups. II. *J. Biol. Chem.*, *12*, 275.

———. 1913–1914. The gasometric determination of aliphatic amino nitrogen in minute quantities. *J. Biol. Chem.*, *16*, 121.

———. 1915a. Improvements in the method for analysis of proteins by determination of the chemical groups characteristic of the different amino acids. *J. Biol. Chem.*, *22*, 281.

———. 1915b. Note on the micro-method for the gasometric determination of aliphatic amino nitrogen. *J. Biol. Chem.*, *23*, 407.

———. 1917. Studies of acidosis. VII. The determination of β-hydroxy-butyric acid, aceto-acetic acid, and acetone in urine. *J. Biol. Chem.*, *32*, 455.

———. 1929a. The determination of acetone bodies in blood and urine. *J. Biol. Chem.*, *83*, 415.

———. 1929b. Manometric determination of primary amino nitrogen and its application to blood analysis. *J. Biol. Chem.*, *83*, 425.

——— and Cullen, G. E. 1914. A permanent preparation of urease, and its use in the determination of urea. *J. Biol. Chem.*, *19*, 211.

_____ and Dillon, R. T. 1938. Gasometric determination of carboxyl groups in amino acids. *Compt. rend. trav. lab. Carlsberg, 22,* 480.

_____, _____, MacFadyen, D. A., and Hamilton, P. B. 1941. Gasometric determination of carboxyl groups in free amino acids. *J. Biol. Chem., 141,* 627.

_____ and Folch, J. 1940. Manometric carbon determination. *J. Biol. Chem., 136,* 509.

_____, Hiller, A., and Dillon, R. T. 1942. Solubilities and compositions of the phospho-12-tungstates of the diamino acids and of proline, glycine, and tryptophane. *J. Biol. Chem., 146,* 137.

_____, _____, and MacFadyen, D. A. 1941. The determination of hydroxylysine in proteins. *J. Biol. Chem., 141,* 681.

_____, _____, _____, Hastings, A. B., and Klemperer, F. W. 1940. On hydroxylysine. *J. Biol. Chem., 133,* 287.

_____, MacFadyen, D. A., and Hamilton, P. B. 1942. Application of the gasometric ninhydrin-CO_2 method to determination of amino acids in blood. *Federation Proc., 1,* 139.

_____, _____, and _____. 1943. The gasometric determination of amino acids in urine by the ninhydrin—carbon dioxide method. *J. Biol. Chem., 150,* 251.

_____ and Palmer, W. W. 1920. Studies of acidosis. XVI. Determination of organic acids in urine. *J. Biol. Chem., 41,* 567.

Van Slyke, L. L. and Baker, J. C. 1918. The preparation of pure casein. *J. Biol. Chem., 35,* 127.

_____ and Bosworth, A. W. 1913. Method of preparing ash-free casein and paracasein. *J. Biol. Chem., 14,* 203.

_____ and Carpenter, D. C. 1924. Quoted by Zoller, H. F. Casein and the Dairy Industry. In Bouge, R. H., The Theory and Application of Colloidal Behavior. McGraw-Hill Book Company, Inc., New York, *2,* 784.

Vauquelin and Robiquet. 1806. Decouverte d'un nouveau principe végétal dans les asperges (*Asparagus sativus, Linn.*) *Ann. chim. et. phys.* (1) *57,* 88.

Vickery, H. B. 1946. Position of Arnold in relationship to the Kjeldahl method. *J. Assoc. Offic. Agr. Chemists, 29,* 358.

_____ and Leavenworth, C. S. 1929. The separation of cystine from histidine: the basic amino acids of human hair. *J. Biol. Chem., 83,* 523.

_____ and Pucher, G. W. 1943. Amide metabolism in etiolated seedlings. I. Asparagine and glutamine formation in *Lupinus angustifolius, Vicia atropurpurea,* and *Cucurbita pepo. J. Biol. Chem., 150,* 197.

_____, _____, Wakeman, A. J., and Leavenworth, C. S. 1937. Chemical investigations of the tobacco plant. VI. Chemical changes that occur in leaves during culture in light and in darkness. *Connecticut Agr. Exp. Sta. Bull., 399.*

_____ and Schmidt, C. L. A. 1931. The history of the discovery of the amino acids. *Chem. Revs., 9,* 169.

_____ and White, A. 1932. The use of cysteine cuprous mercaptide in the determination of cystine. *J. Biol. Chem., 99,* 701.

du Vigneaud, V. 1941. Interrelationships between choline and other methylated compounds. *Biol. Symposia, 5,* 234.

_____. 1942—1943. Significance of labile methyl groups in the diet and their relation to transmethylation. *Harvey Lectures, 38,* 39.

_____ and Irish, O. J. 1938. The role of the acetyl derivative as an intermediary stage in the biological synthesis of amino acids from keto acids. *J. Biol. Chem., 122,* 349.

_____ and Meyer, C. E. 1932. The racemization of amino acids in aqueous solution by acetic anhydride. *J. Biol. Chem., 98,* 295.

Virtanen, A. I., and Rautanen, N. 1947. Determination of certain amino-acids by ninhydrin oxidation to volatile aldehydes. *Biochem. J., 41,* 101.

Virtue, R. W., and Lewis, H. B. 1934. The iodometric determination of cystine in the urine. *J. Biol. Chem., 104,* 415.

Vischer, E., and Chargaff, E. 1948a. The separation and quantitative estimation of purines and pyrimidines in minute amounts. *J. Biol. Chem., 176,* 703.

_____ and _____. 1948b. The composition of the pentose nucleic acids of yeast and pancreas. *J. Biol. Chem., 176,* 715.

_____, Magasanik, B., and Chargoff, E. 1949. Chromatographic separation of ribonucleotides and its application to the study of ribonucleic acid structure. *Federation Proc., 8,* 263.

_____, Zamenhof, S., and Chargoff, E. 1949. Microbial nucleic acids: the desoxypentose nucleic acids of avian tubercle bacilli and yeast. *J. Biol. Chem., 177,* 429.

Volhard, J. 1874. Über eine neue Methode der maassanalytischen Bestimmung des Silbers. *J. prakt. Chem., 9,* 217.

_____. 1878. Die Anwendung des Schwefelcyanammoniums in der Massanalyse. *Ann., 190,* 1.

Volz, G. W., and Caldwell, M. L. 1947. A study of the action of purified amylase from *Aspergillus oryzae,* taka-amylase. *J. Biol. Chem., 171,* 667.

Vredenburg, R. M. 1950. Guide to Photometric Analysis. Fisher Scientific Company, Pittsburgh, Pa.

Waddell, J., and Kennedy, G. H. 1947a. The antirachitic potency of pure crystalline vitamin D_3 in comparison with the U.S.P. reference cod liver oil when assayed by the chick method. *J. Assoc. Offic. Agr. Chemists,* 30, 190.

_____ and _____. 1947b. The assay of vitamin D by the chick method. *Biol. Symposia,* 12, 435.

Waelsch, H., and Prescott, B. A. 1945. A chemical method for the determination of glutamic acid. *Federation Proc.,* 4, 108.

Wagner, E. C. 1940. Titration of ammonia in presence of boric acid. *Ind. Eng. Chem., Anal. Ed.,* 12, 771.

Waldschmidt-Leitz, E., and Akabori, S. 1934. Bestimmung von Oxyprolin. Zur Methode nach K. Lang. *Z. physiol. Chem.,* 224, 187.

Warner, R. C. 1944. Separation of α- and β-casein. *J. Am. Chem. Soc.,* 66, 1725.

Waser, E., and Brauchli, E. 1924. Untersuchungen in der Phenylalanin-Reihe. V. Hydrierung des Tyrosins. *Helv. Chim. Acta,* 7, 740.

Webb, B. H., and Ramsdell, G. A. 1944. The manufacture of crude and technical lactose from cheese whey. *Natl. Butter Cheese J.,* 35, No. 7, 18, No. 8, 18.

Weber, C. J. 1930. A modification of Sakaguchi's reaction for the quantitative determination of arginine. *J. Biol. Chem.,* 86, 217.

Weiss, M. 1919. Über den quantitativen Nachweis des Tyrosins mittels der Millonschen Reaktion. *Biochem. Z.,* 97, 170.

Weissberger, A. 1946. Physical Methods of Organic Chemistry, Vol. 2. Interscience Publishers, New York.

Welker, W. H. 1915. A disturbing factor in Barfoed's test. *J. Am. Chem. Soc.,* 37, 2227.

West, C. D. 1947. X-ray diffraction by addition compounds of halogens with hydrophilic organic polymers. *J. Phys. Chem.,* 15, 689.

Weygand, F. 1940. Über N-glycoside. IV. Mitteil. Theorie der Osazonbildung. *Ber.,* 73B, 1284.

Wheeler, H. J., and Tollens, B. 1889. Über die Xylose (Holzzucker) und das Holzgummi. *Ber.,* 22, 1046.

_____ and Johnson, T. B. 1907. IV. Researches on pyrimidines: on a color test for uracil and cytosin. *J. Biol. Chem.,* 3, 183.

Wheeler, J. E., and György, P. 1948. Studies on urinary excretion of methionine by normals and by patients having liver disease. *Am. J. Med. Sci.,* 215, 267.

Whistler, R., and Hilbert, G. 1944. Extraction of fatty substance from starch. *J. Am. Chem. Soc.,* 66, 1721.

White, E. V. 1946. The constitution of mesquite gum. I. The methanolysis products of methylated mesquite gum. *J. Am. Chem. Soc.,* 68, 272.

_____. 1947. The constitution of mesquite gum. II. Partial hydrolysis of mesquite gum. *J. Am. Chem. Soc.,* 69, 622.

Whitmoyer, R. B. 1934. Determination of small amounts of glucose, fructose, and invert sugar in absence and presence of sucrose. *Ind. Eng. Chem., Anal. Ed.,* 6, 268.

Whittier, E. O. 1925–1926. Lactose — a review. *Chem. Revs.,* 2, 85.

_____. 1944. Lactose and its utilization: a review. *J. Dairy Sci.,* 27, 505.

Wijs, J. J. A. 1898. Zur Jod-Additionsmethode. *Ber.,* 31, 750.

Willgeroth, G. B., Halpin, J. L., Halloran, H. R., and Fritz, J. C. 1944. Use of turkeys for assay of vitamin D. *J. Assoc. Offic. Agr. Chemists,* 27, 289.

Williams, R. J., Schlenk, F., and Eppright, M. A. 1944. The assay of purified proteins, enzymes, etc., for "B vitamins." *J. Am. Chem. Soc.,* 66, 896.

Williams, R. T., and Synge, R. L. M. 1950. Partition Chromatography. Cambridge University Press, London.

Williamson, M. B. 1944. The amino acid composition of human milk proteins. *J. Biol. Chem.,* 156, 47.

Willstätter, R., Waldschmidt-Leitz, E., and Hesse, A.R.F. 1923. Über Pankreas-Amylase. *Z. physiol. Chem.,* 126, 143.

Wilson, R. H., and Lewis, H. B. 1927. The cystine content of hair and other epidermal tissues. *J. Biol. Chem.,* 73, 543.

Windaus, A., Lettré, H., and Schenck, F. 1935. Über das 7-Dehydro-Cholesterin. *Ann.,* 520, 98.

Winnick, T., Friedberg, F., and Greenberg, D. M. 1947. Incorporation of C^{14}-labeled glycine into intestinal tissue and its inhibition by azide. *Arch. Biochem.,* 15, 160.

Winterstein, E. 1901–1902. Über eine Methode zur Abscheidung der organischen Basen aus den Phosphorwolfram-säureniederschlägen und über das Verhalten des Cystins gegen Phosphorwolframsäure. *Z. physiol. Chem.,* 34, 153.

Winzler, R. J. 1944. Azide inhibition of anaerobic assimilation of glucose by yeast and its application to the determination of fermentable sugar. *Science,* 99, 327.

Wise, L. E., and Appling, J. W. 1944. Quantitative determination of *d*-galactose by selective fermentation. *Ind. Eng. Chem., Anal. Ed.,* 16, 28.

_____ and _____ . 1945. Quantitative determination of *d*-xylose by selective fermentation. *Ind. Eng. Chem., Anal. Ed.,* 17, 182.

_____ , Ratliff, E. K., and Browning, B. L. 1948. Determination of mannose. Mannans in hardwoods. *Anal. Chem.,* 20, 825.

Wittenberg, J., and Shemin, D. 1949. The utilization of glycine for the biosynthesis of both types of pyrroles in protoporphyrin. *J. Biol. Chem.,* 178, 47.

Wohlgemuth, J. 1908. Über eine neue Methode zur Quantitativen Bestimmung des Diastatischen Ferments. *Biochem. Z.,* 9, 1.

Wood, H. G., Geiger, C., and Werkman, C. H. 1939—1940. Nutritive requirements of the heterofermentative lactic acid bacteria. *Iowa State Coll. J. Sci.,* 14, 367.

Woodard, H. Q. 1934. Colorimetric determination of iodine by the starch-iodine reaction. *Ind. Eng. Chem., Anal. Ed.,* 6, 331.

Woodhouse, D. L. 1949. A method for the colorimetric micro-estimation of thymine. *Biochem. J.,* 44, 185.

Woodson, H. W., Hier, S. W., Solomon, J. D., and Bergheim, O. 1948. Urinary excretion of amino acids by human subjects on normal diets. *J. Biol. Chem.,* 172, 613.

Woolley, D. W., and Peterson, W. H. 1937—1938. Some observations on the Kapeller-Adler method for the determination of histidine. The histidine content of yeast. *J. Biol. Chem.,* 122, 207.

Wu, H. 1920. Contribution to the chemistry of phosphomolybdic acids, phosphotungstic acids and allied substances. *J. Biol. Chem.,* 43, 189.

Yamafuji, K., and Yoshida, T. 1939. Eine Micromethode zur Zuckerbestimmung mittels α-Naphthol. *Biochem. Z.,* 301, 61.

_____ , _____ , and Fukuura, T. 1941. Zur Zuckerbestimmung mittels α-Naphthol. *Biochem. Z.,* 308, 128.

Yeh, H. L., Frankl, W., Dunn, M. S., Parker, P., Hughes, B., and György, P. 1947. The urinary excretion of amino acids by a cystinuric subject. *Am. J. Med. Sci.,* 214, 507.

Yemm, E. W. 1935. The respiration of barley plants. I. Methods for the determination of carbohydrates in leaves. *Proc. Roy. Soc. (London),* 117B, 483.

Yoe, J. H. 1928. Photometric Chemical Analysis. John Wiley & Sons, Inc., New York.

Young, E. G., and Conway, C. F. 1942. On the estimation of allantoin by the Rimini-Schryver reaction. *J. Biol. Chem.,* 142, 839.

_____ , MacPherson, C. C., Wentworth, H. P., and Hawkins, W. H. 1944. The estimation of allantoin in blood. *J. Biol. Chem.,* 152, 245.

Young, L. 1939. The detoxication of carbocyclic compounds. *Physiol. Revs.,* 19, 323.

Zechmeister, L. 1950. Advances in Chromatography, 1938-1947. Chapman & Hall, Ltd., London.

_____ and Cholnoky, L. 1941. Principles and Practice of Chromatography. John Wiley & Sons, Inc., New York.

Zimmermann, W. 1930. Über den Nachweis kleiner Mengen Glykokool, *Z. physiol. Chem.,* 189, 4.

Ziskin, D. E., Gibson, J. A., Skarka, A., and Bellows, J. W. 1943. Effect of large daily doses of vitamin D on teeth and jaws of rats and on humans. *J. Dental Research,* 22, 457.

Zittle, C. A., and O'Dell, R. A. 1941. The determination of cystine: the use of cuprous oxide for simultaneous reduction and precipitation of cystine as the cuprous mercaptide. *J. Biol. Chem.,* 139, 753.

Zoller, H. F. 1921. Precipitation of grain-curd casein from pasteurized milk including sweet cream buttermilk. *Ind. Eng. Chem.,* 13, 510.

INDEX

Glycylglycine hydrochloride, preparation of, from
glycine anhydride, 6, 7
preparation of glycylglycine from, 8
Glyoxal-2,4-dinitrophenylosazone, formation of,
from aspartic acid, 37, 43
from malic acid, 43
Glyoxylic acid, formation of, from reducing
carbohydrates, 80
from serine, 41
from threonine, 41
reaction of, with tryptophan, 36, 42
Grapefruit juice, ascorbic-acid content of, 89
determination of ascorbic acid in, 88
Guaiacol, reaction of, with carbohydrates, 77
Guanadinoacetic acid (see Glycocyamine)
Guanidine, reaction of methyl derivatives of, with
hypohalite and α—naphthol, 43
Guanine, detection of, with diazobenzenesulfonic
acid, 85
with potassium-bismuth iodide, 86
with silver salt reagent, 85
fluorescence of, under ultraviolet light, 86
formation of xanthine from, 84
in nucleic acids, 84
reaction of, with diazobenzenesulfonic acid, 87
salt of HI and BiI_3, 87
Guinea pigs, scurvy in, 88

H

Hair, animal and human, cystine in, 25
isolation of tyrosine from, 25
Hanus method of determination of iodine number, 51
Hemoglobin, determination of papain proteolytic
activity with, 106
Hexoses, determination of, with orcinol, 80
interference of, in detection, of disaccharides, 79
of pentoses, 75
Hippuric acid, determination of liver function with, 114
determination of, in urine, 114
excretion of, after ingestion of foods, 114
formation of, from glycine, 2
in kidney, 9
in liver, 9
synthesis of, from glycine, 9
synthesis of phenylalanine from, 10
in urine, 9, 110, 114
Histamine, reaction of, with bromine-acetic acid, 43
with sodium nitroprusside, 42
Histidine, detection of, 34, 37
detection of interference of amino acids in, 43
determination of nitrogen in, 13
excretion of, in urine, 114
interference of, in detection, of lysine, 37
of phenylalanine, 42
reaction of, with bromine-acetic acid, 43
with nitrous acid, 15
with sodium nitroprusside, 42
separation of, with phosphotungstic acid, 34, 35
Histidine phosphotungstate, solubility of, in
hydrochloric acid, 40
Hog hair, isolation of cystine from, 25
Homocystine, formation of methionine from, 96
Homogentisic acid (see 2,5-Dihydroxyphenylacetic
acid)
Hopkins apparatus for condensing vapors, 148
Hormones, adrenal, sterol types of, 53
sex, relation of cholesterol to, 108
sterol types of, 53
in urine, 110

Horse hair, isolation of cystine from, 25
Hübl method of determination of iodine number, 51
Human hair, cystine in, 25
Hydrazine, determination of cysteine with, 28
Hydrocarbons, carcinogenic, relation of cholesterol
to, 108
Hydrogen chloride, preparation of, 4
Hydrogen cyanide, stimulation of papain proteolytic
activity by, 106
Hydrogen electrode, determination of pH with, 150
Hydrogen sulfide, stimulation of papain activity by, 106
Hydrolysis of proteins, 20
Hydroxyanthranilic acid, formation of nicotinic acid
from, 91
β-Hydroxybutyric acid, excretion of, in diabetes, 113
formation of acetone from, 113
in urine, 110, 113
7-Hydroxycholesterol, dibenzoate of, 98
formation of 7-dehydrocholesterol from, 98
formation of, from 7-ketocholesterol, 98
p-Hydroxydiphenyl, reaction of, with acetaldehyde,
38, 44, 73, 75
with aldehydes, 44
p-Hydroxydiphenyl-periodic acid, reaction of, with
desoxysaccharides, 73, 75
5-Hydroxylevulinaldehyde, formation of, from
5-(ω-hydroxymethyl) furfural, 78
Hydroxylysine, determination of, with periodic acid, 41
5-(ω-Hydroxymethyl) furfural, formation from, of formic
acid, 77
of 5-hydroxylevulinaldehyde, 78
of levulinic acid, 77
formation of, from fructose, 77
reaction of, with α-naphthol, 78
p-Hydroxyphenylpyruvic acid, excretion of, in
tyrosinuria, 10
in urine, 110
Hydroxyproline, detection of, 33, 36
reaction of, with p-dimenthylaminobenzaldehyde, 33,
40
with isatin, 36, 40
Hypoxanthine, detection of, with potassium-bismuth
iodide, 86
with silver salt reagent, 85
formation of, from adenine, 84
in natural materials, 84
reaction of, with diazobenzenesulfonic acid, 87

I

Iminodiacetic acid, formation of ammonium salt of, in
glycine synthesis, 2
Inorganic ions in urine, 110, 114
Inositol in purified amylase, 102
Inulin, detection of, 72, 74
formation of product on heating of, 80
solubility of, 73
Iodimetry, determination by, of acetaldehyde bisulfite,
114
of acetone, 113
of amino acids, 114
of ascorbic acid, 88, 89
of cysteine, 28
of reducing substances, 114
of tyrosine, 22
Iodine, complexes of, with basic acetates, 79
with hydroxides, 79
with α-pyrone, 79
with γ-pyrone, 79
detection with, of acetone, 113
of starch, 103

– 189 –

Iodine, determination of ascorbic acid with, 88
  oxidation of amino acids by, 15
Iodine number, methods of determination of, Aschmann, 51
    Hanus, 51
    Hübl, 51
    Kaufman bromine, 51
    with pyridine sulfate dibromide, 51
    Wijs, 51
    Winkler, 51
Iodoform, formation of, from acetone, 113
Ion exchange, adsorption of ammonia by, 115
  separation by, of acidic amino acids, 40
    of arginine, 43
    of lysine, 43
    of nucleic acid derivatives, 84
Isatin, reaction with, of hydroxyproline, 36, 40
    of proline, 36, 40
    of pyrrole, 40
Isobarbituric acid, formation of, from dibromoxy-hydrouracil, 87
    phenylhydrazone of, 87
Isodialuric acid, formation of, from pyrimidines, 87
    phenylosazone of, 87
Isoelectric point, of cystine, 25
    of tyrosine, 20
Isoleucine, detection of, 35, 38
    formation of methyl ethyl ketone from, 41, 44
Ivory-nut waste, isolation of α-D-mannose from, 64

K

Kaufman bromine method of determination of iodine number, 51
Keratins, cystine in, 25
7-Ketocholesterol, formation of, from cholesterol, 98
    formation of 7-hydroxycholesterol from, 98
Ketohexoses and ketopentoses, reaction of, with resorcinol, 80
Kidney, hemorrhages of, in choline deficiency, 95
Kjeldahl method of determinations, of nitrogen, 13
    of protein, 114
    of uric acid, 114
Koettstorfer number (see Saponification number)

L

Lactic acid, determination of, in urine, 114
  excretion of, in pathological conditions, 114
  formation of acetaldehyde from, 114
  in urine, 110, 114
Lactobacillus arabinosus 17-5, determination of nicotinic acid with, 91
Lactobacillus casei, determination with, of nicotinamide, 91
    of nicotinic acid, 91
    of nicotinuric acid, 91
Lactosazone, solubility of, 76
Lactose, analysis of, by polarimetry, 68
  in commercial products, 66
  detection of, 72, 74—76
  determination of, as nonfermentable carbohydrate, 81
  differentiation of microorganisms with, 66
  formation of mucic acid from, 82
  history of, 66
  isolation of, from whey powder, 66
  in milk, 66
  mutarotation of, 67
  oxidation of, by acidic cupric acetate, 80
  precipitation of, by ethanol, 73

Lactose, specific rotation of, 67, 68
  utilization of, by animals, 66
    by microorganisms, 66
  in whey powder, 67
Lanthanum nitrate, hydrolysis of pyrimidine nucleotides by, 86
Lecithin, isolation of choline from, 95
  solubility of, in acetone, 53
    in ethylene dichloride, 53
Leucine, detection of, 35, 38
  determination of, by photometry, 41
  extraction of, from crude tyrosine, 20
Leuconostoc mesenteroides, determination with, of nicotinamide, 91
    of nicotinic acid, 91
    of nicotinuric acid, 91
Levulinic acid, formation of, from 5-(ω-hydroxymethyl)-furfural, 77
Liebermann-Burchard reagent (*see* Acetic anhydride)
Lipids, acid numbers of, 49
  iodine numbers of, 51
  saponification numbers of, 50
Liver, choline deficiency of, deposition of fat in, 95
  neoplasms of, 95
  excretion of amino acids in diseases of, 114
  formation of vitamin D in fish, 100
Liver function, determination of, with hippuric acid, 114
Liver oils, iodine numbers of, 51
Lumisterol, formation of, from ergosterol, 98
Lupine sprouts, isolation of asparagine monohydrate from, 29
Lysine, detection of, 34, 37
  amino acids interfering in, 37, 43
  determination of nitrogen in, 13
  reaction of, with nitrous acid, 15
    with phosphotungstic acid-phosphomolybdic acid, 37
  separation of, by ion exchange, 43
    with phosphotungstic acid, 34, 35
Lysine phosphotungstate, solubility of, in hydrochloric acid, 40
Lysine picrate, melting point of, 43
  solubility of, 43

M

Magnesium ammonium phosphate, determination of phosphorus as, 47
Magnesium ion, activation of phosphatase by, 104
Magnesium pyrophosphate, determination of phosphorus as, 47
Malic acid, formation of, from aspartic acid, 43
Malt, amylase in, 102
Maltosazone, solubility of, 76
Maltose, detection of, 72, 75, 76
  determination of amylase as, 102
  formation of, from glycogen, 102
    from starch, 102
  oxidation of, by acidic cupric acetate, 80
  solubility of, 80
Mannose, detection of, 72, 76
  determination of, as phenylhydrazone, 83
  fermentation of, by brewer's yeast, 81
  formation of β-D form from α-D form, 64
  history of, 64
  isolation of, from ivory-nut waste, 64
  melting point of, 65
  mutarotation of, 65
  in natural materials, 64
  specific rotation of, 65
  utilization of, by microorganisms, 64
    by rabbits, 64
Mannose benzhydrazone, formation of, 83
Mannose methyl glycoside, formation of, 64
Mannose phenylhydrazone, formation of, 64, 76, 83
  melting point of, 76

Melanin, formation of, from tyrosine, 57
Melting-point technique, description of, 149
Mercuric acetate, effect of, in iodine-number
  determination, 51
Mercuric chloride, purification of tyrosine with, 20
Mercuric iodide complex, formation of, during
  deamination, 15
Mercuric nitrite reagent (*see* Millon reagent)
Mercuric sulfate, acetone as complex of, determination
  of, 113
  separation of, 38, 44
  precipitation with, of cystine, 25
  of tryptophan, 23, 42
Mercury salts, identification of nucleic acid
  derivatives as, 84, 87
Mesquite gum, anhydrogalactomethoxytetragalacturonic
  acid in, 62
  isolation of L-arabinose from, 62
  properties of, 62
  sources of, 62
Metal salts, formation of purines and pyrimidines as, 87
Methanol, in glycine purification, 3
  in glycylglycine purification, 8
  preparation of glycine methyl ester hydrochloride
  from, 4
Methionine, detection of, 33, 36
  excretion of, in liver disease, 114
  formation from, of choline, 95
  of creatine, 96
  formation of, from choline, 96
  from homocystine, 96
  reaction of, with sodium nitroprusside, 36, 42
Methyl ethyl ketone, formation of, from isoleucine, 41
  reaction of, with mercuric sulfate, 44
  with salicylaldehyde, 41, 44
  separation of, from acetone, 41, 44
Methylamine, reaction of, with reducing disaccharides,
  72, 79
5-Methylcytosine, detection of, with potassium-bismuth
  iodide, 86
  in tubercle bacilli, 84
Methylene blue, determination of ascorbic acid with, 88
5-Methylfurfural, formation of, from rhamnose, 77
Methylglyoxal, reaction of, with p-hydroxydiphenyl, 44
N^1-Methylnicotinamide, determination of, by fluorometry,
  91
  formation of, from nicotinic acid, 96
Methylpentoses, determination of, 80
Methylpurines, separation of, from purines, 86
Microbiological assay, dependability of, 92
  determination by, of amino acids, 114
    of choline, 95
    of nicotinamide, 91
    of nicotinic acid, 91
    of riboflavin, 92
    of tyrosine, 23
  principles of, 92
Microdiffusion, determination of ammonia by, 115
Microorganisms, action on cholesterol, 108
  amylase in, 102
  determination with, of nicotinic acid, 91, 92
    of xylose, 60
  differentiation of, with lactose, 66
  formation by, of muscarine, 95
    of neurine, 95
  isolation of amylase from, 102
  liberation of tyrosine from proteins by, 20
  neutralization of toxins of, by cholesterol, 108
  nutritional requirements of, 91
  utilization by, of D- and L-arabinose, 62
    of lactose, 66
    of mannose, 64
    of xylose, 60
Milk, lactose in, 66
  preparation of casein from, 45
  tyrosine decarboxylase in, 24
Millon reagent, detection of tyrosine with, 36
  determination of tyrosine with, 22, 23
  reaction of, with proteins, 42
    with tyrosine, 42

Molisch reagent, detection of carbohydrates with, 77
  interfering substances in tests with, 78
Molybdivanadophosphoric acid, determination of
  phosphorus with, 47
Monosaccharides, fermentation of, by brewer's yeast, 81
  fermentation products of, 82
  oxidation of, by acidic cupric acetate, 80
    by nitric acid, 82
Mucic acid, formation of, from galactose, 76, 82
  from lactose, 82
  melting point of, 76
Muscarine, formation of, from choline, 95
Mutarotation of L-arabinose, 63
  of D-lactose, 67
  of D-mannose, 65
  of D-xylose, 61

N

α-Naphthol, compounds reacting with, 43
  reaction of, with arginine, 42
  with carbohydrates, 77
β-Naphthol, reaction of, with carbohydrates, 77
  with 5-(ω-hydroxymethyl) furfural, 78
β-Naphthoquinone sulfonic acid (*see* 1,2,
  Naphthoquinone-4-sulfonic acid)
1,2,Naphthoquinone-4-sulfonic acid, determination with,
  of amino acids, 114
  of cysteine, 28, 36, 41
  reaction of, with amino acids, 40
Nerves, choline in, 95
  liberation of acetylcholine from, 95
Nessler reagent, detection of ammonia with, 35
  determination with, of ammonia, 112
    of total nitrogen, 112
  interference of sodium chloride with, 115
  reaction of, with ammonia, 115
Neurine, formation of, from choline, 95
Neurospora crassa, inhibition of, by phenylalanine
  analogues, 10
Nicotinamide, determination of, by microbiological
  assay, 91
Nicotine, preparation of nicotinic acid from, 91
Nicotinic acid, in coenzymes I and II, 91
  daily allowances of, for humans, 91
  deficiency symptoms of, 91
  determination of, with cyanogen bromide-pyridine, 91
    by microbiological assay, 91
    by photometry, 91
  in foods, 91
  formation from, of N^1-methylnicotinamide, 96
    of nicotinuric acid, 96
    of trigonelline, 96
  formation of, from hydroxyanthranilic acid, 91
  function of, in glycolysis, 91
    in respiration. 91
  history of, 92
  interference of, in utilization of choline, 95
  isolation of, from rice, 91
  methylbetaine of, 96
  in natural materials, 91
  preparation of, from nicotine, 91
  in purified amylase, 102
  treatment of natural products for assay of, 94
Nicotinuric acid, determination of, by microbiological
  assay, 91
  formation of, from nicotinic acid, 96
Ninhydrine, determination of amino acids with, 114
  reaction of, with alanine, 44
    with amino acids, 33, 39
    with glutamic acid, 43
    with glycine, 44
Nitric acid, detection with, of aromatic amino acids,
  33, 40
  of proteins, 40, 111, 113
p-Nitrobenzoyl chloride, reaction of, with amino acids, 40
Nitrochromic acid, compounds reacting with, 79
  reaction of, with carbohydrates, 72, 79
Nitrogen, detection of, in starch preparations, 56
  determination of, with Nessler reagent, 112

R

Rabbit, utilization of mannose by, 64
Rabbit hair, cystine in, 25
Rabbit intestine, determination of acetylcholine
    with, 96
Raffinose, detection of, 72, 74—76
    reaction of, with diazouracil, 81
    solubility of, 73, 80
Rat, bioassay of vitamin D by line test with, 99
    cholesterol in blood of, 108
    dispensability of glycine for growth of, 2
    exsanguination of, 104
    inhibition of, by phenylalanine analogues, 10
    lethal dose of choline for, 95
    phosphatase in blood of, 104
    potency of vitamins D_2 and D_3 for, 99
    utilization by, of lactose, 66
      of xylose, 60
    vitamin D unit for, 99
Rat hair, cystine in, 25
Reducing substances, detection of, 111, 113
    with bismuth reagent, 113
    with copper reagent, 113
    by optical rotation, 113
    with phenylhydrazine, 113
    determination of, with dinitrosalicylic acid, 114
    by fermentation with yeast, 113
    with ferricyanide, 114
    by iodimetry, 114
    with phosphomolybdic acid, 114
    by photometry, 114
    with picric acid, 114
    in urine, 114
    formation of cuprous thiocyanate in oxidation of, 114
    in potatoes, 56
    in urine in pathological conditions, 114
Reinecke salt, determination of choline with, 96
Resorcinol, reaction of, with carbohydrates, 74, 77
    with furfural, 81
    with ketohexoses, 80
    with ketopentoses, 80
R_f values of purines and pyrimidines, 85, 86
Rhamnose, detection of, 72, 75
    formation of furfural from, 77
    solubility of, 73, 80
Rhamnose benzhydrazone, formation of, 83
Riboflavin, determination of, by microbiological
    assay, 92
    reaction of, with benzidine, 81
Ribose in pentose nucleic acids, 84
Rice, isolation of nicotinic acid from, 91
Rotation (*see* Specific rotation)

S

Saccharic acid, formation of, from glucose, 82
    monopotassium salt of, 82
    silver salt of, 82
Saccharin, taste of, 2
Saccharogenic activity, variations in, 102
Saccharogenic time, definition of, 102
Salicylaldehyde, detection of acetone with, 111
    formation of dihydroxybenzalacetone from, 41, 111
    reaction of, with acetone, 36, 38, 41, 44, 111
    with methylethylketone, 36, 38, 41, 44
Saliva, isolation of amylases from, 102
Sapogenins, sterol types of, 53
Saponification number, determination of, 50
Sarcosine, formation of choline from, 95

Scurvy, symptoms of, 88
Seed oils, iodine numbers of, 51
    saponification numbers of, 50
Seeds, α- and β-amylase in, 102
    α-D-mannose in, 64
Sericin in silk, 20
Serine, detection of, 35, 38
    determination of, with periodic acid, 41, 44
    formation of, from glycine, 2
    reaction of, with nitrous acid, 15
    with periodic acid, 41, 44
Shigella paradysenteriae, determination of
    nicotinic acid with, 91
Silica gel, adsorption of biological substances on,
    84
Silk, isolation of tyrosine from, 20
    sericin in, 20
    silk fibroin in, 20
Silk fibroin, in silk, 20
    tyrosine in, 20
Silver chloride in chloride-ion determination, 19
Silver chromate in chloride-ion determination, 19
Silver fluoresceinate in chloride-ion determination, 19
Silver salt, detection of saccharic acid as, 82
Silver salts, purines as, detection of, 85
    determination of, 87
Skin, formation of antirachitic substances in, 99
Sodium azide, inhibition of anerobic fermentation by,
    82
Sodium bisulfite, reaction of, with acetaldehyde, 114
Sodium fusion in detection, of nitrogen, 56
    of sulfur, 33
Sodium nitroprusside, detection of acetone with, 113
    determination of cysteine with, 28
    reaction of, with amino acids, 42
    with methionine, 36, 42
Solubility, analysis of casein by, 45
Soybean, isolation of amylase from, 102
    stigmasterol in, 53
Soybean sprouts, isolation of asparagine monohydrate
    from, 29
Specific gravity of urines on high- and low-protein
    diets, 111
Specific rotation, of acetyl-D-phenylalanine, 107
    of β-L-arabinose, 63
    of L-cystine, 27
    of α-D-lactose, 67
    of α-D-mannose, 65
    of phenylalanine antipodes, 107
    of starch, 58
    of α-D-xylose, 61
Spectrophotometry, determination by, of ascorbic
    acid, 88
    of starch, 58
    of tyrosine, 23
Spinal cords, isolation of cholesterol from, 53
Starch, action of amylase on, 102
    adsorption of nucleic acid derivatives on, 84
    amylopectin in, 55, 58
    amylose in, 55, 58
    constitution of, 55, 58
    detection of, 72, 74, 103
    with iodine, 103
    detection of nitrogen in, 56
    determination of amylase activity by hydrolysis of, 102
    determination of glucose in, 58
    determination of, by fermentation, 58
    by gravimetric analysis, 58
    as iodide complex, 58
    by polarimetry, 58
    by spectrophotometry, 58

Tyrosine, preparation of tyramine hydrochloride from, 24
    purification of, by crystallization from water, 20
        as ethyl ester hydrochloride, 20
        as mercuric chloride complex, 20
        as phosphotungstate, 20
    reaction of, with Millon reagent, 36, 42
        with nitric acid, 33, 40
        with phosphotungstic acid, 28
    in silk fibroin, 20
    solubility of, in water, 40
L-Tyrosine, separation of, from L-cystine, 25
Tyrosine decarboxylase, in natural materials, 24
Tyrosine ethyl ester, extraction of, from crude cystine
    ethyl ester, 25
Tyrosinuria, excretion of p-hydroxyphenylpyruvic acid
    in, 10

U

Ultraviolet light, formation of antirachitic substances
    in skin by, 99
Uracil, detection of, with iron-bromine-ammonia, 85
    determination of, with arsenophosphotungstic acid, 87
    formation of, from cytosine, 86
    formation of dialuric acid from, 86
    in pentose nucleic acids, 84
    reactions of, with bromine water, 86
        with diazobenzenesulfonic acid, 87
Uranium phosphate, precipitation of phosphate by, 47
Uranyl salts, identification of nucleic acid derivatives
    as, 84, 87
Urea, decomposition of, with urease, 112
    excretion of, in normal and pathological conditions, 115
    formation of ammonia from, 112
    reaction of, with nitrous acid, 15
    in urine, 110—112, 115
        determination of, 112
Urea nitrogen, excretion of, 114
    in urine, on high- and low-protein diets, 111
Urease, decomposition of urea with, 112
Uric acid, copper salt of, 114
    determination of, as ammonium urate, 115
        with arsenophosphotungstic acid, 115
        with 2,6-dichloroquinone chloroimide, 115
        with phosphotungstic acid, 115
        by photometry, 113, 115
        with potassium permanganate, 115
    in urine, 113, 114
    formation of, from 8-aminoxanthine, 87
        from glycine, 2
    hydrochloride of, 114
    in urine, 110, 111, 113, 115
Uric acid nitrogen, determination of, by Kjeldahl
    method, 114
    in urine, on high- and low-protein diets, 111
Uridine, determination of, with arsenophosphotungstic
    acid, 87
Uridylic acid, destruction of, during hydrolysis, 86
Urine, acetone bodies in, 110, 111, 113
    acid content of, in normal and pathological
        conditions, 110
    alkalinity, causes of, 110
    allantoin in, 110, 113
    ammonia nitrogen of, on high- and low-protein
        diets, 111
    bacterial decomposition of, 110
    carbohydrates in, 110, 111, 113
    creatinine nitrogen of, on high- and low-protein
        diets, 111
    detection of pentoses in, 81

Urine, determination in, of acetone, 113
    of acidity, 114
    of amino acids, 39, 114
        with ninhydrin, 39
    of ammonia, 112
    of creatinine, 113
    of hippuric acid, 114
    of nicotinamide, 91
    of nicotinic acid, 91
    of nicotinuric acid, 91
    of organic acids, 114
    of protein, 114
    of purines, 114
    of reducing substances, 114
    of total nitrogen, 112
    of urea, 112
    of uric acid, 113, 114
    excretion in, of amino acids, 114
        of ammonia, 115
        of aspartic acid, 114
        of choline, 95
        of glutamic acid, 114
        of histidine, 114
        of methionine, 114
        of phosphatase, 104
    formation of, by filtration of plasma, 110
    glucose in, 110—112
    hippuric acid in, 9, 110, 114
    inorganic ions in, 110, 114
    nitrogen of, on high- and low-protein diets,
        total, 111
        undetermined, 111
        uric acid, 111
    nitrogen compounds in, 110, 115
    organic acids in, 110, 114
    pH of, 110
    properties of normal and pathological, 110
    purines in, 110, 114
    reabsorption of constituents in, 110
    specific gravity of, 110
        on high- and low-protein diets, 111
    testosterone in, 53
    tyrosine decarboxylase in, 24
    volume of, excreted under normal and pathological
        conditions, 110
        on high- and low-protein diets, 111
        influence of drugs on, 110
Urocanic acid in urine, 110

V

Vaccinia virus, inhibition of, by phenylalanine
    analogues, 10
Valine, detection of, 35, 38
    determination of, by photometry, 41
Van Slyke factors, conversion of nitrogen volume to
    weight by, 17, 18
Van Slyke method of determination of amino nitrogen, 15
Vapors, apparatus (Hopkins) for condensing, 148
Vetch sprouts, isolation of asparagine monohydrate
    from, 29
Vitamin C (see Ascorbic acid)
Vitamin D, allowances of, for humans, 99
    bioassay of, by chick bone-ash method, 99
        by rat line test, 99
    determination of, by chick bone-ash method, 98
        comparative studies on, 99
        with turkeys, 99
    discovery of, 98
    disease symptoms of chicks in deficiency of, 99

W

X

Y

Z

DATA SHEET FOR EXPERIMENT 1

_____ _____ _____
(Date) (Desk No.) (Student's name)

G. of unknown organic acid	
Ml. of_____N NaOH:	
Trial 1..	
Trial 2..	
Trial 3..	
Average	
Average equivalents of NaOH	
Equivalent weight of unknown acid	
Theoretical equivalent weight of unknown acid _____ _____ (name)[a] (formula)	
Percentage error in the equivalent weight determined experimentally	

[a]Furnished by the instructor after the equivalent weight has been determined and submitted.

DATA SHEET FOR EXPERIMENT 9

_____   _____   _____
(Date)   (Desk No.)   (Student's name)

	No._____	No._____	No._____
Unknown			
Ml. of_____ N NaOH in titration:			
(a) First flask...			
(b) Second flask...			
(c) Third flask			
(d) Average			
(e) First blank		—	—
(f) Second blank..		—	—
(g) Average			
Average ml. of_____ N NaOH equivalent to ammonia from aliquot corrected for ammonia in reagents			
Equivalents of nitrogen in the ammonia from the unknown in the 25.00-ml. aliquot			
Theoretical per cent of nitrogen in the unknown .... _____ _____ (name)[a] (formula)			
Per cent purity of the unknown[b]			

[a]Furnished by the instructor.

[b]Or percentage error in the determination of the per cent of nitrogen if an analytically pure amino acid unknown was supplied by the instructor.

DATA SHEET FOR EXPERIMENT 10

_____   _____   _____
    (Date)   (Desk No.)   (Student's name)

Trial	1	2	3
G. of unknown amino acid, No._____			
G. of unknown amino acid per 5.00-ml. aliquot			
Ml. of nitrogen liberated from reagents (blank)			
Ml. of nitrogen liberated from 5.00-ml. aliquot, corrected for blank value			
Temperature, °C.			
Atmospheric pressure (corrected),[a] mm. Hg			
Mg. of amino nitrogen per ml. of nitrogen at observed temperature and corrected pressure (factor from table)			
G. of amino nitrogen from 5.00-ml. aliquot			
Average g. of amino nitrogen from 5.00-ml. aliquots			
Per cent of amino nitrogen in unknown amino acid			
Theoretical per cent of amino nitrogen in unknown _____ _____ (name)[b] (formula)			
Percentage error in the per cent of amino nitrogen determined in the experiment			

[a]See Appendix.

[b]Furnished by the instructor after the per cent of amino nitrogen has been determined and submitted.

DATA SHEET FOR EXPERIMENT 11

_____   _____   _____
      (Date)   (Desk No.)   (Student's name)

	Unknown No._____	Unknown No._____	Unknown No._____
Sample...			
G. of hydrochloride unknown			
G. of sample in 25-ml. aliquot........................			
Ml. of _____ N AgNO$_3$..............................			
Ml. of _____ N KSCN			
First trial			
Second trial			
Third trial			
Average			
Equivalents of AgNO$_3$			
Average equivalents of KSCN			
Equivalents of AgNO$_3$ used by chloride................			
Per cent of chloride in unknown hydrochloride...........			
Theoretical percentage of chloride in unknown			
_____ _____ (name)[a] (formula)			
Per cent purity of unknown hydrochloride			

[a]Furnished by the instructor.

DATA SHEET FOR EXPERIMENT 13

_____   _____   _____

(Date)   (Desk No.)   (Student's name)

Sample..	Unknown No._____	Unknown No._____	Unknown No._____
G. of unknown tyrosine...................................			
Mm. thickness of standard solution	20.0	20.0	20.0
Mm. thickness of unknown solution matching color of standard solution			
Mg. of tyrosine per ml. undiluted standard solution...			
Mg. of tyrosine per 25 ml. final dilution of unknown solution			
G. of tyrosine per 500 ml. original solution...			
Per cent purity unknown tyrosine			

DATA SHEET FOR EXPERIMENT 14

| (Date) | (Desk No.) | (Student's name) |

Sample	Casein	Casein plus tyrosine
G. of casein		
G. of casein in 10-ml. aliquot		
Mm. thickness of colored standard L-tyrosine solution	20.0	20.0
Mg. of tyrosine per 5 ml. of standard solution..		
Mg. of tyrosine per 10 ml. of unknown solution..		
Per cent tyrosine in casein		
Mg. of tyrosine recovered...............................		
Mg. of tyrosine added[a]		
Per cent recovery of tyrosine...........................		

[a]Furnished by instructor after the milligrams of tyrosine recovered has been reported

DATA SHEET FOR EXPERIMENT 14

DATA SHEET FOR EXPERIMENT 17

_____ _____ _____
(Date)   (Desk No.)   (Student's name)

Sample...	Unknown No._____	Unknown No._____	Unknown No._____
G. of L-cystine per 50-ml. solution			
Zero reading, average deg.			
Observed rotation, average deg.			
Observed rotation, corrected			
Temperature, °C., of L-cystine solution			
Specific rotation at observed temperature			
Specific rotation of pure L-cystine at observed temperature			
Per cent purity of sample...			

DATA SHEET FOR EXPERIMENT 18

_____ (Date)   _____ (Desk No.)   _____ (Student's name)

Sample	Unknown No.____	Unknown No.____	Unknown No.____
G. of unknown cystine			
Mm. thickness of standard solution	20.0	20.0	20.0
Mm. thickness of unknown solution matching color of standard solution			
Mg. of cystine per ml. undiluted standard solution..			
Mg. of cystine per 50 ml. final dilution of unknown solution....................................			
G. of cystine per 250 ml. of original solution.............			
Per cent purity unknown cystine..................................			

DATA SHEET FOR EXPERIMENT 20

_____   _____   _____
(Date)   (Desk No.)   (Student's name)

STANDARD-CURVE DATA

Ml. of_____N NH$_4$OH...........	1	2	3	4	5	6	7	8	9	10
pH										

Sample..	Unknown asparagine monohydrate No. _____	Unknown + added asparagine monohydrate
G. of asparagine sample.......................................		
G. of asparagine in 5-ml. aliquot...........................		
pH of ammonia-borate solution		
Equivalents of ammonia from 5-ml. aliquot		
G. of asparagine calculated from equivalents of ammonia...........................		
Per cent purity of asparagine monohydrate		————
G. of asparagine monohydrate recovered from 5-ml. aliquot..............................		
G. of asparagine monohydrate added[a]		
Per cent recovery		

[a]To be obtained from the instructor after grams of asparagine monohydrate recovered has been determined and submitted.

DATA SHEET FOR EXPERIMENT 23

_____   _____   _____
(Date)   (Desk No.)   (Student's name)

Sample..	Unknown casein No. _____	Unknown casein plus added phosphate
G. of casein		
G. of casein in 10-ml. aliquot		
Mm. thickness of colored standard phosphate solution...........................	20.0	20.0
Depth in mm. of colored unknown solution...................................		
Mg. of phosphorus per 10.0 ml. of standard phosphate solution........................		
Mg. of phosphorus per 10.0 ml. of unknown solution analyzed............................		
Per cent phosphorus in casein...........................		
G. of phosphorus recovered (from 10-ml. aliquot)		
G. of phosphorus added[a]...............................		
Per cent recovery of phosphorus........................		

[a]To be obtained from the instructor after grams of phosphorus recovered has been determined and submitted.

DATA SHEET FOR EXPERIMENT 24

_____   _____   _____

(Date)   (Desk No.)   (Student's name)

Trial	1	2	3
G. of unknown lipid, No._____........................			
Ml. of_____N KOH to titrate sample			
Ml. of_____N KOH to titrate blank			
First trial		——	——
Second trial		——	——
Average..			
Ml. of_____N KOH to titrate sample, corrected for blank value			
Equivalents of fatty acid in sample			
Acid number of lipid			
Average acid number of lipid........................			

DATA SHEET FOR EXPERIMENT 25

_____   _____   _____
(Date)   (Desk No.)   (Student's name)

Trial	1	2	3
G. of unknown lipid, No._____			
Ml. of_____ N H_2SO_4 to titrate excess base in sample mixture			
Equivalents of base in 25.0 ml. of _____ N alcoholic KOH			
Equivalents of H_2SO_4 to titrate excess base in sample mixture			
Equivalents of base to saponify sample (uncorrected for free acid)			
Saponification number[a] of lipid.....................................			
Average saponification number of lipid			

[a]Corrected for the free acid in the lipid. The acid number of the unknown lipid will be furnished by the laboratory instructor.

DATA SHEET FOR EXPERIMENT 26

_____ _____ _____
(Date)   (Desk No.)   (Student's name)

Trial	1	2	3
G. of unknown lipid, No._____			
Ml. of_____ N $Na_2S_2O_3$ to titrate blank			
First trial		——	——
Second trial		——	——
Average			
Ml. of_____ N $Na_2S_2O_3$ to titrate IBr (as I_2) unabsorbed by sample			
Ml. of_____ N $Na_2S_2O_2$ equivalent to IBr absorbed by sample...			
Equivalents of IBr absorbed by sample			
Iodine number of lipid......................................			
Average iodine number of lipid			

DATA SHEET FOR EXPERIMENT 27

_____   _____   _____
(Date)   (Desk No.)   (Student's name)

G. of moist spinal cords..	
G. of mixture of dry spinal cords and celite	
G. of celite added	
G. of dry spinal cords	
Per cent moisture in spinal cords................................	
G. of cholesterol, first crop crude	
G. of cholesterol, first crop recrystallized	
G. of cholesterol, second crop crude	
G. of cholesterol, second crop recrystallized...............	
Per cent total recrystallized cholesterol of moist spinal cords...	
Per cent total recrystallized cholesterol of dry spinal cords..	
Melting point, cholesterol sample No. _____ Observed... Corrected...	
Melting point, cholesterol sample No. _____ Observed... Corrected	
Melting point, cholesterol sample No. _____ Observed... Corrected	
Melting point, cholesterol (corrected literature value)..	148°

DATA SHEET FOR EXPERIMENT 28

------------------ ------------------ ------------------
(Date)   (Desk No.)   (Student's name)

1. _____ g. of purified, dry starch was prepared from 500 g. of macerated slices of peeled potatoes of the _____variety.

2. In the color tests the following color changes were noted: sliced potatoes standing in air, _____ to _____ ; sliced potatoes suspended in water and heated for 15 min., _____ to _____ ; and the supernatant liquids obtained in the preparation of purified starch, _____ to _____ .

3. _____ g. of dry colloid was obtained in the last section from 100 ml. of aqueous extract. The total colloid in 500 g. of potato slices is calculated to be _____ g.

4. The test for nitrogen in dry starch was _____ and in dry colloid_____ . (Indicate each answer as positive or negative.)

5. Observations on the reducing substances, presumably principally glucose, present in aqueous extracts of potato pulp and from starch purification:

Aqueous extract of potato pulp	Results from Benedict test	Aqueous fluid from starch purification	Results from Benedict test
1		1	
2		2	
3		3	
4		4	
5		5	

DATA SHEET FOR EXPERIMENT 29

_____   _____   _____
(Date)   (Desk No.)   (Student's name)

Sample...	Purified starch	Starch-protein, unknown No. _____
G. of sample..		
Ml. of 0.02 M ceric sulfate solution to titrate 5-ml. aliquot of hydrolysate		
Trial 1...		
Trial 2...		
Trial 3...		
Average...		
Mg. of glucose equivalent to 1 ml. of the 0.02 M ceric sulfate solution		
G. of glucose in 1,000 ml. of hydrolysate...		
Starch factor...		
Percentage of starch in unknown		

DATA SHEET FOR EXPERIMENT 34

_____   _____   _____
(Date)   (Desk No.)   (Student's name)

Sample No................		Log α, time most sample dissolved	
G. of sample............		α, time most sample dissolved	
Temperature of solution...............		Specific rotation $[\alpha]_D^t$	
Zero reading............		Per cent purity	

Time, min.	Observed rotation (corrected)	Log corrected rotation
0	(Water added)	
	(Most sample dissolved)	

DATA SHEET FOR EXPERIMENT 35

_____   _____   _____
(Date)   (Desk No.)   (Student's name)

Sample..	Unhydrolyzed		Hydrolyzed	
	Corn sirup	Corn sirup + glucose	Corn sirup	Corn sirup + glucose
Mg. of corn sirup _____.................................... (brand)				
Mg. of corn sirup in 2-ml. aliquot				
Mm. depth of colored standard..	20.0	20.0	20.0	20.0
Mm. depth of colored unknown				
Mg. of glucose per 2-ml. standard...................................				
Mg. of glucose per 2-ml. aliquot				
Per cent glucose in corn sirup..				
Mg. of glucose recovered (from 2-ml. aliquot)				
Mg. of glucose added[a]..				
Per cent recovery of glucose..				

[a]Furnished by instructor after milligrams of glucose recovered has been calculated and submitted.

DATA SHEET FOR EXPERIMENT 35

OPTIONAL PROCEDURE

_____   _____   _____

(Date)   (Desk No.)   (Student's name)

Glucose concentration, mg. per 2 ml.....................	0	0.070	0.120	0.200	0.300
Optical density	0				

Sample...	Unhydrolyzed		Hydrolyzed	
	Corn sirup	Corn sirup + glucose	Corn sirup	Corn sirup + glucose
Mg. of corn sirup _____ .... (brand)		———		———
Mg. of corn sirup in 2-ml. aliquot...........................				
Optical density of colored unknown				
Mg. of glucose per 2-ml. aliquot				
Per cent glucose in corn sirup...............................				
Mg. of glucose recovered (calculated for 2-ml. aliquot)				
Mg. of glucose added[a]...				
Per cent recovery of glucose				

[a]Furnished by instructor after milligrams of glucose recovered has been calculated and submitted.

DATA SHEET FOR EXPERIMENT 38

_____   _____   _____
(Date)   (Desk No.)   (Student's name)

Sample	Grapefruit juice			Grapefruit juice + ascorbic acid		
Trial	1	2	3	1	2	3
Ml. of_____N KIO$_3$ to titrate aliquot						
Ml. of _____N KIO$_3$ to titrate aliquot after dye titration..						
Ml. of _____N KIO$_3$ equivalent to ascorbic acid in aliquot						
Average equivalents of_____N KIO$_3$ equivalent to ascorbic acid in aliquot..						
Equivalents of KIO$_3$ in average titration volume						
Mg. of ascorbic acid in aliquot						
Mg. of ascorbic acid per 100 ml. of grapefruit juice..						
Mg. of ascorbic acid recovered (from 25-ml. aliquot)						
Mg. of ascorbic acid added[a]						
Per cent recovery..						

[a]To be obtained from instructor after milligrams of ascorbic acid recovered has been determined and submitted.

DATA SHEET FOR EXPERIMENT 39

_____   _____   _____
(Date)   (Desk No.)   (Student's name)

Vitamin tablet, name.....................................	
Vitamin tablet, manufacturer	
Vitamin tablet, g..	
Vitamin-tablet solution, ml..........................	

Ml. of standard nicotinic acid solution (_____ μg per ml.) per tube...................	0	0.25	0.50	0.75	1.00	1.25	1.50	1.75	2.00	2.50
μg of nicotinic acid per tube........................	0									
Ml. of _____ N NaOH to titrate acid per tube										
1..										
2..										
Average...........................										

Ml. of vitamin solution	Ml. of _____ N NaOH to titrate sample			Nicotinic acid			
	1	2	Average	μg per tube	μg per ml.	Deviation from the mean μg per ml.	Per cent mean deviation from the mean
0.5							
1.0							
1.5							
2.0							
2.5							
Mean...							

Ml. of vitamin-recovery solution	Ml. of _____N NaOH to titrate sample			Nicotinic acid			
	1	2	Average	μg per tube	μg per ml.	Deviation from the mean μg per ml.	Per cent mean deviation
0.5							
1.0							
1.5							
2.0							
2.5							
Mean..							

Mg. of nicotinic acid per tablet (on label)............................	
Mg. of nicotinic acid per tablet (found)................................	
Mg. of nicotinic acid recovered...	
Mg. of nicotinic acid added[a]	
Per cent recovery..	

[a]Furnished by instructor after milligrams of nicotinic acid recovered has been determined and submitted.

DATA SHEET FOR EXPERIMENT 40

_____   _____   _____
(Date)   (Desk No.)   (Student's name)

Ml. of standard choline solution (_____ μg per ml.) per tube	0.5	1	2	3	4	5
μg of choline per tube	0					
Mg. of mycelium per tube						

		Choline			
Ml. of sample solution	Mg. of mycelium	μg per tube	μg per ml.	Deviation from the mean μg per ml.	Per cent mean deviation from the mean
1.0					
2.0					
3.0					
4.0					
5.0					
Mean...					

Ml. of sample-recovery solution	Mg. of mycelium	Choline			
		μg per tube	μg per ml.	Deviation from the mean μg per ml.	Per cent mean deviation from the mean
1.0					
2.0					
3.0					
4.0					
5.0					
Mean..					

Mg. of egg yolk	
Mg. of choline per ml. of egg solution assayed	
Mg. of choline per 100-ml. aliquot of egg solution....................................	
Per cent choline in egg yolk	
Mg. of choline recovered per ml. of solution assayed	
Mg. of total choline recovered..	
Mg. of choline added[a]	
Per cent recovery of choline	

[a]Furnished by instructor after milligrams of choline recovered has been determined and submitted.

DATA SHEET FOR EXPERIMENT 41

_____   _____   _____
(Date)   (Desk No.)   (Student's name)

Total number of chicks used	
Average weight of chicks, g...........	
First day....................................	
Last day	

	Tibiae		Middle toes	
	Left	Right	Left	Right
Bones, g. after heating to 100°				
Ash, g. after heating bones to 800°...........................				
Ash, per cent in bones				
Ash, average per cent in bones...................................				
Vitamin D, units per g. of oil No._____[a]				

[a]Determined by interpolating standard curve plotted from data furnished by instructor:

Units of vitamin D per g. of standard oil										
Per cent ash in bones..										

DATA SHEET FOR EXPERIMENT 42

_____   _____   _____
(Date)   (Desk No.)   (Student's name)

Starch solution, per cent	Time		
	Start	Finish	Elapsed
0.2............................			
0.5............................			
1.0............................			
1.5............................			
2.0............................			
2.5............................			
Unknown No._____			
Unknown No._____			

Per cent starch in	
Unknown No._____	
Unknown No._____	
Ml. to which_____ml. saliva diluted	
Units of amylase activity..	

DATA SHEET FOR EXPERIMENT 43

_____   _____   _____
(Date)   (Desk No.)   (Student's name)

Sample	Total[a] phosphorus	Total[a] plus added phosphorus	Preformed phosphorus	Blank phosphorus
Ml. of blood serum in final 10-ml. volume				
Ml. depth of standard phosphorus solution	20.0	20.0	20.0	20.0
Mg. of phosphorus in 10-ml. final volume of standard solution				
Mm. depth of unknown phosphorus solution matching the standard solution				
Mg. of phosphorus in final 10-ml. volume				
Mg. of phosphorus in final 10-ml. volume corrected for blank............................			——	——
Mg. of phosphorus per 100 ml. of blood serum..................................				——
Units of phosphatase activity per 100 ml. of blood serum				
Mg. of phosphorus recovered (calculated for original 0.40 ml.).....................................				
Mg. of phosphorus added[b].................................				
Per cent recovery				

[a]Preformed phosphorus plus phosphorus liberated from β-glycerophosphate.

[b]Furnished by instructor after milligrams of phosphorus recovered has been submitted.

DATA SHEET FOR EXPERIMENT 43

OPTIONAL PROCEDURE

_____   _____   _____
(Date)   (Desk No.)   (Student's name)

Ml. of standard phosphorus (_____ mg. per ml.) solution.............................	0	1	2	3
Mg. of phosphorus per ml. final volume............	0			
Optical density	0			

Sample..	Total[a] phosphorus	Total[a] plus added phos-phorus	Preformed phosphorus	Blank phosphorus
Ml. of blood serum in final 10-ml. volume				
Optical density of unknown solution...............				
Mg. of phosphorus in final 10-ml. volume........				
Mg. of phosphorus in final 10-ml. volume, corrected for blank			——	——
Mg. of phosphorus per 100 ml. blood serum..				——
Units of phosphatase activity per 100 ml. of blood serum				
Mg. of phosphorus recovered (calculated for original 0.40 ml. of serum)............................				
Mg. of phosphorus added[b]................................				
Per cent recovery..				

[a] Preformed phosphorus plus phosphorus liberated from β-glycerophosphate.

[b] Furnished by instructor after milligrams of phosphorus recovered has been submitted.

DATA SHEET FOR EXPERIMENT 45

_____   _____   _____
    (Date)   (Desk No.)   (Student's name)

Ml. of standard (_____mg. per ml.) cholesterol solution........	0	1	2	3	5
Cholesterol concentration (mg. per 5 ml.)	0				
Optical density..	0				

Sample	Serum	Serum plus cholesterol
Ml. of blood in final 5-ml. aliquot................		
Optical density of unknown		
Mg. of cholesterol in 5-ml. aliquot		
Mg. of cholesterol per 100 ml. blood serum................................		—————
Mg. of cholesterol recovered (calculated for 5-ml. aliquot)...................		
Mg. of cholesterol added[a].............................		
Per cent recovery..		

[a]Furnished by instructor after milligrams of cholesterol recovered has been determined and submitted.

DATA SHEET FOR EXPERIMENT 46

_____   _____   _____
(Date)   (Desk No.)   (Student's name)

Diet	
Volume of urine excreted in 24 hr.	
Final volume of urine after dilution	

Constituent	Nitrogen found		Nitrogen recovery		
			Mg. N/50 ml.		Per cent recovery
	Mg.	Per cent of total	Found	Added[a]	
Total nitrogen......................					
Urea..................................					
Ammonia					
Creatinine...........................					
Uric acid.............................					
Undetermined nitrogen (by difference)					

	Original urine	Urine plus added components
Albumin[b]		
Glucose[c]		
Acetone[b]		

[a]Furnished by the instructor after milligrams of nitrogen recovered has been calculated and submitted.

[b]Record as present or absent.

[c]Record the relative quantities as described in Note 2, Exp. 46.